T0327666

# Ceramic Materials and Multilayer Electronic Devices

# Related titles published by The American Ceramic Society

*Morphotropic Phase Boundary Perovskites, High Strain Piezoelectrics, and Dielectric Ceramics (Ceramic Transactions Volume 136)*
Edited by Ruyan Guo, K. M. Nair, Winnie K. Wong-Ng, Amar Bhalla, Dwight Viehland, D. Suvorov, Carl Wu, and S-I. Hirano
©2003, ISBN 1-57498-151-x

*Phase Diagrams for Electronic Ceramics I: Dielectric Ti, Nb, and Ta Oxide Systems*
*ACerS-NIST Phase Equilibria Diagrams*
Robert S. Roth, Editor
©2003, ISBN 1-57498-172-2

*Recent Developments in Electronic Materials and Devices (Ceramic Transactions Volume 131)*
Edited by K.M. Nair, A.S. Bhalla, and S.-I. Hirano
©2002, ISBN 1-57498-145-5

*Dielectric Materials and Devices*
Edited by K.M. Nair, Amar S. Bhalla, Tapan K. Gupta, Shin-Ichi Hirano, Basavaraj V. Hiremath, Jau-Ho Jean, and Robert Pohanka
©2001, ISBN 1-57498-118-8

*Electronic Ceramic Materials and Devices (Ceramic Transactions Volume 106)*
Edited by K.M. Nair and A.S. Bhalla
©2000, ISBN 1-57498-098-x

*Dielectric Ceramic Materials (Ceramic Transactions Volume 100)*
Edited by K.M. Nair and A.S. Bhalla
©1999, ISBN 1-57498-066-1

*Multilayer Electronic Ceramic Devices (Ceramic Transactions Volume 97)*
Edited by Jau-Ho Jean, T.K. Gupta, K.M. Nair, and K. Niwa
©1999, ISBN 1-57498-064-5

For information on ordering titles published by The American Ceramic Society, or to request a publications catalog, please contact our Customer Service Department at:

Customer Service Department
735 Ceramic Place
Westerville, OH 43081, USA
614-794-5890 (phone)
614-794-5892 (fax)
info@ceramics.org

Visit our on-line book catalog at www.ceramics.org.

Ceramic Transactions

Volume 150

# Ceramic Materials and Multilayer Electronic Devices

Proceedings of the High Strain Piezoelectric Materials, Devices, and Applications and Advanced Dielectric Materials and Multilayer Electronic Devices Symposia held at the 105th Annual Meeting of the American Ceramic Society, April 27–30, 2003 in Nashville, Tennessee.

Edited by

**K. M. Nair**
E. I. duPont de Nemours & Co. Inc.

**A. S. Bhalla**
The Pennsylvania State University

**S.-I. Hirano**
Nagoya University

**D. Suvorov**
Jozef Stefan Institute

**R. W. Schwartz**
University of Missouri-Rolla

**W. Zhu**
Nanyang University

Published by
**The American Ceramic Society**
**735 Ceramic Place**
**Westerville, Ohio 43081**
**www.ceramics.org**

*Proceedings of the High Strain Piezoelectric Materials, Devices, and Applications and Advanced Dielectric Materials and Multilayer Electronic Devices Symposia held at the 105th Annual Meeting of The American Ceramic Society, April 27–30, 2003 in Nashville, Tennessee.*

COVER PHOTO: "Structure of multilayer ceramic capacitor" is courtesy of Yoshinori Fujikawa, Fumikazu Yamane, Takeshi Nomura, and Yasuyuki Kitano and appears as figure 1 in their paper "Characterization of $BaTiO_3$ Powders by Transmission Electron Microscopy and Scanning Transmission Electron Microscopy," which begins on page 115.

For information on ordering titles published by The American Ceramic Society, or to request a publications catalog, please call 614-794-5890.

Printed in the United States of America.

4 3 2 1–07 06 05 04

ISSN 1042-1122
ISBN 1-57498-205-2

# Contents

## Microstructure and Properties of Materials

## Electronic Devices: Design and Properties

# Preface

The growth of materials research, development of technology, and product innovation has been extraordinary during the last century. Our understanding of science and technology behind dielectric materials played a major role in satisfying the social needs by developing electronic devices for automotive, telecommunications and medical applications. Dielectric technology development still has an enormous potential role to play in developing future materials for electronic applications. We will continue our growth efforts during this century to satisfy the increased demands of our society.

Materials societies like The American Ceramic Society (ACerS) understand their social responsibility. For the last many years, ACerS has organized several international symposia covering many aspects of the advanced electronic materials systems by bringing together leading researchers and practitioners of electronics and publishing proceedings of the conferences in the Ceramic Transaction series.

This volume contains a collection of selected papers from two symposia: Advanced Dielectric Materials and Multilayer Electronic Devices and High Strain Piezoelectric Materials, Devices and Applications that were held during the 105th Annual Meeting of The American Ceramic Society, April 27-30, 2003, Nashville, Tennessee. Major topics of the symposium were: fundamental and historical perspectives of dielectric materials; relaxor materials and devices; high strain piezoelectric devices; advanced aspects of powder preparation, characterization and properties; thin films; materials for low and high frequency applications; processing-structure-property-relationships; and potential areas of applications. Over fourteen invited and twenty-five contributed papers are peer-reviewed and included in this volume.

We, the editors, acknowledge and appreciate the contributions of the speakers, conference and session chairs, manuscript reviewers, and the ACerS staff for making this endeavor a successful one.

Finally, we dedicate this volume to the memory of professor W. D. Kingery and his contributions to modern ceramics.

K. M. Nair,
A.S. Bhalla
S-I. Hirano
D. Suvorov
W. Zhu
R. W. Schwartz

# Design and Preparation of Materials

# THE ROLE OF CRYSTAL CHEMISTRY IN THE DESIGN OF DIELECTRIC MATERIALS

William B. White
Materials Research Institute
The Pennsylvania State University
University Park, PA 16802

## ABSTRACT

To a surprisingly accurate approximation, the crystal structure of a compound depends only on electrostatic forces holding ions together. On the order of 95% of the lattice energy can be ascribed to Coulomb forces. As a result, ions with the same size and charge can often be substituted interchangeably. A relatively small number of primary structures, with their distorted, ordered, and superstructure variants, account for a very large number of compounds. Phase transitions, structural and electronic ordering, and domain structures represent only a very small percentage of the total lattice energy but can sometimes be addressed by crystal chemical mapping.

## INTRODUCTION

Crystal chemistry is concerned above all with the systematics of crystal structures. Although the emphasis is on structure, crystal chemistry is not crystallography. Crystal structures determined by the methods of x-ray, neutron, and electron diffraction are only the feedstock from which crystal chemical principles are sorted out.

When the experimental methods and underlying theory for extracting crystal structures from diffraction patterns were worked out in the early years of the 20th Century, there followed an outpouring of structure determinations. It was quickly recognized that some sets of compounds with quite different chemical composition had the same atomic arrangement. Thus NaCl, MgO, and MnS all have the same cation and anion positions within a face-centered cubic unit cell. The cell constants are different but these only serve to scale otherwise identical crystal structures. By the early 1920's a sufficient library of crystal structures had been built up that it was possible to search for systematic patterns. Crystal chemistry had been born.

The guiding principles are empirical. The concept of a structure type and the systematic organization of crystal structures was proposed by Goldschmidt[1] in 1926. There are Pauling's rules[2] which first appeared in 1929. By 1933 Neuburger[3] could write a full treatise on the principles of crystal chemistry and by 1939, Evan[4] had published the first edition of his classic textbook.

Because the roots of crystal chemistry go so deep into the past, the subject sometimes has a musty smell, as though it is a relict that should have long since been superceded by the modern theory of chemical bonding. What is important is that the broad empirical principles of crystal chemistry remain as valid today as they were 80 years ago. And even more importantly, they remain useful as a practical guide to materials design. At a certain level, the back-of-the-envelope principles of crystal chemistry can compete with the elegant molecular orbital and band theoretical calculations that are now used to rationalize molecular and crystal structures.

PRINCIPLES OF CRYSTAL CHEMISTRY
Packing Principles
        The fundamental premise of crystal chemistry is that ions can be treated as charged spheres that are then held together by electrostatic forces. An assemblage of ions will arrange themselves to minimize the potential energy. Rather than details of chemical bonding, many of the primary features of crystal structures are a matter of pure geometry. Anions are usually larger than cations so it is convenient to examine the ways in which large spheres can be packed around smaller ones. The arrangements are most stable when all ions just touch. This provides the best balance between Coulomb attraction and the onset of the repulsion forces. If the central cation is too small, anion-anion repulsion will destabilize the structure, anions will be rejected, and a new arrangement with fewer anions will appear. If the central cation is too large, the anions will be spread out and Coulomb attraction will pull in additional anions. The controlling variable is the ratio of cation radius to anion radius, not the absolute values of the radii.

        The number of anions that can pack around a cation is the *coordination number*. The clusters consisting of a central cation and its coordinating anions form coordination polyhedra. Because of anion-anion repulsion, the coordination polyhedra take regular forms of triangles, tetrahedra, octahedra and cubes. If the most stable polyhedra are those in which the cation and anions just touch, simple geometry gives the ideal radius ratios (Table I). Of course, not all combinations of ions will produce ideal radius ratios. The interionic repulsion forces increase as the 8 – 9 power of the interatomic distances (or exponentially depending on the potential function used) and rapidly destabilize the polyhedra for radius ratios smaller than the ideal value. For ratios higher than the ideal value the destabilization depends on the Coulomb attractive force which varies slowly with distance. Thus the stability interval ranges from the ideal ratio up to the ratio of the next higher coordination number.

## Multicomponent Systems

The concepts of coordination polyhedra and sphere packings assumed that there were only two sizes of spheres – large anions and small cations. This is appropriate for binary compounds. In systems with larger numbers of components there will be the possibility of more than one kind of coordination polyhedron and a competition among the cations as to which fits into which. Cations may have different charges and this will affect the distribution of cations among available polyhedra.

A master principle in any structural arrangement is that of charge neutrality. It is essential that positive and negative charges balance and further that they do so over short distances within the structure. An unyielding guideline in distributing ions within crystal structures is that local charge balance must be maintained.

Table I. Radius ratios for coordination polyhedra

| Coordination No. | Radius Ratio | Configuration | Example |
|---|---|---|---|
| 2 | $0 - 0.155$ | Linear | $CO_2$ |
| 3 | $0.155 - 0.224$ | Planar Triangle | $CO_3^{2-}$ |
| 4 | $0.224 - 0.414$ | Tetrahedron | $SiO_2$ |
| 4 | $0.414 - 0.732$ | Planar Square | $CuO$ |
| 6 | $0.414 - 0.732$ | Octahedron | $MgO$ |
| 8 | $0.732 - 1.0$ | Cube | $CaF_2$ |

## Linkages

Although many structures can be considered examples of the closest packing of spheres, many other structures are more loosely packed and can best be described in terms of the coordination polyhedra and the ways in which the polyhedra can be linked to form continuous structures. The silicates are the most common example. The structural building block (at ambient pressures) is the $SiO_4$ tetrahedron. However, the tetrahedra can be linked in a great variety of dimers, chains, rings, sheets, and three-dimensional frameworks if one considers only the possibilities within corner-sharing.

Polyhedra can appear as isolated units, with shared corners, with shared edges, and with shared faces. As noted by Pauling long ago, shared edges, and more significantly shared faces, tends to destabilize the polyhedra. An examination of a many crystal structures reveals the trends shown in Table II. The concept of structural buildup from coordination polyhedra works for both closed packed and non-close-packed structures. Structures built of close-packed spheres also contain close-packed polyhedra.

Table II.  Trends in polyhedral linkages

|  | Tetrahedra | Octahedra | Cubes |
| --- | --- | --- | --- |
| Isolated Units | Common | Occasionally | Extremely Rare |
| Corner-Sharing | Common | Common | Rare |
| Edge-Sharing | Very Rare | Common | Common |
| Face-Sharing | Never | Rare | Common |

A Summary of Principles

(1)  Crystals are composed of cations and anions, each treated as spheres with a specified charge and radius.

(2)  Sphere packing is controlled by the balance between attractive and repulsive electrostatic forces and leads to polyhedra of various geometries depending essentially on the ratio of cation radius to anion radius, not the absolute values of these parameters.

(3)  Charge balance must be maintained over short distance scales.

(4)  Because ion size and charge are the key parameters, ions of similar size and charge are largely interchangeable regardless of their chemistry.

(5)  Because of principle (4), the number of essentially different kinds of structural constituents in a crystal tends to be small (Pauling's fifth rule; also called the "rule of parsimony").  Likewise, the number of essentially different crystal structures is much smaller than the number of compounds that take those structures.

CHEMICAL BONDING
The Ionic Bond:  Electrostatic Models

Solid materials represent a great variety of chemical bonding.  There are halides and oxides which are close to ideal ionic solids, there are polymers and organic compounds made of covalently bonded molecules held together in the solid by van der Waals or hydrogen bonding, there are metals, there are semiconductors with both metallic and covalent character, there are silicates, phosphates, and carbonates with mixed covalent and ionic character within the same compound.  Traditionally, the strong bonds were characterized as ionic, covalent, and metallic.  Each is based on a different conceptual framework and each has a different theoretical structure.  As suggested in Fig 1, many classes of materials are not ideally described by any of the models.

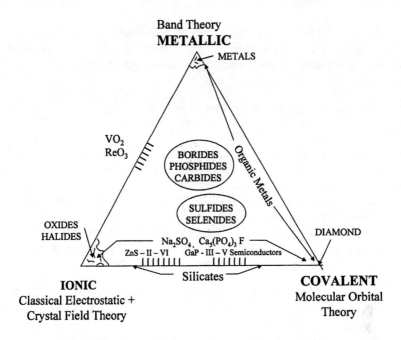

*Figure 1: The three types of strong chemical bonds with corresponding theoretical model. Typical compounds with various pure and mixed bond types are illustrated.*

The ionic model is based on classical electrostatic forces between charged ions. The attractive force pulling ions together is a Coulomb force that increases slowly with the inverse of the distance between the ions. When ions approach each other to a distance where the outer electron shells begin to overlap, there is a short-range repulsive force that increases very rapidly as the interatomic distance decreases further. The balance between attractive and repulsive forces defines the equilibrium interatomic distance and is expressed by a potential function of the form

$$V = -\frac{e^2 z_+ z_- A}{r} + B e^{-\frac{r}{\rho}}$$

Several expressions have been used for the repulsive potential. The one given here is the Born potential. Although there is some quantum mechanical justification for this function, the parameter, $\rho$, is generally taken as an empirical parameter with a numerical value of 0.345. It should be noted that as a theory of the chemical bond, the electrostatic model doesn't actually display any bonds. The electrons remain localized on their parent ions, the electrostatic fields are spherically distributed, and the charge density between the ions trends toward zero.

The potential function applies to individual ion pairs. By fixing r = equilibrium distance and multiplying by the number of ion pairs per mole of material, $N_0$, equation (1) leads immediately to the lattice energy, U.

$$ U = -\frac{e^2 z_+ z_- A N_0}{r_{equil}} (1 - \frac{\rho}{r_{equil}}) $$

In these equations, e is the charge on the electron, $z_+$ and $z_-$ are the formal charges on the cation and the anion respectively, and A is known as the Madelung constant. The repulsive force acts only over short distances and varies little with next nearest neighbors. However, the Coulomb attractive forces varies slowly with distance and thus for a target cation, the attraction by nearest neighbor anions, repulsion by next nearest neighbor cations, more attraction by next-next-nearest neighbor anions and so on, gives rise to a long series of terms which converges only slowly. The sum of the series is the Madelung constant, A. The Madelung constant is a dimensionless parameter determined only by the arrangement of the ions and not by their actual interatomic distances. As a result, each crystal structure type has its own unique value of the Madelung constant.

In spite of its theoretical simplicity and classical forces, the ionic model works remarkably well. Calculated lattice energies are usually within five percent of measured values. The modern reincarnation of the electrostatic model is in molecular dynamics. These calculations use potential functions not very different from those described above.

The main problem with the classical electrostatic model as a theory of the solid state is that equation (2) gives only the ground state of the system. There is no provision for excited states and no provision for any sort of transport properties. To some extent, these limitations can be overcome by superimposing crystal field theory[5] on the simple ionic model. Crystal field theory assumes a fixed and pre-determined anion arrangement which provides an electrostatic field that interacts with the orbital states of d- and f-electrons of the cations. The resulting energy levels are determined by the symmetry of the crystallographic site occupied by the transition metal or rare earth ion, and by the interatomic distances. Although crystal field energy levels are in principle determined by d-orbital and f-orbital wave functions, the calculations are compacted into a few empirically derived parameters so that crystal field theory is very useful in describing magnetic properties, color, and luminescence of ionic compounds. The contribution of crystal field energies to the overall lattice energy is small but sufficient to account for unusual crystal chemical behavior in ions such as $Cr^{3+}$ and $Ni^{2+}$.

The Covalent Bond: Molecular Orbital Models

The conceptual picture of molecules is that they are arrays of atoms held together by bonds. The molecular orbital model describes the bonds as being built up from mixtures of the atomic orbitals derived from the atoms being bonded. One must assume a structure and estimate interatomic distances. The orbital combinations are in large part determined by the symmetry of the assumed structure because allowed combinations are required to transform properly under the operations of the molecular point group. Once the orbital structure is determined, the orbitals are populated with the available electrons drawn from all atomic orbitals outside the closed noble gas cores. The more orbitals and the more electrons that can be included, the more accurate the calculated energy levels. Early molecular orbital calculations were limited by available computing power and many simplifications had to be made. The current generation of molecular orbital models such as GAUSSIAN98 have large basis sets and can be used as working tools without too much concern for the internal mathematics. Many useful calculations can be made[6,7]. These programs are particularly useful for excited states, transient species, surface species and other molecular units where direct observation is difficult.

Molecules are intrinsically closed systems whereas crystals are not. Direct application of molecular orbital methods to the energy level structure and overall stability of crystalline solids required extracting clusters or fragments that are small enough to allow computation. By repeating the calculations for various combinations of crystallographic parameters, the combination that produces the minimum energy can be identified. Good results have been obtained for structures as complex as spinel and olivine[8].

The Metallic Bond: Band Models

Band theory was created in order to understand the electrical conductivity, thermal conductivity, and other properties of metals. The basic concept was that of an array of atomic cores, arranged according to the known crystal structure of the metal. The valence electrons, rather then being localized on any particular atom were treated as an electron gas, completely delocalized throughout the crystal structure. The wave functions for the valence electrons would all mix generating a number of states comparable to the number of atoms in the crystal. Because of the Pauli exclusion principle, there would remain closely spaced, but discrete energy states so that the overall energy levels would have spread to form bands from fractions of an electron volt to several electron volts wide. The guiding symmetry is the translational symmetry of the metal structure. Because electrons are delocalized, they also carry momentum. The results of band structure calculations are plotted as energy as a function of momentum along specified directions in the Brillouin zone.

Band theory is the most comprehensive of the various theories of the chemical bond. It can accommodate insulators and semiconductors and indeed metals become simply structures with partially filled bands. The main drawback of the band model is that it lacks the intuitive or interpretive aspects associated with the chemical bonds of molecular orbital theory and full calculations must be made for quantitative interpretation, something that is difficult for complex structures. However, in recent years, good success has been achieved in blending band concepts with both crystal chemistry and with more traditional views of the chemical bond[9,10]. There has been a convergence of the three models into hybrids that can be adapted to structures of interest.

## STRUCTURE TYPES AND STRUCTURE FIELD MAPS

The reason why crystal chemistry remains an effective model for organizing and predicting crystal structures, in spite of the impressive improvements in theoretical models for the chemical bond, is that all of the theories produce potential functions of roughly the same shape (Fig. 2). Further, the central variable is the interatomic distance. So at the sophistication level of crystal chemistry's back-of-the-envelope calculations, the detailed theory of the chemical bond doesn't really matter all that much so long as some aspect of ionic character remains. It is possible to proceed with an organizational scheme that utilizes as variables only ionic radii, ionic charge, and to a lesser extent ionic polarizability and special electronic features of ions.

### Binary Compounds

The structures of binary compounds consist mostly of arrangements of a single kind of cation coordinated by a single kind of anion. Because of the necessity of local charge neutrality, the possible arrangements of ions depends both on the ionic radii and charge and on proportions of the ions. Thus comparisons are made for structures with the same stoichiometry: $AX$, $AX_2$, $A_2X_3$, and any others of interest.

Examination of a very large number of compounds with the same stoichiometry reveals that they can be represented by only a small number of structure types. Many compounds will be isostructural which implies (i) same stoichiometry, properly defined, (ii) same relative atomic arrangement meaning same coordination numbers and same polyhedral linkages, and (iii) same space group. For each structure type, one compound is defined as a prototype. The choice of prototype is usually historical and certainly arbitrary. If the prototype occurs in nature, its mineral name makes a convenient label for the structure type. The advantage of the mineral name is that it implies both a composition and a structure. Thus we speak of the rutile structure (but not the $TiO_2$ structure), the calcite structure (but not the $CaCO_3$ structure), the spinel structure, the garnet structure, the perovskite structure and others. Something like 30 – 40 structure

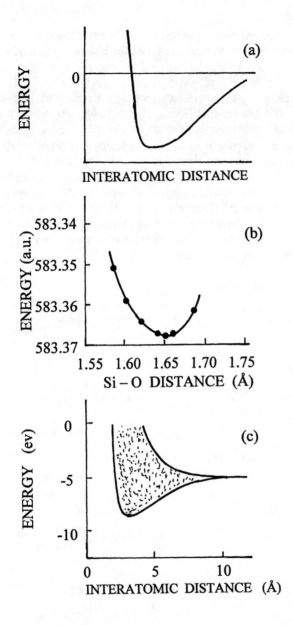

*Figure 2: Potential functions for the three models of the chemical bond. A) Sketch of classic electrostatic potential. B) Potential function for SiO bond determined by earlier molecular orbital calulation[11] and C) 3s band of sodium.*

types are sufficient to describe most of the compounds of interest to materials science. Some of the more important structure types for binary compounds are given in Table III.

For binary compounds, there are three primary plotting variables: anion/cation ratio, the cation radius, and the anion radius. If one holds the composition constant, all compounds with that composition can be plotted in terms of cation and anion radius. The result is known as a structure field map. A set of structure field maps for the AX composition are shown in Fig. 3 using Shannon-Prewitt crystal radii[12,13]. The anions have been separated into three groups by charge and the transition metal ions are also plotted separately. These maps demonstrate that ionic radii alone map the structures effectively but that the position of structure field boundaries also depends on charge. Note the trend in coordination numbers. As the anion charge is increased, lower coordination structures dominate. The 8-coordinated CsCl structure appears only among the

Table III. Some important binary structure types.

| Structure | Prototype | Coordination No. | Space Group |
|---|---|---|---|
| **AX** | | | |
| Boron Nitride | BN | 3 | $P6_3/mmc$ |
| Sphalerite | ZnS | 4 | $F\bar{4}3m$ |
| Wurtzite | ZnS | 4 | $P6_3mc$ |
| Halite | NaCl | 6 | Fm3m |
| Niccolite | NiAs | 6 | $P6_3mc$ |
| CsCl | CsCl | 8 | Pm3m |
| | | | |
| **AX$_2$** | | | |
| Quartz | $SiO_2$ | 4 | $P3_121, P3_221$ |
| Rutile | $TiO_2$ | 6 | $P4_2/mnm$ |
| Brucite | $Mg(OH)_2$ | 6 | $P\bar{3}m1$ |
| Fluorite | $CaF_2$ | 8 | Fm3m |
| Cotunnite | $PbCl_2$ | 9 | Pnam |
| | | | |
| **A$_2$X$_3$** | | | |
| Corundum | $Al_2O_3$ | 6 | $R\bar{3}c$ |
| Bixbyite | $Mn_2O_3$ | 6 | Ia3 |
| A-Type | $La_2O_3$ | | $P\bar{3}m1$ |

halides. Note also the overlap between the 6-coordinated NiAs structure of the transition metal chalcogenides with the NaCl structure of the alkaline earth chalcogenides. This is indicative of the importance of the d-orbitals in certain cases. The NiAs structure is composed of face-sharing octahedral which are stabilized by d-orbital overlap across the shared faces.

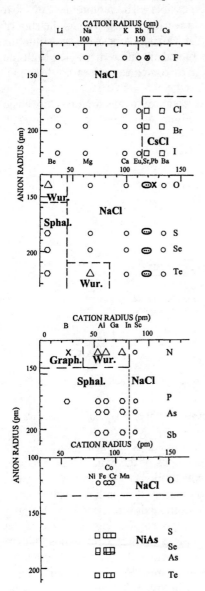

*Figure 3: Structure field maps for AX compounds. The maps are arranged $A^+X^-$, $A2^+X2^-$, $A3^+X3^-$, and $M2^+X2^-$ where M is a divalent transition metal ion.*

## Building-Up Principles

Ternary compounds have two cations, Quaternary compounds have three cations and more complex compositions are possible. The requirement of local charge neutrality requires only that the sum of the cation charges equal the sum of the anion charges. This provides for a great variety of possible substitutions because charges on the cation sites can be mixed in different ways. Multiple substitutions mean that increasing the number of components does not lead to a great increase in the number of distinct structure types.

Some ternary structures are built up as compositional variations on basic binary structures; others are uniquely ternary. Figure 4 outlines the possibilities.

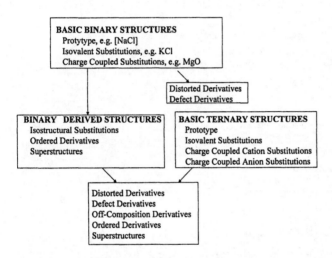

*Figure 4: Schematic outline showing derivative structures of primary parent structures.*

For each of the basic binary structures there is a defined prototype, for example NaCl. Most ions within the size constraints of the structure field can be substituted for $Na^+$ or $Cl^-$ as isovalent substitutions. For many of these substitutions there will be complete solid solution so that partial substitution is also possible. Other families of isostructural compounds are formed by changing both cation and anion charge, as for example, replacing $Na^+$ by $Mg^{2+}$ and at the same time replacing $Cl^-$ by $O^{2-}$. These substitutions produce compounds that are strictly isostructural with the prototype. However, other closely related structures may occur as small distortions of the primary structures. $VO_2$ is monoclinic but is only slightly distorted from the rutile structure. In Fig. 3, TlF appears in the field of the NaCl structure but it has an orthorhombic distortion of the NaCl structure.

One can simply replace half of the ions of the binary compound randomly with a different isovalent ion to form a ternary compound but this does not form a ternary structure, only a solid solution (e.g. $NaKCl_2$). There are ternary compounds belonging to binary structure types although the end members do not have the binary structure. $LiNdS_2$ is a disordered compound with the NaCl structure but is not a solid solution. In contrast, if the cations are inserted in an ordered way, a new ternary structure may be formed. $LiLuS_2$ is related to NaCl but $Li^+$ and $Lu^{3+}$ are arranged in alternate cation positions. As a result, symmetry is lost, the structure is elongated along the diagonal of the NaCl unit cell and a trigonal ordered derivative structure results. In general, substitution of two ions of the same charge will produce a solid solution whereas substitution of pairs of ions of differing charge will result in an ordered derivative structure.

Superstructures are also ordered arrangement but ordered arrangements that require defining larger unit cells to accommodate the ordered ions. Usually a superstructure is built with unit cells composed of two or more cells of the parent structure stacked in an ordered array. For example, the chalcopyrite structure, prototype $CuFeS_2$, is composed of two cubic sphalerite cells stacked on top of each other to produce a tetragonal cell with roughly the same a-axis as the sphalerite cell but twice the c-axis. Superstructures are found with very long stacking sequences.

Primary ternary structures are those that have no immediate structural relationship with any of the primary binary structures. Usually, this means that there will be more than one cation site, often with different coordination numbers, polyhedral linkages or both. Once the ternary structures have been identified, the structural variants of distorted derivatives, defect and off-composition derivatives, ordered derivatives and superstructures can often be found.

Ternary and Higher Systems

Table IV summarizes some of the more important ternary structures. Much more detail may be found in Muller and Roy's book[14]. The structures are organized by chemical composition as with the binary structures. The convention is to list the larger cation (usually higher coordination number) as A and the smaller cation as B. Considering all possible ternary compositions, it is obvious that there are a large number of possible cation/cation and cation/anion ratios. Table IV is limited to the simpler ratios $ABX_2$, $ABX_3$, $ABX_4$, and $A_2BX_4$ (which keeping with the cation size convention must also include $AB_2X_4$).

Although there are useful materials that fall into most of the structures, some structure types are more important than others. Within the $ABX_2$ family certain of the chalcopyrite compounds are optical materials. Within the $ABX_3$ family, calcite and aragonite are geologically important. However, the perovskite structure and its many derivatives are the core of the entire field of dielectric materials. The $ABX_4$ family is something of a hodge-podge. There are many structures, not all of them listed, based on packings of tetrahedra with various sizes of large A-ion. The zircon structure appears in ceramic pigments and in speciality refractories. In contrast, the $A_2BX_4$ family includes many important structures. Olivine is a major mineral in the earths crust and mantle and its phase transitions in the deep mantle are of important in geophysics. Among the spinel structure compounds are chromite refractories, aluminate optical materials, and ferrite magnetic materials. Spinel superstructures include the β-alumina family of fast ion conductors.

CRYSTAL CHEMISTRY OF DIELECTRIC MATERIALS

The title of this section is rather overly pretentious. Dielectric materials include substances from wax paper to $BaTiO_3$. The term is often used in a broad sense to include ferroelectrics, piezoelectrics, pyroelectrics and other electrically and optically interesting insulators. Included in this very large assemblage of materials would be organic salts (e.g. triglycine sulfate), ionic salts (e.g. potassium dihydrogen phosphate), and a variety of polymers as well as ceramic compounds that fit into crystal chemical categories. The discussion that follows is not only limited to ionic compounds, but is further restricted to compounds related to the perovskite structure. Within this limitation, however, are a very large variety of phenomena at many levels of structural subtlety. Although the perovskite structure allows for a long and complex catalog of derivative structures, a similar catalog could be prepared for most of the structures listed in Table IV.

A huge number of compounds take the perovskite or one of its derivative structures[15]. In addition to dielectric materials, transition metal perovskites have application as catalysts[16] and as fuel cell materials. The high temperature superconductors are also built on perovskite-like structural units[17, 18].

Non-Spherical Ions

The dielectric behavior of materials is described by the dielectric permittivity, both the real part which describes the dielectric response and the imaginary part which describes the dielectric losses. The permittivity in turn is a function of the polarizability of the material. Polarizability is determined in part by the intrinsic polarizability of the ions and in part by dipoles within the structure.

If ions are to be regarded as charged spheres, their polarizability generally increases with ionic radius, larger ions being more polarizable than smaller ions[19]. $Ba^{2+}$ is highly polarizable; $Al^{3+}$ is not. Some ions receive additional contributions to the polarizability from d-electrons and from non-bonding lone pair electrons.

Ions with filled d-shells, $Zn^{2+}$, $Cd^{2+}$, and $Ga^{3+}$ for example, tend to occur in 4-fold coordination when their ionic radii would predict 6-fold coordination. Mixing of metal d-orbitals with ligand p-orbitals enhances a tendency to covalent bonding and the greater polarizability of the shared electron bond.

Certain ions, listed as a "periodic table" in Table V, have filled outer s-orbitals. These electrons do not participate in chemical bonding, but they are space-filling and make the ions decidedly non-spherical. The large and extended lone pair orbitals make these ions highly polarizable. This property is the reason that so many lead and bismuth compounds are interesting dielectric materials.

Table IV. Some important ternary structure types

| Structure | Prototype | Coor. No. A | Coor. No. B | Space Group |
|---|---|---|---|---|
| **ABX$_2$** | | | | |
| Chalcopyrite | $CuFeS_2$ | 4 | 4 | $I\bar{4}2d$ |
| β-NaFeO$_2$ | β-NaFeO$_2$ | 4 | 4 | Pna2$_1$ |
| α-NaFeO$_2$ | α-NaFeO$_2$ | 6 | 6 | $R\bar{3}m$ |
| α-LiFeO$_2$ | α-LiFeO$_2$ | 6 | 6 | I4$_1$/amd |
| Delafossite | $CuFeO_2$ | 2 | 6 | $R\bar{3}m$ |
| | | | | |
| **ABX$_3$** | | | | |
| Calcite | $CaCO_3$ | 6 | 3 | $R\bar{3}c$ |
| Aragonite | $CaCO_3$ | 9 | 3 | Pbnm |
| Ilmenite | $FeTiO_3$ | 6 | 6 | $R\bar{3}$ |
| Perovskite | $SrTiO_3$ | 12 | 6 | Pm3m |
| | | | | |
| **ABX$_4$** | | | | |
| Silica Isotypes | $AlPO_4$ | 4 | 4 | P3$_1$21 |
| Wolframite | $FeWO_4$ | 6 | 6 | P2/c |
| Zircon | $ZrSiO_4$ | 8 | 4 | I4$_1$/amd |
| Scheelite | $CaWO_4$ | 8 | 4 | I4$_1$/a |
| Monazite | $CePO_4$ | 8 | 4 | P2$_1$/n |
| Fergusonite | $YTaO_4$ | 8 | 4 | I2 |
| Anhydrite | $CaSO_4$ | 8 | 4 | Cmcm |
| Barite | $BaSO_4$ | 12 | 4 | Pnma |
| | | | | |
| **A$_2$BX$_4$** | | | | |
| Phenakite | $Be_2SiO_4$ | 4 | 4 | $R\bar{3}$ |
| Olivine | $Mg_2SiO_4$ | 6 | 4 | Pbnm |
| Spinel | $Al_2MgO_4$ | 6 | 4 | Fd3m |
| Thenardite | $Na_2SO_4$-V | 6 | 4 | Fddd |
| Sr$_2$PbO$_4$ | $Sr_2PbO_4$ | 7 | 6 | Pbam |
| K$_2$NiF$_4$ | $K_2NiF_4$ | 9 | 6 | I4/mmm |
| CaFe$_2$O$_4$ | $CaFe_2O_4$ | 8 | 6 | Pnam |
| BaAl$_2$O$_4$ | $BaAl_2O_4$ | 9 | 4 | P6$_3$22 |
| Th$_3$P$_4$ | $CaLa_2S_4$ | 8 | 8 | $I\bar{4}3d$ |

Table V. A "periodic table" of non-bonding, lone pair ions

| | | $As^{3+}$ |
|---|---|---|
| | $Sn^{2+}$ | $Sb^{3+}$ |
| $Tl^{+}$ | $Pb^{2+}$ | $Bi^{3+}$ |

The Primary Structure: Perovskite
The ideal perovskite structure consists of a three dimensional network of corner-sharing octahedra with a large ion in the 12-coordinated site created by the space between the octahedra (Fig. 5).

## THREE VIEWS OF PEROVSKITE

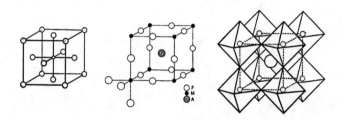

*Figure 5: Three views of the perovskite structure, AMX₃. Left) Unit cell with 6-coordination M-ion at center. Middle) Unit cell with 12-coordination A ion at center. Right) Unit cell displaying framework of corner-sharing octahedral.*

The ideal structure is cubic, space group Pm3m, with a single $ABX_3$ formula in the primitive unit cell. The mineral perovskite, $CaTiO_3$, is an orthorhombic distortion of the ideal structure so $SrTiO_3$ is often taken as the prototype. The ideal cubic perovskite structure is relatively unstable against distortions of various kinds but the overall structural arrangement is extremely stable and permits a great variety of ionic substitutions. Goldschmidt pointed out long ago that the stability range of the perovskite structure could be described by a tolerance factor defined as

$$ t = \frac{(R_A + R_X)}{\sqrt{2}\,(R_B + R_X)} $$

The tolerance factor ranges from 0.8 to 0.9 for perovskite structures and from 0.7 to 1.0 if various distorted derivatives are included.
The examples given below all have the basic perovskite arrangement but not all have the ideal cubic perovskite structure. The term "perovskite" structure is applied to the entire set of related structures whereas the Pm3m cubic structure is called the "ideal perovskite structure".

The prototype is a II-IV perovskite with 12-coordinated divalent ions and 6-coordinated tetravalent ions. This permits a series of isovalent substitutions such as

$SrTiO_3$
$BaTiO_3$
$PbTiO_3$
$PbZrO_3$
$SrPbO_3$

Some perovskites have defect structures

$SrFeO_{2.84}$
$La_{0.94}Mn_{0.98}\square_{0.02}O_3$

Halide structure perovskites exist based on charge-coupled substitutions such as

$KMgF_3$
$RbMnF_3$
$CsCaCl_3$
$CsCdBr_3$

In spite of structural stability over a large range of cation sizes, anion substitution is more limited. Chalcogenide perovskites are extremely rare. The replacement of the ionic oxide and halide ions by the more covalent sulfide, selenide and telluride ions destabilizes the structure.

Because the requirement of local charge balance can be satisfied in different ways over the two cation sites, there are matched valence substitutions such as

| | |
|---|---|
| $LaAlO_3$ | III-III perovskite |
| $NaNbO_3$ | I-V perovskite |
| $\square ReO_3$ | 0-VI perovskite |

Multiple substitutions on one or both of the cation sites, sometimes known as half-breed derivatives, are limited only by ionic size and the requirement for local charge balance. There are hundreds of possibilities but some have been extensively investigated because of their useful dielectric properties. A few examples are

$[KNd]^{xii}[Ti_2]^{vi}O_3$
$[Pb_3]^{xii}[MgNb_2]^{vi}O_9$     alternatively $PbMg_{1/3}Nb_{2/3}O_3$ (PMN)
$[Ba_3]^{xii}[ZnNb_2]^{vi}O_9$     (BZN)
$[BaNa]^{xii}[NbTi]^{vi}O_6$
$[Pb_2]^{xii}[ScTa]^{vi}O_6$

It is not, of course, necessary that integral substitutions be made. Most combinations of either the $ABX_3$ compositions or the half-breed derivatives permit wide ranges of solid solutions. One such is $Pb(Zr_{1-x}Ti_x)O_3$, the lead zirconate-titanate (PZT) series of transducer perovskites. In the more complex substitutions, the ions may be randomly distributed over A or B sites in which case the perovskite structure is maintained, or they may be ordered in various ways to produce ordered derivative structures. Particular compositions are selected to optimize specific device applications[20].

First Level Subtlety: Distorted Derivatives of the Perovskite Structure

The corner-sharing octahedral framework of the perovskite structure is only weakly stable against distortions arising from rotation or shearing of the octahedra. If the balance of Coulomb potentials of the A and B cations is not close to the value needed for the ideal perovskite structure, the structure will distort.

Rotation of the octahedra around the [111] axis reduces the symmetry from cubic to rhombohedral[21,22]. $LaAlO_3$ is the prototype with space group $R\bar{3}c$ (Fig. 6A). The distortion from cubic symmetry is very small. At high temperatures, 435 °C, for $LaAlO_3$ itself, the distortion is relaxed and the compounds take on the ideal perovskite structure[23].

Most common of the distorted perovskites is the $GdFeO_3$ structure[24,25]. It is orthorhombic, space group Pbnm (Fig. 6B). The distortion from the ideal perovskite structure is substantially larger. Four of the 12 A-O distances have been extended so far that it is probably more accurate to describe the A-ion as having 8-fold coordination. The framework of corner-sharing octahedra is preserved although in distorted form.

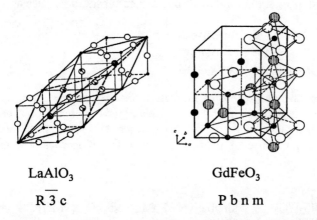

$LaAlO_3$            $GdFeO_3$

$R\bar{3}c$              P b n m

*Figure 6: The crystal structures of A) trigonal $LaAlO_3$ and B) orthorhombic $GdFeO_3$*

Both rhombohedral and orthorhombic distortions appear mainly in the III-III perovskites. The energetics of these distortions are sufficiently large that distinct structure fields can be mapped (Fig. 7). The structure field maps show that nearly ideal perovskite structures appear mainly among the II-IV compounds. These plots do not take account of distortions arising from spontaneous polarization.

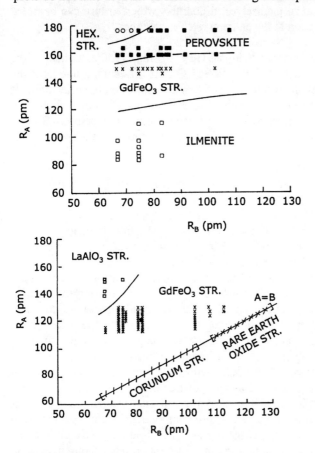

*Figure 7: Structure field map for II-IV perovskites and II-III perovskites. (Structural data from Muller and Roy[14] and crystal radii from Shannon[13])*

Second Level Subtlety:   Phase Transformations, Spontaneous Polarization and Domain Structures

The ions that comprise most compounds of dielectric interest have rather unexceptional electronic structures. The alkali and alkaline earth ions have noble-gas cores with a polarizability determined only by the distortion of the spherical closed shells under the influence of an electric field. $Pb^{2+}$ and $Bi^{3+}$ which also appear as the A ion are more highly polarizable because of the extended electron cloud of the non-bonding outer s-orbitals. Many of the B-ions can be considered transition metal ions with empty d-orbitals. Overall, one would expect the sphere packing model of crystal chemistry to work rather well. Unfortunately it doesn't. Not predicted, the B-ions tend to move off the center of symmetry of the ideal perovskite structure producing a strong electric dipole. In many of these materials, the dipoles arrange themselves in domains which in turn can be poled to produce a bulk polarization to the entire crystal or ceramic.

Ferroelectricity was described in $BaTiO_3$ in the 1940's although the phenomenon was known much earlier[26]. In $BaTiO_3$, the off-center ion reduces the symmetry from cubic with the resulting symmetry dependent on the orientation of the dipoles. The energy minima of the possible orientations differ only slightly so that orientations can be changed by changing temperature or pressure. $BaTiO_3$ undergoes three phase transitions associated with reorientation of the spontaneous dipoles[15].

Trigonal (-90 °C) → Orthorhombic (0 °C) → Tetragonal (120 °C) → Cubic

Each polymorph corresponds to a different dipole orientation, [111] for trigonal, [110] for orthorhombic, and [001] for tetragonal. The cubic, paraelectric, form has randomly oriented dipoles and the ideal perovskite structure. None of the polymorphs differs much from the ideal perovskite structure
Dipole ordering is at least part of the explanation for why ideal perovskites are so rare. Many perovskite compounds are ferroelectrics or antiferroelectrics and as such are lower symmetry distortions of the ideal structure. At some temperature, the Curie temperature, the dipoles relax and the material takes on the cubic structure of the ideal perovskite. The spontaneous polarization it difficult to construct structure field maps because these assume ambient temperature.
Shifts in the orientation of the dipoles with corresponding small changes in crystal structure can also be induced by compositional changes. One of the best known systems is $PbZrO_3$-$PbTiO_3$. At room temperature, $PbZrO_3$ is rhombohedral and $PbTiO_3$ is tetragonal. These compounds form a complete solid solution $PbZr_{1-x}Ti_xO_3$. At x in the range of 0.45 to 0.48, the dipoles reorient and the structure shifts over a very narrow composition range from rhombohedral to tetragonal. The boundary between the two structures, known as a morphotropic phase boundary, is essentially independent of temperature up to the Curie temperature, a property useful in PZT materials.

Third Level Subtlety: Dynamic Disorder and Nanodomains
The main crystal chemical classifications are based on crystal structure determinations, mainly by X-ray diffraction. The relationship of distorted derivatives to the parent structure can also be identified by comparison of the crystal structures. Ordering of dipoles such as those described above for $BaTiO_3$ reveal themselves in slight distortions of the ideal crystal structure which can be

identified by X-ray patterns taken at appropriate temperatures or by polarizing light microscopy. According to X-ray data, the paraelectric form of $BaTiO_3$ should have the $Ti^{4+}$ ion on the center of symmetry of the cubic cell. Detailed structure determinations at temperatures between 120 and 180 °C reveal a more complicated structural arrangement[27]. The $Ti^{4+}$ ion is displaced from the center of symmetry along the [111] direction giving eight local disorder positions. It was also found that $Ba^{2+}$ was displaced from the cell corner along [110] giving twelve possible positions and that the $O^{2-}$ were distributed in rings around their face-centered positions (Fig. 8). What appears as a cubic cell above the Curie temperature is a statistical distribution among many equally probable positions. This may be termed "dynamical disorder" and is to be distinguished from structural disorder in which ions or vacancies are distributed in disordered but fixed positions in the unit cell.

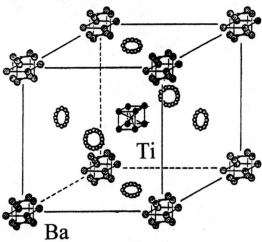

*Figure 8: Possible positions for displacement of ions from their ideal equipoint in cubic BaTiO3 (After Itoh et al[27]).*

Some insight into dynamical disorder involving dipole orientations may be obtained from the temperature dependence of Raman line widths. Figure 9 compares the Raman spectra of $TiO_2$, which has no ferroelectric domain structure at two temperatures[28]. The pronounced sharpening of the Raman lines at low temperature is an indication of freezing the dipoles into a single minimum energy orientation. Measurement of Raman line widths, for example in PMN, as a function of temperature sometimes reveals abrupt changes which may be the signature of subtle order-disorder phase transitions[29].

The domain structure taken by ferroelectric and antiferroelectric materials has a specific crystallographic orientation and switchable. A more subtle domain structure appears in compounds with complex compositions. There may appear regions is which the composition or degree of ordering is shifted in one direction and other nearby regions when the compositions or ordering is shifted in a different direction. These regions are typically small and intergrown. They may be referred to as "nanodomains". Compounds with nanodomain internal structure often exhibit broad and rather diffuse phase transitions between ferroelectric and paraelectric states in contrast to the sharp transitions in well ordered homogeneous compounds. The dielectric properties reflect the broad transitions giving rise to a class of compounds known as "relaxor ferroelectrics[30].

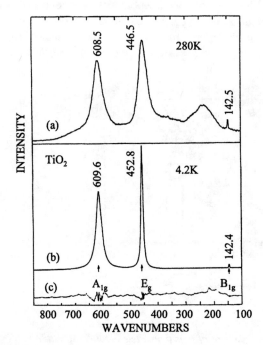

Figure 9: Raman spectra of rutile, TiO2, at room temperature and at liquid helium temperature (After Betsch et. al.[27]).

Ordered Derivatives of the Perovskite Structure

If two or more different ions randomly occupy the same site in a crystal there is no change in crystal structure or symmetry. The site occupancy is of an "average" ion with size intermediate between that of the two end-member ions. If the substituting ions have the same charge and are not too different in size, the substitution is likely to be random. However, if there is a substantial charge mismatch, there will be a tendency for the substituting ions to occupy the sites in an ordered way. The driving force is from the interaction of the next-nearest neighbor cation charges. The greater the charge difference, the more likely is an ordered structure. In an ordered structure, cation sites that were equivalent in the parent phase become inequivalent, resulting in a loss of symmetry and a derivative space group. Ordering occurs in perovskite structure on both A and B sites with various arrangements possible[31].

B-site 1:1 order is found in compounds such as $Pb_2ScTaO_6$ (often written $PbSc_{1/2}Ta_{1/2}O_3$). The ordered structure is face-centered cubic with a unit cell roughly twice that of the parent perovskite cell. This ordering scheme gives compounds isomorphic with the $(NH_4)_3FeF_6$ structure. Many such ordered compounds are known where the $B^{3+}$ - $B^{5+}$ combination drives the ordering process[32].

Ordering at 1:2 ratios occurs in a variety of compounds such as $Ba_3SrTa_2O_9$ where both the $Sr^{2+}$ - $Ta^{5+}$ charge mismatch and also a substantial size mismatch drive the ordering process. Most 1:2 ordered compounds have a hexagonal superstructure and contain the II-V valence combination on the B sites. Included with this family is $Ba_3ZnTa_2O_9$, an important microwave ceramic. Recently an example of I-IV valence combination, $La_3LiTi_2O_9$, has been synthesized[33].

Superstructures of the Perovskite Structure

Structural ordering often results in the formation of a superstructure which is usually composed of a small integral number of parent cells which themselves differ only by the distribution of ordered ions. A more elaborate form of superstructure can be constructed by mixing more than one parent structure – rather like the structural equivalent of a binary compound. Consider $Sr_2TiO_4$. This compound is often classified as an $A_2BX_4$ composition with the $K_2NiF_4$ structure. However, one can think of the compound as the 1$^{st}$ member of a series (with $SrTiO_3$ itself as the 0$^{th}$ member): $SrO.SrTiO_3$, $SrO.2SrTiO_3$, $SrO.3SrTiO_3$ .......$SrO.nSrTiO_3$. The compounds in this sequence are known as Ruddlesden-Popper phases (Fig. 10(A)). They consist of n perovskite layers separated by a single NaCl-like SrO layer and thus should be considered as superstructure derivatives of the perovskite structure[34]. Distinct single-phase compounds exist up to $Sr_4Ti_3O_{10}$ but complex intergrowth structures appear at larger values of n[35].

Similar superstructures can be formed with $Bi^{3+}$ compounds such as $Bi_4Ti_3O_{12}$ (Fig. 10(B)). These are known as Aurivillius phases. Again there are varying numbers of perovskite layers but in the Aurivillius phases, the $Bi_2O_2$ layer consists of square pyramids rather than NaCl-structures because of the non-bonding lone pair of 6-s electrons in the $Bi^{3+}$ ions.

Structures Near Perovskite

One could construct an structure field map for all compounds with the $ABX_3$ composition but we here consider only those that immediately border the perovskite structure. There is the case of A-ions that are too small to fit into the 12-coordinated A-site and there is the case of structures where the B-sites lose their corner-sharing arrangement.

$ABX_3$ compositions with A-ion sizes too small for the 12-coordinated site in perovskite take on 6-6 coordinated structures derived from the corundum structure. Corundum, $Al_2O_3$, has both $Al^{3+}$ ions in equivalent 6-coordinated sites

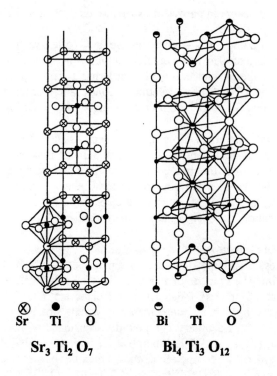

| ⊗ | ● | ○ | | ⊖ | ● | ○ |
|---|---|---|---|---|---|---|
| Sr | Ti | O | | Bi | Ti | O |

$$Sr_3 Ti_2 O_7 \qquad\qquad Bi_4 Ti_3 O_{12}$$

*Figure 10: A) $Sr_3Ti_2O_7$, a two-layer Ruddlesden-Popper phase. B) $Bi_4Ti_3O_{12}$, a three layer Aurivillius phase.*

in space group $R\bar{3}c$. It can be made into a ternary compound by replacing one $Al^{3+}$ by one kind of ion and the other $Al^{3+}$ by a different ion. If the substituting ions have different charges, there are two possible structural orderings. The II-IV valence combination generally leads to the ilmenite structure, $FeTiO_3$, with space group $R\bar{3}$. The I-V valence combination leads to the $LiNbO_3$ structure with space group R3c. The two ordering schemes arise from two different cation arrangements. $LiNbO_3$ and the isomorphic $LiTaO_3$ are ferroelectric and are often classified with the perovskite structure.

At temperatures above 1460 °C the perovskite form of $BaTiO_3$ converts into a hexagonal form structurally different from perovskite. Hexagonal $BaTiO_3$ is one member of a complex family of structures based on hexagonal packing with some face-sharing octahedra (Fig. 11). The sequence of structures has varying degrees of hexagonal packing[14].

BaNiO$_3$ structure:  2 layers, hhh packing, 100% face sharing
BaRuO$_3$ structure:  9 layers, chh packing, 67% face sharing
BaMnO$_3$ structure:  4 layers, chch packing, 50% face sharing
Hex BaTiO$_3$ structure:  6 layers, cch packing, 33% face sharing
Perovskite structure:  3 layers, ccc packing, 0% face sharing

These structures also appear in a series of CsMF$_3$ compounds where M = Mg, Ni, Zn, Co, Fe, and Mn[36]. At high pressures, these structures interconvert with the BaNiO$_3$ structure appearing at the lowest pressure and perovskite at the highest pressure.

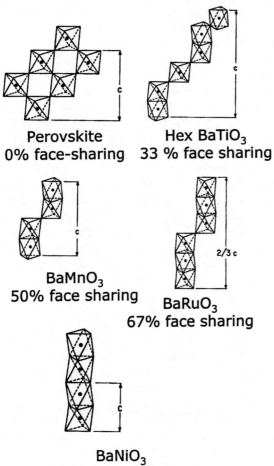

**Perovskite** **Hex BaTiO$_3$**
**0% face-sharing** **33 % face sharing**

**BaMnO$_3$**
**50% face sharing** **BaRuO$_3$**
**67% face sharing**

**BaNiO$_3$**
**100 % face sharing**

*Figure 11: ABX$_3$ compounds with various degrees of hexagonal packing. (Adapted from Longo and Kafalas[36])*

## Structures Off-Composition from Perovskite

Crystal chemists usually discuss the systematics of crystal structures with respect to small integral cation/cation and cation/anion ratios. However, it is legitimate to also consider the structural arrangements for other bulk compositions. Only two examples are considered here: the tungsten bronze structures and the pyrochlore structure.

$WO_3$ has a small distortion of the perovskite structure making it an example of the 0-VI variety. When alkali metals are added to $WO_3$ (or $MoO_3$) the alkali ion enters the empty 12-fold site. Electrical neutrality is maintained by reducing $W^{6+}$ or $Mo^{6+}$ to $W^{4+}$ or $Mo^{4+}$. Because of the mixed valence states on the B-sites, some bronzes are semiconductors and some are metallic. For example potassium molybdenum bronze is described by $K_xMoO_3$. A red compound with x = 0.26 is a semiconductor. A metallic blue compound with x = 0.28 is metallic[37]. These compounds take the perovskite structure but without the ideal $ABX_3$ composition. Insulator tungsten bronze structures also exist without the mixed valence state composition. $PbNb_2O_6$ is typical but there are many other compounds[38]. The compound is a tetragonal distortion of the perovskite structure and is ferroelectric.

The pyrochlore structure intrudes onto investigations of perovskite ferroelectrics because of its similar chemical composition and some pyrochlores are themselves ferroelectric. The prototype is $Cd_2Nb_2O_7$, the mineral pyrochlore. The coordination scheme is $A_2^{viii}B_2^{vii}O_7$. With one less oxygen, the structure would be clearly related to perovskite. However, there are really two additional anion sites with one of them an ordered vacancy so the formula should really be written $A_2B_2O_7\square$. The pyrochlore structure is a superstructure based on the fluorite structure. Both have full cubic symmetry, space group Fm3m, but the cell edge of the pyrochlore cell is about twice that of the fluorite cell. The pyrochlore cell consists of eight octants each of which is a fluorite cell with one missing anion in an ordered arrangement.

## CONCLUSIONS

Traditional crystal chemistry provides broad brush principles that do well at defining primary structures (NaCl, rutile, fluorite, perovskite, spinel, garnet and many others). These involve energy minima that are so large that consideration of composition, ionic size and ionic charge are sufficient to define the minima. At the next step down, details of ionic size and charge account in a reasonable fashion for distorted structures ($LaAlO_3$ and $GdFeO_3$ as distorted derivatives of perovskite) and for ordered structures. More subtle levels of structural variability such as phase transitions, nanodomains, and dynamic disorder involve energy differences that are so small, that the rather crude measures of ionic size, charge, and polarizability are no longer good predictors.

Crystal chemistry is a useful guidebook to get the materials designer close to the final goal. Once the goal is approached, it is time to turn to the much more powerful but also much more highly focused models for the chemical bond and for subtleties in crystal structure.

## ACKNOWLEGEMENT

This tutorial is drawn in part from lecture notes for a graduate course in Crystal Chemistry that I taught at Penn State for many years. The course was inherited from a similar course taught by Professor Rustum Roy for many more years and from which I learned Crystal Chemistry. I am very grateful to Professor Roy for that long ago training in crystal chemistry. I am also very grateful to E.L. White for her assistance in preparation of the figures.

## REFERENCES

[1] V.M. Goldschmidt, "Geochemische Verteilungsgesetze der Elemente VII: Die Gesetze der Kristallchemie," *Skrifter Norsk Videnskaps Akademie Oslo*, No. 2 (1926). V.M. Goldschmidt, "Some principles of crystal chemistry in relation to Geochemistry"; Chap. 6, pp. 80-125 in *Geochemistry*, Oxford University Press, London, 1958.

[2] L. Pauling "The principles determining the structure of complex ionic crystals," *Journal of the American Chemical Society* **51** 1010-1026 (1929). L. Pauling, *The Nature of the Chemical Bond*, Cornell University Press, Ithaca, 644 pp., 1960.

[3] M.C. Neuburger, "Kristallchemie der anorganischen Verbindungen," *Sammlung chemischer und chemisch-technischer Vorträge*, No. 17, 115 pp. (1933).

[4] R.C. Evans, *An Introduction to Crystal Chemistry*, 2nd Ed., Cambridge University Press, Cambridge, 411 pp., 1964.

[5] B.N. Figgis and M.A.Hitchon, *Ligand Field Theory and Its Applications*, John Wiley, New York, 2002.

[6] A. Hinchliffe, *Modelling Molecular Structures*, 2nd Ed., John Wiley, New York, 336 pp, 2000.

[7] J.A. Tossell and D.J. Vaughan, Theoretical Geochemistry: Application of Quantum Mechanics in the Earth and Mineral Sciences, Oxford University Press, New York, 514 pp, 1992.

[8] P. D'Arco, B. Silvi, C. Roetti and R. Orlando, "Comparative study of spinel compounds: A pseudopotential periodic Hartree-Fock calculation of $Mg_2SiO_4$, $Mg_2GeO_4$, $Al_2MgO_4$, and $Ga_2MgO_4$," *Journal of Geophysical Research*, **96** 6107-6112 (1991).

[9] R. Hoffmann, "How chemistry and physics meet in the solid state," *Angewandte Chemie, International Edition*, **26** 846-878 (1987).

[10] J.K. Burdett, *Chemical Bonding in Solids*, Oxford University Press, New York, 319 pp, 1995.

[11] G.V. Gibbs, "Molecules as models for bonding in silicates," *American Mineralogist* **67** 421-450 (1982).

[12] R.D. Shannon and C.T. Prewitt, "Effective ionic radii in oxides and fluorides," *Acta Crystallographica* **B25** [5] 925-946 (1969).

[13] R.D. Shannon, "Revised effective ionic radii and systematic studies of interatomic distances in halides and chalcogenides," *Acta Crystallographica* **A32** [5] 751-767 (1976).

[14] O. Muller and R. Roy, *The Major Ternary Structural Families*, Springer-Verlag, Berlin, 487 pp, 1974.

[15] F.S. Galasso, *Structure, Properties and Preparation of Perovskite-Type Compounds*, Pergamon Press, Oxford, 207 pp, 1969.

[16] M.A. Peña and J.L.G. Fierro, "Chemical structures and performance of perovskite oxides," *Chemical Reviews* **101** 1981-2017 (2001).

[17] M.T. Anderson, J.T. Vaughey and K.R. Poeppelmeier, "Structural similarities among oxygen-deficient perovskites," *Chemistry of Materials* **5** 151-165 (1993).

[18] R.J. Cava, "Oxide superconductors," *Journal of the American Ceramic Society* **83** [1] 5-28 (2000).

[19] R.D. Shannon, "Dielectric polarizabilities of ions in oxides and fluorides," *Journal of Applied Physics* **73** 348-366 (1993).

[20] K. Uchino, *Ferroelectric Devices*, Marcel Dekker, New York, 308 pp, 2000.

[21] C. Michel, J.M. Moreau and W.J. James, "Structural relationships in compounds with $R\bar{3}c$ symmetry," *Acta Crystallographica* **B27** 501-503 (1971).

[22] H.D. Megaw and C.N.W. Darlington, "Geometrical and structural relations in the rhombohedral perovskites," *Acta Crystallographica* **A31** 161-173 (1975).

[23] M. Marezio, P.D. Dernier and J.P. Remeika, "The crystal structures of orthorhombic $SmAlO_3$ and of trigonal $NdAlO_3$," *Journal of Solid State Chemistry* **4** 11-19 (1972)

[24] S. Geller and E.A. Wood, "Crystallographic studies of perovskite-like compounds. I. Rare earth orthoferrites and $YFeO_3$, $YCrO_3$, $YAlO_3$," *Acta Crystallographica* **9** 563-568 (1956).

[25] S. Geller and V.B. Bala, "Crystallographic studies of perovskite-like compounds. II. Rare earth aluminates," *Acta Crystallographica* **9** 1019-1025 (1956).

[26] L.E. Cross and R.E. Newnham, "History of ferroelectrics", in *Ceramics and Civilization. III. High Technology Ceramics – Past, Present and Future*, The American Ceramic Society, Columbus, OH, pp. 289-305.

[27] K. Itoh, L.Z. Zeng, E. Nakamura, and N. Mishima, "Crystal structure of $BaTiO_3$ in the cubic phase," *Ferroelectrics* **63** 29-37 (1985).

[28] R.J. Betsch, H.L. Park and W.B. White, "Raman spectra of stoichiometric and defect rutile," *Materials Research Bulletin* **26** 613-622 (1991).

[29] H. Idink and W.B. White, "Raman spectroscopic study of order-disorder in lead magnesium niobate," *Journal of Applied Physics* **76** [3] 1789-1793 (1994).

[30] L.E. Cross, "Relaxor ferroelectrics," *Ferroelectrics* **76** 241-267 (1987).

[31] H. Gui, X. Zhang and B. Gu, "Possible order-disorder phase transitions in $(A'_xA"_{1-x})BO_3$ and $A(B'_xB"_{1-x})O_3$ complex perovskites," *Journal of Physics of Condensed Matter* **8** 1491-1501 (1996).

[32] N. Setter and L.E. Cross, "The contribution of structural disorder to diffuse phase transitions in ferroelectrics," *Journal of Materials Science* **15** 2478-2482 (1980).

[33] A.Y. Borisevich and P.K. Davies, "La($Li_{1/3}Ti_{2/3}$)$O_3$: a new 1:2 ordered perovskite," *Journal of Solid State Chemistry* **170** 198-201 (2003).

[34] I.B. Sharma and D. Singh, "Solid state chemistry of Ruddlesden-Popper type complex oxides," *Bulletin of Materials Science* **21** 363-374 (1998).

[35] W. Tian, X.Q. Pan, J.H. Haeni and D.G. Schlom, "Transmission electron microscopy study of n = 1-5 $Sr_{n+1}Ti_nO_{3n+1}$ epitaxial thin films," *Journal of Materials Research* **16** 2013-2026 (2001).

[36] J.M. Longo and J.A. Kafalas, "The effect of pressure and B-cation size on the crystal structure of $CsBF_3$ compounds (B = Mn, Fe, Co, Ni, Zn, Mg)," *Journal of Solid State Chemistry* **1** 103-108 (1969).

[37] J. Graham and A.D. Wadsley, "The crystal structure of the blue potassium molybdenum bronze, $K_{0.28}MoO_3$," *Acta Crystallographica* **20** 93-100 (1966).

[38] E.C. Subbarao and J. Hrizo, "Solid solutions based on ferroelectric $PbNb_2O_6$," *Journal of the American Ceramic Society* **45** 528-531 (1962).

# COMPUTER SIMULATION OF P-E CURVES OF NON-LINEAR DIELECTRICS

Takkaaki Tsurumi, Song-Min Nam,
Youichi Kubota, Hirofumi Kakemoto
and Satoshi Wada
Tokyo Institute of Technology
Department of Metallurgy and
Ceramics Science
2-12-1 Ookayama, Meguro,
Tokyo 152-8552, JAPAN

Youn-Kyu Choi
Samsung Electro-
Mechanics, Co.Ltd.
314 Meatan-3Dong, Paldal-Gu
Suwon, Kyunggi-Do, 442-743
Korea

ABSTRACT

Non-linear dielectrics such as ferroelectrics, relaxors and tunable capacitors are desired to be handled in circuit simulators such as the SPICE. We have developed a software package to simulate a wide variety of non-linear dielectrics in the SPICE. In the simulation of the polarization vs. electric field curve (P-E curve) using program code of "P-E simulator", a P-E curve was divided into two parts, a non-linear dielectric part and a domain switching part. In the former, the polarization was calculated as a linear expansion in terms of electric field, while in the latter, the polarization due to domain switching was calculated by assuming that the distribution of domain-switching probability was represented by Gaussian distribution functions. Two Gaussian distribution functions were required to accurately simulate the P-E curves of ferroelectric materials with the 180 degree and the non-180 degree domains. A circuit model with two capacitors and an arbitrary voltage source was proposed for non-linear dielectrics in the SPICE. The netlist data to the SPICE were automatically generated using program code of "Mk-netlist" from the parameters determined by the P-E simulator. The P-E curves of a PZT thin film and multi-layered ceramics capacitors were successfully simulated in the SPICE without try-and-error process.

INTRODUCTION

Recently, it is becoming important in many electronic circuits to use non-linear dielectrics in which the polarization vs. electric-field curve (P-E curve) shows non-linear relation with even hysteresis. Typical non-linear dielectrics are ferroelectric capacitor films for non-volatile memories, multi-layered ceramics capacitors (MLCCs) with high capacitance, frequency tunable capacitors, piezoelectric micro-actuators and so on. In the ferroelectric thin film memories, the incorporation of ferroelectric films with standard CMOS processing is a nontrivial procedure for which the interrelationships between the film properties, processing conditions and circuit design should be understood. The thickness of dielectric layers in MLCCs is reducing every year to reach under 1 µm these days. The electric field applied to each dielectric layer is therefore continuously increasing. The dielectric layers in MLCCs consist of the grain cores of barium titanate and the grain shells of relaxors surrounding the grain cores.[1] These materials show highly non-linear behaviors,[1,2] and it is becoming difficult to ignore the effects of the non-linear dielectricity on the operation of electric circuits. In the frequency tunable capacitors, non-linear dielectrics such as strontium barium titanate are used to change the dielectric permittivity with dc-bias field[3]. The piezoelectric micro-actuator is a key devise in many MEMS applications. The actuator is usually made of PZT-based thick films, where the P-E curve is non-linear even in the uni-polar driving.

Although these non-linear capacitors are currently used in many electric circuits, capacitors are still regarded as a linear devise in most circuit simulators such as the SPICE. It is therefore becoming difficult to precisely simulate the response of a circuit. Moreover, there are a lot of scientific studies on non-linear dielectrics in the field of material science but this knowledge is not incorporated into the circuit design at present.

In this study, we are making a bridge to connect the material science and the circuit design in the field of non-linear dielectrics by developing a software package to handle all kinds of non-linear dielectrics including relaxors and ferroelectrics in the SPICE that is regarded as the de-facto standard circuit simulator. We have developed software called "PE-simulator" to simulate the P-E curves of all kind of non-linear dielectrics and to obtain parameters to represent the P-E curve of materials, and software called "Mk-netlist" to automatically produce the netlist date for the SPICE from the parameters.

SIMULATION TECHNIQUE
P-E Simulator
The P-E simulator is software to simulate the P-E curve of non-linear dielectrics. We have selected three conditions to be satisfied in the P-E simulator. The first condition is the universality of the software. The P-E simulator should be applied to any non-linear dielectrics such as tunable dielectrics, relaxors and normal ferroelectrics as well as any material morphology such as bulk ceramics,

single crystals and thin films. The second condition is the uniqueness of the solution. It is possible to simulate any P-E curves if there is no restriction in the number of parameters. However, to obtain the unique solution becomes difficult with increasing parameters. The P-E simulator should be designed to represent the P-E curves with the smallest number of parameters. The third condition is to keep the physical picture of the domain switching in the simulation. Simple mathematical fitting process is not adequate for the P-E simulator because the results of this fitting are not always useful for the improvement and the development of materials.

In the P-E simulator, it was assumed that the P-E curve of non-linear dielectrics could be divided into the two parts, a non-linear dielectric part without hysteresis and a purely domain switching part. In the non-linear dielectric part, the polarization was represented by a linear expansion in terms of electric field, whereas in the domain switching parts, we have employed two Gaussian distribution functions to represent the distribution of coercive field for the domain switching[4]. These two distributions may be corresponding to the 180 degree domain switching and non-180 degree domain switching. Parameters were refined to fit the experimental result by means of the non-linear least-squares procedure.

Circuit Model and Netlist Data

There are some reports proposing circuit models for ferroelectric materials in the SPICE. Yamamoto et al.[5] has employed the Schmitt trigger circuit to produce an electric response with hysteresis, and represented the hysteresis curve of ferroelectric films using many branches with the Schmitt trigger circuit. The Schmitt trigger circuit uses two operational amplifiers. To obtain a smooth curve, the number of branches should be increased, which requires a lot of memories for simulation. It should be also noted that the current into the circuit is not always equal to that from the circuit in this circuit model, indicating that the ferroelectric capacitor is not a passive or symmetric component. Sheikholeslami et al.[6] used a voltage controlled current source (VCCS) and a voltage controlled capacitor (VCC) to generate an electric response with hysteresis. It was also necessary in this circuit to increase the number of branches in order to obtain a smooth hysteresis curve. Moreover, in the two circuit models mentioned above, circuit parameters in each branch should be determined by additional experiments or try-and-error process.

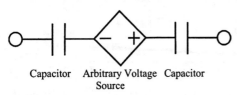

Capacitor    Arbitrary Voltage    Capacitor
Source

Fig.1    Circuit    model    of    non-linear capacitor used in B²Spice.

Our circuit model used in this study is shown in Fig.1. The circuit consists of two linear capacitors and one arbitrary voltage source. This circuit is basically the same as that proposed by Dunn[7]. The non-linear capacitance and hysteresis were generated by controlling the voltage of the source, which was programmed according to the parameters determined in the P-E simulator. Additional experiments or try-and-error process was not necessary to determine the operation of the circuit. The Mk-netlist software was designed to automatically produce the netlist, which is the data format of the SPICE. We used B$^2$Spice A/D 2000 (Beige Bag Software Inc.) to perform the simulation.

RESULTS·AND DISCUSSION
Simulation with the P-E Simulator

Figure 2 (a) shows the observed and simulated P-E curve of a PZT thin film prepared by sol-gel process. The observed result was taken from a reterature[8]. A very good agreement between the observed and simulated results was obtained. The non-linear dielectric part and the purely domain switching part are shown in Fig.2 (b) and (c), respectively. The non-liner dielectric part is not negligible in the case of thin films because the electric field applied to the specimen is extremely high in comparison to the case of bulk specimens. The distribution of domain switching probability was shown in Fig.2(d). Two Gaussian distribution functions

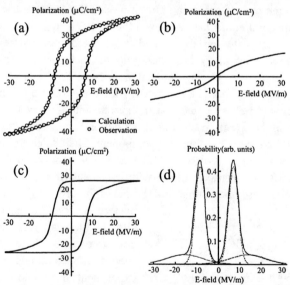

Fig.2 Results of P-E simulator for PZT thin film. (a) observed[8] and calculated P-E curves, (b) the nonlinear dielectric part, (c) the domain switching and (d) Gaussian distributions to represent the domain switching probability.

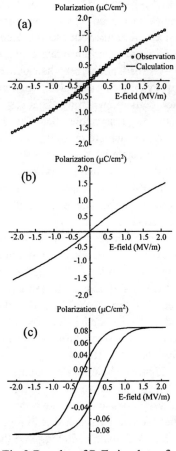

(a) Polarization ($\mu C/cm^2$)

- Observation
— Calculation

E-field (MV/m)

(b) Polarization ($\mu C/cm^2$)

E-field (MV/m)

(c) Polarization ($\mu C/cm^2$)

E-field (MV/m)

Fig.3 Results of P-E simulator for strontium titanate thin film. (a) observed [9] and calculated P-E curves, (b) the non-linear dielectric part and (c) the domain switching part.

were necessary to represent the P-E curve of the PZT film. We believe that the sharp and intense distribution corresponds to the 180 degree domain switching while the broad and week distribution to the non-180 degree domain switching. The parameters used to simulate the P-E curve are as follows: spontaneous polarization = 26.02 $\mu C/cm^2$, coercive field of the center of 1st peak = 7.78 MV/m, sigma of the 1st Gaussian peak = 0.7, coercive field of the center of 2nd peak = 14.78 MV/m, sigma of the 2nd Gaussian peak = 2.58, weight of the 2nd Gaussian peak = 0.357, offset of P-E curve = -0.792 MV/m and 1st to 4th order coefficients of non-linear susceptibility determined by a linear least-squares fitting to Fig.2 (b). Only eight independent parameters were required to fit the experimental data.

Figure 3 (a) shows the observed and simulated P-E curve of a strontium titanate thin film measured at 5 K. This sample is a typical case of the tunable capacitors. The observed curve was calculated from the dc-bias dependence of permittivity reported by Rogers et al.[9] We have also got a good fitting between observed and simulated results. The non-linear dielectric part and the domain switching are shown in Fig.3 (b) and (c), respectively. It is obvious that the P-E curve of the tunable capacitor mainly consists of the former part. However, a small amount of domain switching was necessary to explain the slight hysteresis in the P-E curve. A single Gaussian distribution of domain switching was enough to represent the P-E curve within the accuracy of experimental data.

Figure 4(a) shows the result of a barium titanate single crystal. The observed curve was taken from a reterature[10]. The non-linear dielectric part could not be detected from the experimental curve. The distribution of domain switching

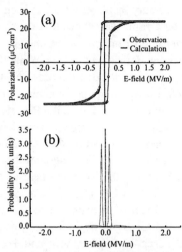

Fig.4 Results of P-E simulator for barium titanate single crystal. (a) observed[10] and calculated P-E curves and (b) Gaussian distributions to represent the domain switching probability.

probability is shown in Fig.4(b). It is interesting that the two Gaussian distributions were necessary to represent the P-E curve of a barium titanate single crystal. A broad and week distribution curve provably corresponds to the 90-degree domain switching. This result seems to be reasonable because to prepare barium titanate crystals with the mono-domain state is extremely difficult. The 90-degree domain contribution affected the P-E curve considerably even if its weight in the whole distribution curve was small.

In order to confirm the origin of the two Gaussian distributions in the domain switching probability, a specimen without the non-180 degree domains was examined. Figure 5 (a) shows the observed and simulated P-E curve of a ferroelectric tungsten bronze crystal $(Sr_{0.61}Ba_{0.39}Nb_2O_6)$. The observed curve was taken from data reported by Terabe et al.[11] Figure 5 (b) shows the Gaussian distribution of the domain switching. The observed P-E curve was well explained using single Gaussian distribution because this crystal does not have the non-180 degree domains. This result strongly supports that the two Gaussian distributions observed in other specimens are due to the 180 degree domain switching and the non-180 degree domain switching.

As shown above, the P-E simulator represents the P-E curves of a wide variety of non-linear dielectrics with a small number of parameters. To clarify the origin of the two distributions still needs discussion but it is possible to understand the domain switching behavior as well as the contribution of non-linear dielectricity in materials from the results of simulation.

Simulation with the $B^2$Spice

The response of non-linear capacitors was simulated in $B^2$Spice using the Sawyer - Tower circuit. A sine wave of 1 MHz was applied to the PZT film in Fig.2. The electrode area and the thickness of the PZT film were selected to be 1 $mm^2$ and 1μm, respectively. Figure 6 shows the result of simulation using $B^2$Spice. A good fitting was successfully obtained between the observed and simulated

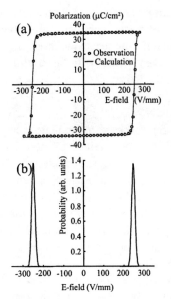

(a) Polarization (μC/cm²)

Observation
Calculation

E-field (V/mm)

(b) Probability (arb. units)

E-field (V/mm)

Fig.5 Results of P-E simulator for ferroelectric tungsten bronze single crystal $(Sr_{0.61}Ba_{0.39}Nb_2O_6)$. (a) observed[11] and calculated P-E curves and (b) Gaussian distribution to represent the domain switching probability.

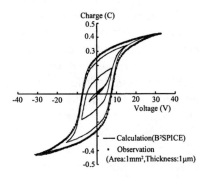

Charge (C)

Voltage (V)

Calculation(B²SPICE)
Observation
(Area:1mm², Thickness:1μm)

Fig.6 Observed and calculated P-E curves of PZT thin film. Calculation was performed using B²Spice.

results. Minor loops were also calculated and shown in the same figure. The shape of minor loops seems to be natural. These results are obtained by the netlist produced from the Mk-netlist software from the parameters determined in the above section. The simulation was performed without try-and-process. We think that the software package developed in this study is useful to simulate the response of ferroelectric capacitors in the SPICE. However, it should be noted that the frequency dependence of the P-E curve was ignored and the response to the arbitrary signals, especially asymmetric signals, could not be simulated at present because of the complicated memory effects of ferroelectrics. We think this is because of the fundamental limit of the SPICE. The improvement of circuit model or even the simulator seems to be necessary for complete circuit design of ferroelectric thin film memories.

Figure 7 shows responses of 4.7 μF and 1.0 μF MLCCs simulated by the B²Spice. The observed curves were calculated form the dc-bias dependences of capacitance of MLCCs. These MLCCs obviously indicated non-linear response in the P-E curve. The only non-linear dielectric part was incorporated in the simulation. Non-linear dielectricity of MLCCs were represented as follows: $Q = 5E\text{-}06V - 8E\text{-}19V^2 - 2E\text{-}08V^3 + 3E\text{-}20V^4$ for 4.7 μF MLCC and $Q = 1E\text{-}06V + 5E\text{-}19V^2 - 5E\text{-}10V^3 - 2E\text{-}21V^4$ for 1.0 μF MLCC. We have successfully simulated the response of MLCCs with high capacitances. As MLCCs are now used in a wide variety of conditions, catalog data of MLCCs

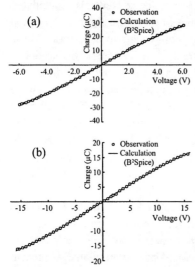

(a)

(b)

Fig.7 Observed and calculated P-E curves of MLCCs. (a) 4.7 μF and (b) 1.0 μF. Calculation was performed using B$^2$Spice.

supplied from manufacturing companies are not always sufficient to predict the response of the circuits. In this sense, the modeling of MLCCs in the SPICE will be useful an important in the future.

CONCLUSION

A software package to simulate electric response of a wide variety of non-linear dielectrics in the SPICE was developed. This package consists of two program cords, the P-E simulator and the Mk-netlist. The former is to simulate the P-E curve of non-linear dielectrics. The P-E curve was divided into two parts, a non-linear dielectric part and a domain switching part. The polarization due to the non-linear dielectric part was represented by a linear expansion in terms of electric field, while that due to the domain switching part was calculated by assuming that the distribution of domain-switching probability was represented by Gaussian distribution functions.

Simulation was done for PZT thin film, strontium titanate thin film, barium titanate single crystal and tungsten bronze single crystal. Two Gaussian distributions, possibly corresponding to the 180 degree domain switching and the non-180 degree domain switching, were required to get good fittings for PZT thin film and barium titanate single crystal. The P-E curve of strontium titanate thin film mainly consisted of the non-linear dielectric part. Single Gaussian distribution was enough to explain the P-E curve of the tungsten bronze crystal.

A circuit model with two capacitors and an arbitrary voltage source was proposed to represent non-linear dielectrics in the SPICE. The parameters determined by the P-E simulator were transferred to the Mk-netlist, which automatically generates the netlist data for the SPICE. The P-E curves of a PZT thin film and multi-layered ceramics capacitors were successfully simulated in the SPICE without try-and-error process.

ACKNOWLEDGEMENTS

The authors are grateful to Dr. K. Kitamura and Dr. K. Terabe for providing experimental results on tungsten bronze single crystals.

# REFERENCES

[1] T. Tsurumi, H. Adachi, H. Kakemoto, S. Wada, Y. Mizuno,H. Chazono and H. Kishi, " Dielectric Properties of BaTiO$_3$-Based Ceramics under High Electric Field", *Jpn. J. Appl. Phys.*, **41**, 6929-6933 (2002).

[2] T. Tsurumi, Y. Yamamoto, H. Kakemoto, S. Wada, H. Chazono and H. Kishi, "Dielectric Properties of BaTiO$_3$-BaZrO$_3$ Ceramics under High Electric-field", *J.Mater.Res.*, **17**, 755-759 (2002).

[3] C. M. Carlson, T. V. Rivkin, P. A. Parilla, J. D. Perkins, D. S. Ginley, A. B. Kozyrev, V. N. Oshadchy, A. S. Palov, G. Golovkov, M. Sugak, D. Kalinikos, L.C. Sengupta, L. Chiu, X. Zhang, Y. Zhu and S. Sengupta, "30 GHz Electronically Steerable Antennas Using Ba$_x$Sr$_{1-x}$TiO$_3$-based Room-temperature Phase Shifters", *Mater. Res. Soc. Symp. Proc.*, **603**, 15 - 25 (2000).

[4] Y. Kubota, H. Kakemoto, S. Wada and T. Tsurumi, "Computer Simulation of P-E Hysteresis of Ferroelectrics", *Trans. Mater. Res. Soc. Jpn*, **28**, 193-196 (2003).

[5] S. Yamamoto, T. Kato and H. Ishihara, "A Novel Simulation with Integrated Circuit Emphasis (SPICE) Model of Ferroelectric Capacitors Using Schmitt Trigger Circuit", *Jpn. J. Appl. Phys.*, 40, 2928 - 2934 (2001).

[6] A. Sheikholeslami, P. G. Gulak, H. Takauchi, H. Tamura, H. Yoshida and T. Tamura, "A Pulse-Based, Prallel-Element Macromodel for Ferroelectric Capacitors", *IEEE Trans. Ultrason., Ferroelect. Freq. Contr.*, **47**, 784 - 791 (2000).

[7] D. E. Dunn, "A Ferroelectric Capacitor Macromodel and Parametrization Algorithm for Spice Simulation", *IEEE Trans. Ultrason., Ferroelect. Freq. Contr.*, **41**, 360 - 369 (1994).

[8] L. L. Boyer, N. Velaaquez and J. T. Evans, Jr., "Low Voltage Lead Zirconate Titanate (PZT) and Lead Niobate Zirconate Tinanate (PNZT) Hysteresis Loops", *Jpn. J. Appl. Phys.*, **36**, 5799 - 5802 (1997).

[9] C. T. Rogers, M. J. Dalberth and J. C. Price, "Microwave Dielectric Tuning and Losses in Epitaxial Lift-off Thin Films of Strontium Titanate", *Mater. Res. Soc. Symp. Proc.*, **603**, 265 - 275 (2000).

[10] B. Jaffe, W. R. Cook and H. Jaffe, "Piezoelectric Ceramics", Academic Press, London, New York (1971) pp.78.

[11] K. Terabe, S. Higuchi, S. Takekawa, M. Nakamura1, Y. Gotoh, and K. Kitamura, "Nanoscale Domain Engineering of a Sr$_{0.61}$Ba$_{0.39}$Nb$_2$O$_6$ Single Crystal Using a Scanning Force Microscope" Ferroelectrics, in press.

# THE EFFECT OF PROCESSING CONDITIONS ON THE POROSITY AND ELECTRICAL PROPERTIES OF IBLC MATERIALS

Stephen J. Lombardo and
Rajesh V. Shende
Department of Chemical Engineering
University of Missouri
Columbia, MO 65211, USA

Daniel S. Krueger
Honeywell
Federal Manufacturing
& Technologies, LLC
Kansas City, Missouri 64141, USA

## ABSTRACT

The influence of sintering conditions on the porosity and on the electrical properties of 0.8 mol% $Y_2O_3$-doped $SrTiO_3$ internal boundary layer capacitor (IBLC) substrates is examined. Powders of $Y_2O_3$ and $SrTiO_3$ were co-milled and then were pressed into pellets which were then sintered in oxidizing or reducing atmosphere at $1450^{\circ}C$ or $1500^{\circ}C$. Both the density and the electrical properties of dielectric constant, dissipation factor and the conductivity were seen to exhibit a strong trend with sintering atmosphere, which in turn suggests that porosity may have a strong influence on the electrical properties.

## INTRODUCTION

Pure strontium titanate has a moderate dielectric constant of about 350 [1-4]. When doped with small amounts of acceptor or donor compound, however, effective dielectric constants (K) of up to 200,000 can be realized [5]. For this type of device, which is termed an internal boundary layer capacitor (IBLC), the mechanism of enhancement in effective dielectric constant is attributed to the formation of thin insulating layers around grains of semiconducting $SrTiO_3$.

To fabricate boundary layer capacitors, a number of processing routes are available [1,5-13]. In one method [8,10,12], the dopant can be applied as a paint onto $SrTiO_3$ substrates previously sintered in reducing atmosphere. The dopant can then be diffused into the substrates under oxidizing conditions. As a consequence of first sintering the $SrTiO_3$ substrate in reducing atmosphere, oxygen vacancies are created and the $SrTiO_3$ becomes n-type semiconducting. During the secondary heat treatment in oxidizing conditions, the dopant diffuses into the grains and creates an insulating layer around each $SrTiO_3$ grain [10].

In an alternative approach [1,13], yttria powder can be mixed or milled directly with $SrTiO_3$ powder. This powder mixture can then be used to form green bodies, which upon sintering will lead to the boundary layer microstructure. The advantage of this approach is that the $Y_2O_3$ powder is well dispersed throughout the $SrTiO_3$ substrate; the disadvantage is that $Y_2O_3$ impedes the sintering of the substrates [14] and can lead to residual porosity in the device.

In the present work, the co-milling approach was used to fabricate compositions of 0.8 mol% $Y_2O_3$–doped $SrTiO_3$. Substrates of this composition were then sintered in oxidizing or reducing atmosphere at 1450°C or 1500°C for 15 h. As a result of the different sintering conditions, different behavior of the electrical properties of dielectric constant (K), dissipation factor (tan δ), and conductivity (σ) were observed. Selected samples, which were first sintered in reducing atmosphere, were then subjected to a secondary heat treatment in oxidizing atmosphere. The effect of this step on the conductivity was also investigated.

## EXPERIMENTAL

The $SrTiO_3$ and $Y_2O_3$ powders used in this work were obtained from Sigma-Aldrich Chemicals (Milwaukee, WI). To prepare the 0.8 mol% $Y_2O_3$–doped $SrTiO_3$ composition, the powders were co-milled in ethanol for 6 h using poly(vinyl butyral) as a binder at 1 wt%. Then ethanol was evaporated and the dried powder was then pressed into cylindrical disks of 1.6 cm diameter

The pressed samples were next sintered in a tube furnace at soak temperatures of 1450°C or 1500°C for 15 h in oxidizing (air) or reducing atmosphere (95% $N_2$+5% $H_2$) at a flow rate of 5-7 cc/min. The sintering cycle used was: ramp at 4°C/min from room temperature to 900°C, then ramp at 8°C/min to the soak temperature for a hold period of 15 h, followed by cooling at 10°C/min to room temperature. The sintered density was determined by the sample weight and dimensions and by the Archimedes technique.

The $Y_2O_3$-doped $SrTiO_3$ specimens are denoted by STY. The samples sintered in oxidizing (OX) or reducing (R) atmospheres are designated as OXSTY or RSTY. The $Y_2O_3$-doped $SrTiO_3$ (STY) specimens previously sintered in reducing atmosphere were subjected for secondary heat treatment in oxidizing atmosphere at 1200°C for 5 h and these samples are designated as RSTYOX.

## RESULTS

The densities of the $Y_2O_3$-doped $SrTiO_3$ substrates sintered in oxidizing or reducing atmospheres are given in Table 1. For samples sintered at 1450°C or 1500°C in oxidizing atmosphere (OXSTY samples), higher densities are obtained as compared with those sintered in reducing atmosphere (RSTY samples). In addition, in either sintering atmosphere, higher densities are achieved as the sintering temperature is increased. For comparison, pure $SrTiO_3$ can be sintered to near full density at 1400°C for 1 h [3]. The results in Table 1 thus show how the presence of $Y_2O_3$ impedes the sintering of $SrTiO_3$. It can also be observed that the density of specimen sintered in reducing atmosphere (RSTY sample) at 1450°C and the density of the specimen heat treated in oxidizing atmosphere (RSTYOX sample) after initial sintering at 1450°C in reducing atmosphere are similar. This behavior is not observed for the corresponding sample sintered at 1500°C, where virtually no change in porosity is observed.

Table 1 Density and porosity of dry-pressed cylindrical specimens containing 0.8 mol% $Y_2O_3$ with $SrTiO_3$ sintered in oxidizing or reducing atmosphere for 15 h.

| Sample designation | Sintering atmosphere | Temp (°C) | Sintered density (g/cc) | Porosity, % |
|---|---|---|---|---|
| OXSTY | Air | 1450 | 4.72 | 7.6 |
| RSTY | 95% $N_2$+5% $H_2$ | 1450 | 4.50 | 11.9 |
| OXSTY | Air | 1500 | 4.81 | 5.7 |
| RSTY | 95% $N_2$+5% $H_2$ | 1500 | 4.57 | 10.1 |
| RSTYOX | 95% $N_2$+5% $H_2$ | 1450 | 4.49 | 12.1 |
| RSTYOX | 95% $N_2$+5% $H_2$ | 1500 | 4.70 | 8.0 |

The dielectric constant as a function of frequency for $Y_2O_3$-doped $SrTiO_3$ substrates sintered in oxidizing or reducing atmosphere is shown in Figure 1. For the specimens sintered at 1450°C for 15 h in oxidizing atmosphere (OXSTY samples), K was 20 times higher as compared to substrates sintered in reducing atmosphere (RSTY samples) at the same temperature-time conditions. For the specimens sintered at 1500°C for 15 h in oxidizing atmosphere, K was also found to be higher for sintering in oxidizing atmosphere as compared with sintering in reducing atmosphere. Although Figure 1 shows how the processing conditions influence the dielectric constant, the figure also shows that the dielectric behavior is correlated with the porosity.

The effect of sintering conditions on the dissipation factor (tan δ) is shown in Figure 2. For the specimens sintered at 1450°C or 1500°C in oxidizing atmosphere (OXSTY samples), the tan δ values were higher as compared with the tan δ values obtained for those specimens sintered in reducing atmosphere (RSTY samples).

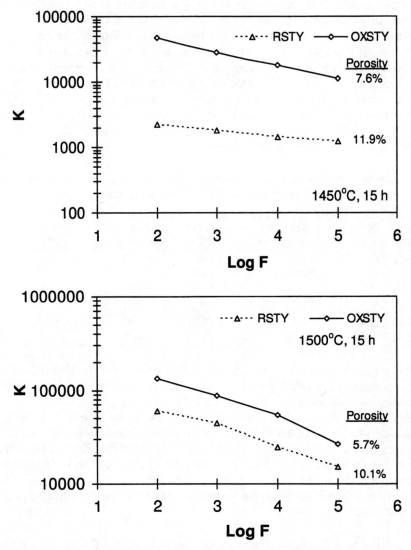

**Fig. 1** K as a function of frequency for $Y_2O_3$-doped $SrTiO_3$ (STY) specimens sintered in oxidizing (OX) or reducing (R) atmospheres.

Ceramic Materials and Multilayer Electronic Devices

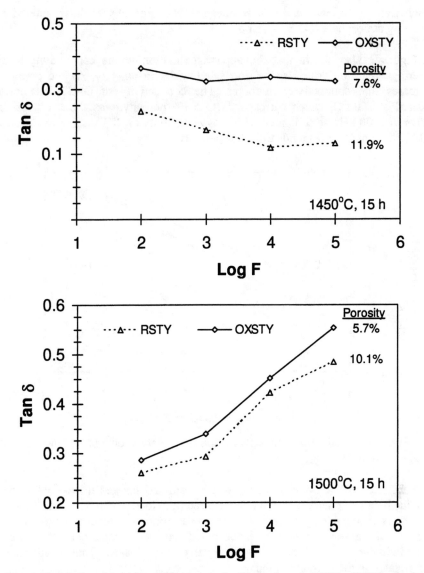

**Fig. 2** Tan δ as a function of frequency for $Y_2O_3$-doped $SrTiO_3$ (STY) specimens sintered in oxidizing (OX) or reducing (R) atmospheres.

The conductivity of $Y_2O_3$-doped $SrTiO_3$ specimens sintered in oxidizing or reducing atmosphere at 1450°C or 1500°C for 15 h is exhibited in Figure 3. For the specimens sintered in reducing atmosphere (RSTY samples), the values of conductivity were lower at all the frequencies as compared with those sintered in oxidizing atmosphere (OXSTY samples).

Figure 3 also shows that the apparent variation in the conductivity with sintering conditions can also be correlated with the porosity. As the porosity decreases, the conductivity increases. The conductivity of OXSTY samples sintered at 1500°C, which corresponds to 5.7% porosity, was about 100 times higher at 1000 kHz as compared with the conductivity of RSTY samples sintered at 1450°C, which corresponds to 11.9% porosity.

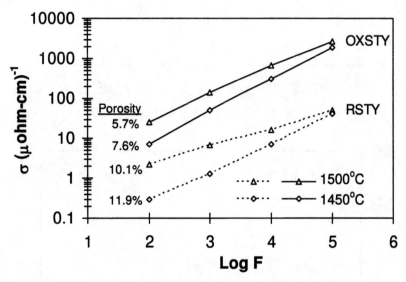

**Fig. 3** Effect of sintering atmosphere and temperature on the conductivity of $Y_2O_3$-doped $SrTiO_3$.

Substrates of $Y_2O_3$-doped $SrTiO_3$, which were first sintered at 1500°C for 15 h in reducing atmosphere, were then heat-treated in oxidizing atmosphere at 1200°C for 5 h. The conductivity measured for these substrates as a function of frequency is shown in Figure 4, where it can be observed that upon secondary heat treatment in oxidizing atmosphere, the conductivity values are enhanced. This enhancement is correlated to the decrease in the porosity.

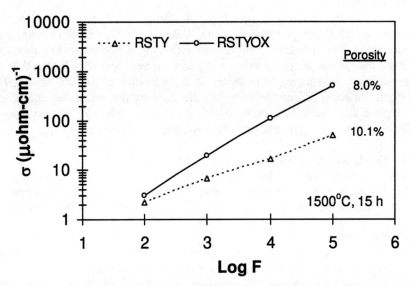

**Fig. 4** Effect of secondary heat treatment at 1200°C for 5 h in oxidizing atmosphere on the conductivity of $Y_2O_3$-doped $SrTiO_3$ specimens previously sintered in reducing atmosphere for 15 h.


## DISCUSSION

For IBLC materials, the enhancement in dielectric constant can be modeled as $K_{eff} = K_1 \, d_g/d_1$ [6-8], where $K_1$ is the dielectric constant of the boundary layer material, $d_g$ is the grain diameter, and $d_1$ is the thickness of the boundary layer. A similar relation holds for the conductivity when the grain boundary resistance is controlling [7]. From the results presented in this work, variations in the dielectric constant and conductivity are both correlated with the porosity. To account for the effect of porosity, $P$, on $K_{eff}$ and $\sigma_{eff}$, relations of the form [15]

$$K_{eff} = K_1 \frac{d_g}{d_1}(1 - \alpha P) \qquad\qquad 1$$

$$\sigma_{eff} = \sigma_1 \frac{d_g}{d_1}(1 - \alpha P) \qquad\qquad 2$$

may be valid, where $\alpha$ describes the reduction in the electrical property with increasing porosity.

## CONCLUSIONS

The influence of sintering conditions on the porosity and on the electrical properties of IBLC composition containing 0.8 mol% $Y_2O_3$ with $SrTiO_3$ has been demonstrated. For substrates sintered in oxidizing atmosphere, the dielectric constant, dissipation factor, and the conductivity were found to be higher than for those sintered in reducing atmosphere at temperatures of 1450°C or 1500°C. Although the electrical properties were influenced by the processing conditions, they were also found to be correlated with the porosity, whereby higher values of dielectric constant and the conductivity corresponded to lower porosity.

## ACKNOWLEDGEMENT

This project was funded by Honeywell Federal Manufacturing & Technologies, which is operated for the United States Department of Energy, National Nuclear Security Agency, under the contract No. DE-AC04-01AL66850.

## REFERENCES

[1] Burns I. and S. Neirman, "Dielectric Properties of Donor-Doped Polycrystalline $SrTiO_3$," *J. Mater. Sci.*, **17**[12], 3510-24 (1982).

[2] C.F. Kao, W.D. Yang, "Preparation and Electrical Properties of Fine Strontium Titanate Powder from Titanaium Alkoxide in a Strong Alkaline Solution," *Mater. Sci. Eng.* **B38**, 127-37 (1996).

[3] R.V. Shende, D.S. Krueger, G.A. Rossetti, S.J. Lombardo, "Strontium Zirconate and Strontium Titanate Ceramics for High-Voltage Applications: Synthesis, Processing, and Dielectric Properties," *J. Am. Ceram. Soc.*, **84**[7] 1648-50 (2001).

[4] S.J. Lombardo, R.V. Shende, D.S. Viswanath, G.A. Rossetti, D.S. Krueger, A. Gorden, "Synthesis, Processing, and Dielectric Properties of Compositions in the Strontium Titanate: Strontium Zirconate Solid Solution System," in *Dielectric Materials and Devices*, pp 227, 2002 (American Ceramic Society, Westerville, Ohio).

[5] N. Yamaoka, M. Masuyama, and M. Fukui, "$SrTiO_3$-Based Boundary Layer Capacitor Having Varistor Characteristics," *Ceramic Bulletin* **62** [6] 698-703 (1983).

[6] R. Wernicke, "Formation of Second-Phase Layers in $SrTiO_3$ boundary Layer Capacitors," in *Advances in Ceramics*, Edited by L.M. Levinson Vol. 1, pp 261, 1981.

[7] R. Wernicke, "Two-Layer Model Explaining Properties of $SrTiO_3$ Boundary Layer Capacitors," in *Advances in Ceramics*, Edited by L.M. Levinson Vol. 1, p 272, 1981.

[8] R. Mauczok and R. Wernicke, "Ceramic Boundary Layer Capacitors," *Philips Tech. Rev.*, **41**[11/12], 338-46 (1983/84).

[9]N. Yamaoka, "$SrTiO_3$-Based Boundary-Layer Capacitors, Ceramic Bulletin," **65** [8] 1149-52 (1986).

[10]S. Komornicki, J.-C. Grenier, J. Ravez and P. Hagenmuller, "Influence of Stoichiometry on Dielectric Properties of Boundary Layer Ceramics Based on Yttrium-Doped Strontium Titanate," *Mat. Sci. Eng.*, **B10**, 95-98 (1991).

[11]P. Hansen, D. Hennings and H. Schreinemacher, "High-*K* Dielectric Ceramics from Donor/Acceptor-Codoped $(Ba_{1-x}Ca_x)(Ti_{1-y}Zr_y)O_3$ (BCTZ)," *J. Am. Ceram. Soc.*, **81**[5] 1369-73 (1998).

[12]M. Fujimoto, W.D. Kingery, "Microstructure of $SrTiO_3$ Internal Boundary Layer Capacitors During and After Processing and Resultant Electrical Properties," *J. Am. Ceram. Soc.*, **68**[4] 169-72 (1985).

[13]S. Neirman and I. Burns, "Method for making a Ceramic Intergranular Barrier-Layer Capacitor," US Patent No. 4,397,886, August 9, 1983.

[14]S.J. Lombardo, R.V. Shende, D.S. Krueger, "Effect of Processing Conditions on the Core-Shell Structure and Electrical Properties of Strontium Titanate Doped With Yttrium Oxide," To appear in the Proceedings of $104^{rd}$ Annual Meeting of the American Ceramic Society, St. Louis, April 2002, (American Ceramic Society, Westerville, Ohio).

[15]D.S. Krueger, "Microstructural and Electrical Characterization of Yttrium Oxide-Doped Strontium Titanate," M.S. Thesis (University of Missouri, Columbia, MO 2003).

# OPTIMIZING THE PERFORMANCE OF TELESCOPING ACTUATORS THROUGH RAPID PROTOTYPING AND FINITE ELEMENT MODELING

Ming-Jen Pan and Alan Leung
Nova Research, Inc.
1900 Elkin Street, Suite 230
Alexandria, VA 22308

Carl C. M. Wu, Barry A. Bender, and Roy J. Rayne
Code 6350
Naval Research Laboratory
4555 Overlook Avenue SW
Washington, DC 20375

ABSTRACT

Developed at the Naval Research Laboratory (NRL), the telescoping actuator utilizes concentric piezoelectric tubes, which are mechanically connected in series and electrically in parallel, to achieve displacement amplification in a compact package. In this paper, we first briefly summarized the previous work on telescoping actuators and then described our recent efforts on using rapid prototyping and finite element analysis to optimize the performance of telescoping actuators. The Laminated Object Manufacturing System (LOMS) was utilized for rapid prototyping of the actuator. We used finite element analysis (FEA) to examine the correlation of key design parameters and to optimize the actuator design. The FEA was used to predict actuator performance and stress distribution within an actuator and therefore will be a useful tool to accelerate the actuator development cycle.

INTRODUCTION

Piezoelectric materials with high energy density, broad frequency response, and large generative force are attractive to smart structure applications. The major disadvantage, however, is the small piezoelectric strain. Many different piezoelectric actuator architectures exist but they fail to provide both large force and large displacement simultaneously. For example, stacked actuators have large generative force but the displacement is on the order of micrometers. On the other hand, bimorphs can displace hundreds of micrometers but only small force on the order of a few newtons.

In contrast, the telescoping actuator, first developed at the US Naval Research Laboratory (NRL), is a device designed to deliver large displacement and reasonable blocking force in a compact package [1]. The design also makes it possible to match mechanical impedance to that of the environment and therefore further enhance the "effective" energy density. In this paper we present a brief description of the evolution as well as recent progress on the optimization of the telescoping actuator through rapid prototyping and finite element analysis.

CONCEPT OF THE TELESCOPING ACTUATOR

The basic design of the telescoping actuator is illustrated in Figure 1. The concentric placement of piezoelectric tubes is an efficient use of space and leads to a compact design. The piezoelectric tubes are assembled in such a way that they are mechanically in series and electrically in parallel to get an additive displacement. During extensional actuation, the outer tube expands in the axial direction, lifting the middle tube. In the meantime, the middle tube undergoes contraction, lifting the inner tube, which expands like the outer tube. In this way, the displacements of all three tubes are added together. Reversing the electric field direction would result in actuator contraction. The electrode arrangement illustrated in Figure 1, in which the tubes are poled in the radial direction, is for the utilization of $d_{31}$ piezoelectric effect. In the case of $d_{33}$ mode operation, the electrodes are placed on the top and bottom surfaces, and the tubes are poled and driven in the axial direction. Note that the $d_{33}$ mode often requires higher driving voltage because of the length of the tubes.

PROTOTYPE TELESCOPING ACTUATOR

To prove the telescoping actuator concept, a prototype was demonstrated using commercial lead zirconate titanate (PZT) materials (EDO, EC65, Navy Type II equivalent) [1]. The configuration of the prototype is shown in Figure 2. The wall thicknesses of the outer, middle, and inner tubes are 3.0, 3.2, and 1.5 mm, respectively. All other dimensions are labeled in Figure 2. The tubes were poled radially, i.e. through the wall thickness, and hence the tubes operated in the $d_{31}$ mode. The "endcaps" used to join the tubes were made of alumina and the joining material is a commercial epoxy.

The electromechanical displacement of the prototype was measured using a laser sensing device (Aromat Corp., ANL-2334A). Figure 3 shows the extension of the actuator as a function of the applied voltage. Note that despite the difference in tube wall thickness, the same voltage was applied to all the tubes and therefore the electric fields are different in the tubes. As designed, the extension of the telescoping actuator is roughly the sum of those of the three individual tubes.

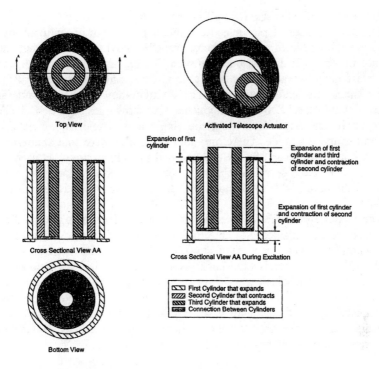

Figure 1 Schematic of a 3-tube telescoping actuator. During extension operation, the outer and inner tubes expand and the middle tube contracts. Reversing the polarity of applied voltage will yield contraction.

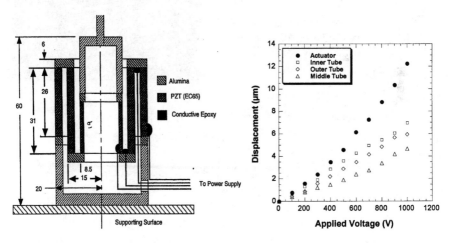

Figure 2 The configuration of the prototype actuator (unit: mm)

Figure 3 The displacements of the actuator and individual tubes

## PIEZOELECTRIC SINGLE CRYSTAL ACTUATOR

The development of piezoelectric single crystals with exceptional $d_{33}$ values (>2000 pC/N) and high coupling factors (>90%) provides an excellent choice of actuator material [2]. In collaboration with The Pennsylvania State University, a new telescoping actuator using lead zinc niobate-lead titanate (PZN-PT) single crystal tubes was constructed [3]. The configuration of the actuator and the dimensions of the PZN-PT components are shown in Figure 4. Unlike the prototype in the previous section, the single crystal telescoping actuator was operated in the $d_{33}$ mode. Therefore, gold electrodes were first sputtered on the top and bottom surfaces of each tube/rod and the silver epoxy between PZN-PT and alumina endcaps served as electrical contacts. Each tube/rod was poled along the axial direction, which coincides with the [001] crystallographic direction of PZN-PT.

The displacement measurements were performed using a modified Sawyer-Tower circuit and a linear variable differential transducer (LVDT) driven by a lock-in amplifier. The electric field applied to the telescoping actuator was limited to <2.5 kV/cm, the coercive field of PZN-4.5%PT, to avoid the depolarization of the middle cylinder, which was driven by a field opposite of the poling direction. Figure 5 shows the displacement as a function of applied electric field. Note that the displacement of the actuator is lower than the sum of the three single crystal elements. This is attributed to the compliant nature of the PZN-PT single crystal and consequently the clamped piezoelectric strain [4].

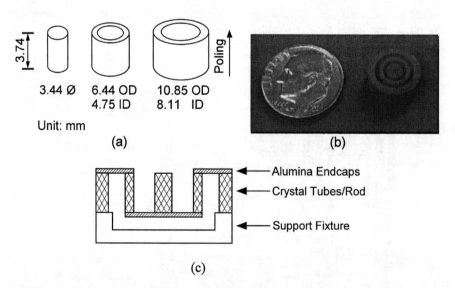

Figure 4    The PZN-PT crystal telescoping actuator: (a) the dimensions of single crystal elements, (b) crystal elements, and (c) the actuator configuration.

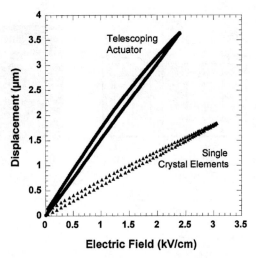

Figure 5    Displacement of the PZN-PT crystal telescoping actuator

TELESCOPING ACTUATOR BY RAPID PROTOTYPING

NRL has the capability of rapid prototyping structure models of functional objects via Laminated Object Manufacturing System (LOMS). Complex three-dimensional objects can be fabricated from paper, ceramic tape, or metallic tape. The LOM process starts with a 3-D computer file of the object to be built. The LOM computer slices the object into layers, each the thickness of the laminating material, and calculates the 2-D design for that layer. The object is then built layer by layer. The cutting of the tape is done by a computer-controlled 50 watt $CO_2$ laser. The unwanted material is cross-hatched by the computer and removed upon completion of the lamination process, yielding the fabricated prototype [5].

Several telescoping actuators were made through the LOM process using PZT-5A ceramic tape. The processing of these actuators was detailed elsewhere [5]. The design of the actuators is shown in Figure 6. In contrast to previous described actuator designs in which endcaps of a different material were joined to the tubes using epoxy adhesive, the actuators made by the LOM process are *monolithic* actuators, i.e., the endcaps are also made of PZT material and co-sintered with the active tubes. Figure 7 shows an as-sintered telescoping actuator.

The piezoelectric behavior of the monolithic actuator was measured using a modified Sawyer-Tower circuit and an LVDT. All of the cylinders were tested at 1000 volts of applied voltage. Consequently, the highest electric field (~7 kV/cm) is seen by the outermost tube, which is roughly 50% of the coercive field of PZT-5A and hence in no danger of depolarization. The electric charge and electromechanical displacement of each tube and the actuator as a whole are plotted in Figure 8. As shown in the figure, the overall extension of the actuator is roughly the sum of the three individual tubes.

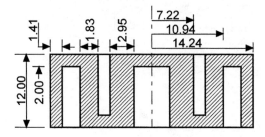

Figure 6    The design and dimensions of the monolithic actuator (unit: mm)

Figure 7 As-sintered monolithic actuator

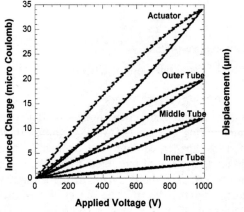

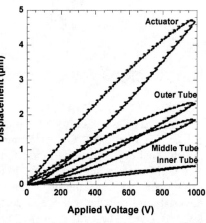

Figure 8    Electric field-induced charge and displacement of the monolithic telescoping actuator.

## FINITE ELEMENT ANALYSIS OF ACTUATOR PERFORMANCE

Although the displacement of actuators can be measured with ease, there are many other characteristics that are difficult to determine. Examples are internal stresses and mechanical impedance, which affect the reliability and operating efficiency, respectively, of an actuator. Finite element analysis (FEA) is a powerful tool for such characterizations. If used in combination with rapid prototyping, it would further accelerate the development cycle of new actuators.

In this study, the FEA was performed using the commercial program ANSYS. Ten node tetrahedral elements were used for the mesh with more than 11000 degrees of freedom. Figure 9 shows the typical mesh distribution.

The properties used in the analysis were taken from the EDO Ceramics catalogue and they are listed in Table 1. Note that these values are low electric field properties, usually measured at 1 volt oscillation. Caution was taken in transforming the Cartesian coordinate properties to cylindrical coordinate during modeling. During actuation, a ground contact and a voltage of 1000 volts (can be

Ceramic Materials and Multilayer Electronic Devices

positive or negative to get contraction or extension, respectively) were applied. Fixed boundary conditions were applied to the base of the outermost tube. Displacement was constrained at the base in the horizontal and vertical directions to simulate the fixture mounting in actual applications.

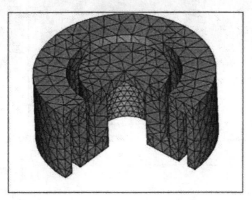

Figure 9  Typical mesh distribution of monolithic telescoping actuator

Table 1 The material properties used in the finite element analysis

| PZT-5A | | | |
|---|---|---|---|
| Density [kg/m$^3$] | | 75000 | |
| Dielectric Constant | | $1.53 \times 10^{-8}$ | |
| Compliance Matrix [N/m$^2$] | | | |
| $s_{11}$ | $14.4 \times 10^{-12}$ | $s_{33}$ | $9.46 \times 10^{-12}$ |
| $s_{12}$ | $-7.71 \times 10^{-12}$ | $s_{44}$ | $25.20 \times 10^{-12}$ |
| $s_{13}$ | $-2.98 \times 10^{-12}$ | $s_{66}$ | $11.05 \times 10^{-12}$ |
| Piezoelectric Matrix [m/V] | | | |
| $d_{31}$ | | $-171 \times 10^{-12}$ | |
| $d_{33}$ | | $374 \times 10^{-12}$ | |
| $d_{51}$ | | $585 \times 10^{-12}$ | |

Our interest in the modeling results primarily focused on the axial displacement and the first (tensile) principal stress. FEA model of the original monolithic actuator showed that the maximum displacement is 2.2 micrometers (Figure 10), which is smaller than the previously measured 4.7 microns. This is attributed to the low field piezoelectric properties used in the FEA as it is common that the high field and low field piezoelectric properties differ by a factor of 2. The maximum principal stress was found to be 14.4 MPa in contraction and 8.7 MPa in extension, and their locations are at the base and the top of middle tube, respectively. Both stresses are much lower than the typical flexural strength of PZT (~90 MPa). The principal stress plots under contraction and extension are shown in Figure 11.

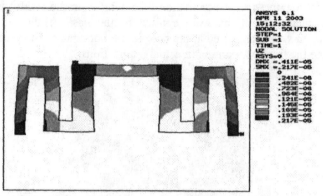

Figure 10   Axial displacement distribution of the original monolithic actuator

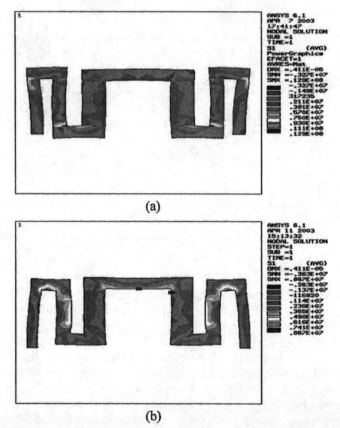

(a)

(b)

Figure 11   Principal stress of the monolithic actuator in (a) contraction and (b) in extension

Ceramic Materials and Multilayer Electronic Devices

After the prototype was modeled, we employed the same FEA code to optimize the actuator design. To have a fair comparison, the outer diameter (28 mm) and the height (12 mm) of actuator were the same as those of the original monolithic actuator. It was also decided that the maximum operating electric field is 8 kV/cm, approximately 60% of the coercive field of PZT-5A, to prevent the depolarization of the piezoelectric elements. By limiting the maximum applied voltage to 1000 volts, the wall thickness of the cylinders was fixed at 1.25 mm. During FEA optimization, we varied the radii of the middle and inner cylindrical sections at 1 mm increments. To determine the optimum design, two criteria were used. The first is the maximum displacement to stress ratio, where a high value is desirable. In addition, the maximum tensile principal stress is required to be less than the PZT flexural strength plus a reasonable safety margin. The final optimized design has a predicted displacement of 3.8 μm, a 70% improvement over the original design. The axial displacement and stress plots are shown in Figure 12.

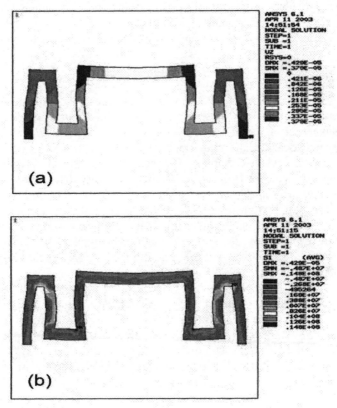

Figure 12 (a) Axial displacement and (b) principal stress distribution in the optimized actuator

## ONGOING RESEARCH EFFORTS

The optimized monolithic actuator is being constructed via the LOM process at NRL. The experimental results will be used to verify the FEA design. In the meantime, the effects of small fillets in sharp corners on reducing local stress are being examined by using FEA. Finally, the effects of external loading on actuator performance are being determined.

## CONCLUSION

The telescoping actuator offers a major advantage over multilayer co-fired actuators: the ease of scaling up to mass production. As there are no embedded electrodes, the fabrication of telescoping actuators does not require sophisticated and often expensive processing control. Previously, in collaboration with Materials Systems, Inc. (Littleton, MA), we have successfully demonstrated the feasibility of using injection molding as a cost-effective way for mass production.

The combination of finite element analysis and rapid prototyping via the LOM process provided great flexibility in manufacturing functional prototypes of different designs and enables rapid design verification and model development. We are continuing our efforts on ways to better utilize these advanced design tools.

## REFERENCES

1. C.C.M. Wu, D. Lewis, M. Kahn, and M. Chase, "High Authority, Telescoping Actuator," pp212-219 in *Proceedings of SPIE Conference on Industrial and Commercial Applications of Smart Structures Technologies, SPIE Vol. 3674.* Newport Beach, California, March 1999.
2. S.-E. Park and T.R. Shrout, "Characteristics of Relaxor-Based Piezoelectric Single Crystals for Ultrasonic Transducers," *IEEE Transactions on Ultrasonic Ferroelectrics and Frequency Control*, **44** [5] 1140-47 (1997).
3. C.C.M. Wu, D. Lewis, and S.-E. Park, "High Authority Telescoping Actuators with Single Crystal Piezoelectric Materials," pp304-311 in *Proceedings of SPIE Conference on Industrial and Commercial Applications of Smart Structures Technologies, SPIE Vol. 3991.* Newport Beach, California, March 2000.
4. M.-J. Pan, P.W. Rehrig, J.P. Kucera, S.-E. Park, and W.S. Hackenberger, "Comparison of Actuator Properties for Piezoelectric and Electrostrictive Materials," in *Proceedings of the SPIE's 7th International Symposium on Smart Structures and Materials*, Newport Beach, CA, March 4-8, 2000.
5. B.A. Bender, C. Kim, D. Lewis, R. Rayne, and C.C.M. Wu, "Mechanical and Piezoelectric Properties of Laminated Object Manufacturing Ceramics," *Ceramic Engineering and Science Proceedings*, **23** [4] p.853, (2002).

# A PROBABILITY APPROACH TO PERCOLATION

David C. Maybury and Rosario A. Gerhardt
School of Materials Science and Engineering
Georgia Institute of Technology
Atlanta, GA 30332-0245

ABSTRACT
Percolation phenomena help to explain water filtering through rocks, distribution of telephone lines in a network as well as catastrophic electrical or mechanical failures. It has always been assumed that when a critical volume fraction of the conducting particles is reached, an interconnected network of conducting particles is formed and thus the electrical resistivity experiences several orders of magnitude change. However, interconnectivity can occur either for the more insulating or the more conducting component and little is known about the exact conditions for this change. Often, massive changes in the sample properties occur for small variations in the sample compositions or in the distribution of the two phases. For these reasons, a purely mathematical attempt is made to locate the onset of the percolation threshold with respect to particle/sample size ratio. In a first thrust, the probability of both the minimal and the super-minimal cases of percolation are calculated from stereological principles. In a second thrust, a finite-element approach is taken by using a partially populated matrix to simulate a loaded solid. In this approach all particles that do not participate in a linked chain are expunged, and the matrix is ultimately summed to give a "percolation score." In both methods, the probability of percolation is found to exponentially increase near the theoretically predicted percolation thresholds in both the two-dimensional and three-dimensional cases ($\phi_c \sim 0.5$ and $0.33$ respectively). A change in the shape of the probability function from a sigmoid to a step function is described.

## INTRODUCTION

The properties of composite materials are often modeled in terms of effective medium models; however, effective medium models are only valid at dilute concentrations of the filler. At some intermediate volume fraction, where there is a cross-over in the electrical response of the composite from that dominated by the matrix behavior to that dominated by the filler phase, the properties are said to be dominated by percolation effects. Percolation occurs when the filler material forms interconnected paths throughout the bulk of the material. A common example in the world ceramic engineering would be to consider what happens when a series of dispersed voids link up to form a continuous path throughout the bulk of a sample. The void interconnectivity would result in a network of open pores leading to the formation of a gas-permeable material. Similarly, the electrical properties of fiber-reinforced composites could be explained using percolation concepts. Other examples of percolating systems with more direct electronic applications include the electrical conductivity of screen printing inks used for metallization of hybrid microelectronic circuits and the resistivity of glass-RuO$_2$ thick film resistors. The distinctive characteristic of percolation behavior is that it is a threshold-type response where, at a particular volume fraction in a given material system, the properties of interest would begin changing drastically. This is illustrated schematically in Fig. 1, where the dielectric loss behavior of an insulating matrix filled with conducting fillers is seen to experience a precipitous change at a given volume fraction.

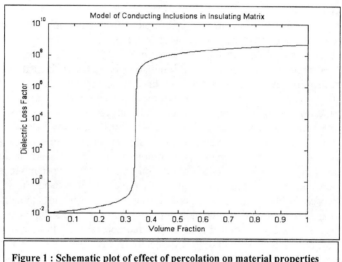

Figure 1 : Schematic plot of effect of percolation on material properties

Most of the previous work dealing with the study of percolation has been focused on predicting the properties of percolating systems, and predicting the volume fraction at which the percolation threshold will occur. Some of the early definitive concepts on percolation theory were published by Balberg and Binenbaum[1,2]. They calculated the critical excluded volume fraction of inclusions in a system and predicted two expected percolation thresholds of roughly 0.55 volume fraction for a two-dimensional system and 0.33 for a three-dimensional system. Their predictions are applicable to monosize spherical particles in an amorphous matrix. Further documentation of the effects of percolation and the mathematics associated with predicting the behavior were done in a series of papers by Drory[3,4,5]. The focus of the Drory papers was the development of a theoretical basis in statistical mechanics to support a continuum percolation model. This paper will continue this focus of a probability-based approached to the continuum percolation model.

MATHEMATICAL MODELING
In order to understand some of the effects that can be exhibited by the alteration of particle size, it is instructive to examine the minimal case of a percolation model, where a system of a given volume fraction has just enough particles to span the space of

Ceramic Materials and Multilayer Electronic Devices

the full composite material. All of the functions in this section will be expressed in terms of $r/s$ or $s/r$, where $s$ is the length of the sample space, and $r$ is the radius of the spherical inclusions. The maximum $r/s$ ratio is easily derived by relating the diameter and volume of the inclusions to the space length to get:

$$\frac{r}{s} = \sqrt[4]{\frac{3v_f}{8\pi}} \tag{1}$$

where $v_f$ is the volume fraction of the inclusions. By assuming $s$ to be equal to unity, the particle radius can be calculated as:

$$r = \left(\frac{3v_f}{4\pi n}\right)^{1/3} \tag{2}$$

where $n$ is the number of particles needed. In order for a chain of these particles to percolate, each one must occupy a particular location with respect to the other particles. For instance, if three particles formed a mutually connected cluster, one particle diameter would not contribute to spanning the sample volume. By taking into account that each particle can only occupy a highly limited volume and still contribute to the chain, the probability of percolation in this minimal system can be derived to be:

$$p_{min} = \left[18r^3(n-1)\arccos\left(\frac{r - \frac{2r-1}{n}}{r}\right)\right]^n \tag{3}$$

The quantity inside the brackets is always less than unity. The most important factors to notice are the influences of $r$, and $n$. While increasing $r$ increases the probability cubically, increasing $n$ results in an exponential decrease in the probability. Since $n$ is an integer function, the resulting probability is the piecewise function, pictured in the log-log plot of probability in Figure 2. This probability plot helps to account for the abrupt threshold behavior often seen in percolating systems.

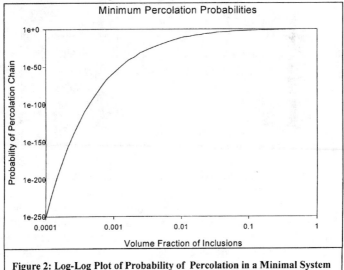

Figure 2: Log-Log Plot of Probability of Percolation in a Minimal System

## NUMERICAL MODELING

A more useful approach to percolation can be accomplished by modeling many successive realizations of a system at a given volume fraction. In developing our models, two approaches were taken. The first model used is the lattice model, where particles are located solely at integer coordinate points. In a lattice system, the geometry of the particles is dictated by the nature of the coordinate system used. For instance, in a Cartesian coordinate system, all particles are assumed to have a cubic geometry. The second approach, to be described in detail later, is the continuum model, where particles can freely occupy any point in space. For the lattice model, an algorithm designated as "Nibbler" was used. For the nibbler algorithm, a two-dimensional matrix of zeros is generated and randomly populated with 1's. A percolation direction, typically left-to-right, though any direction is equally valid, is selected. Each particle is tested in succession to see if the three neighboring points on either side contain a particle (at least one cell labeled L and one cell labeled R in Figure 3 must contain a 1). If the particle is not connected on both sides, it is deleted. The algorithm repeats until the total number of particles stops changing and the score is computed based on the sum of remaining particles. The algorithm is called Nibbler because of the appearance of "nibbling" a chain from one side to the other.

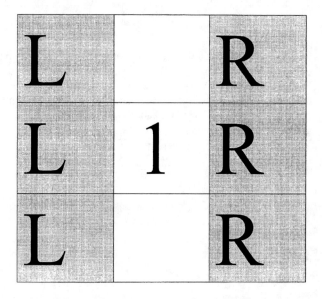

**Figure 3: Illustration of Nibbler Algorithm. At least one cell labeled "L" AND one cell labeled "R" must contain a 1. If not, the central 1 is deleted.**

The main advantage of the Nibbler algorithm is the quick elimination of all particles that do not contribute directly to a chain spanning the sample space. This feature makes the model ideal for evaluating DC and low-frequency electrical properties. It may also be useful for evaluating mechanical properties as well as the relationship between interconnected porosity and gas permeability. The main disadvantages of the Nibbler algorithm are associated with its highly iterative nature, which results in very long process times for large 2D matrices, and consequently even small 3D matrices. Additionally, Nibbler is not readily compatible with the concept of a continuum model. As a result only 2D simulation results from Nibbler are reported in Figure 4. The diagonal line in the plot represents the maximum possible number of percolating particles at a given volume fraction. There are a number of noteworthy features in this plot. First, the wide scatter in the s/r=10 case reflects the relatively low number of particles needed to form a connected chain. As a result, there are several cases when percolation occurs well below the expected threshold of 0.55. Additionally, at higher area fractions, where the number of particles available is more limited because of their large size, it is also considerably more likely for a case to occur where no connection is made by virtue of the low number of opportunities. Secondly, for the larger particles with s/r=10, there is an absence of points with percolation fraction between 0 and 0.1. This is also a product of the large size of the particles, which impose a large minimum area on any connected chain. In the case of s/r=100, the data more closely reflect the expected values of the theoretical physical prediction( ~ 0.55), with comparatively little scatter.

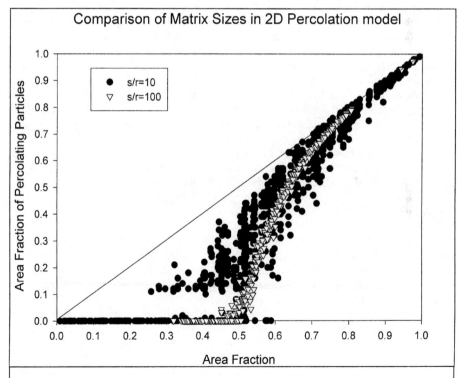

Figure 4: Plot of 2D calculations of the Nibbler algorithm. Notice the gap is results for s/r=10, which reflects the minimum chain diameter for particles of that size.

In order to capture more accurate results at larger volume fractions in 2D and be able to solve 3-D systems more rapidly, we have used the well-known "Wildfire" technique[6,7,8] as modified by Sastry and Yi[9] for continuum percolation. In the Wildfire algorithm, particles in contact with the test side of the sample space are moved into a separate list. Then any particle whose center is within two radii of any of the particles in the test list is also moved into the test list. These particles are tested in succession, until all particles in the cluster are identified. If the cluster spans the sample space, the cluster is scored. It is important to realize that this algorithm is a "soft-core" algorithm, which allows particles to overlap one another. As a result, a correction factor must be introduced to correct for the overlap. In this instance, the volume of two spherical caps is computed as a function of particle separation, and the volume of these caps is subtracted from the particle volume. While this does introduce a new error for areas overlapped by more than two particles, the error is considerably smaller than the error resulting from no action, and the computational costs associated with accounting for this multiplicity outweigh the benefits of the correction. It is also important to note that this correction needs to be carried out both before and after the elimination of non-percolating paths to insure proper scoring.

The chief advantage of the Wildfire algorithm is its relatively short run time, since it does not have to repeatedly test all particles. Additionally, the use of a continuum system allows more degrees of freedom with respect to particle geometry and location, which better simulate a real system. Unlike Nibbler, Wildfire does not remove particles that are not part of the direct line, which makes it better for modeling isolated voids, some mechanical properties, and high-frequency electrical properties, all of which can have drastic effects when the isolated particles are linked to the interconnected network. Looking at the 3-D Wildfire results in Figure 5, the same sort of scattering behavior at low $s/r$ ratios observed for 2-D systems (depicted in Fig. 4) is seen. As the ratio of the sample space to particle radius increases, there is a shift in the "lift off" point, where non-percolating behavior ceases to occur, shifting back to roughly 0.3. The points do not begin conforming to the expected line until a ratio of $s/r$=100 is used. This shows that particle size can have a substantial effect on the appearance of percolation below the expected threshold, and the absence of it above the threshold.

SCALING THE NUMERICAL MODELS

Once a sufficiently large number of iterations have been done for a particular $s/r$ ratio, a probability function can be calculated by dividing the number of percolating systems by the total number of systems tested at the given volume fraction. By using this probability function, the sample space, which has a cubic geometry, can be reduced to a unit cell of a larger lattice model. The probability function then replaces the volume fraction of the loaded space, since the scaled model reduces the previous test volume to a binary percolating/not percolating value. Knowing this, it quickly becomes apparent that the only non-trivial region of the probability function is the region immediately around the percolation threshold for the 3D lattice model. Areas above and below are rapidly reduced to 1 and 0, respectively. As a result, scaling the model leads to an effective shift in the percolation probability function from a sigmoidal-shaped function at small $s/r$ to a step function at very high $s/r$.

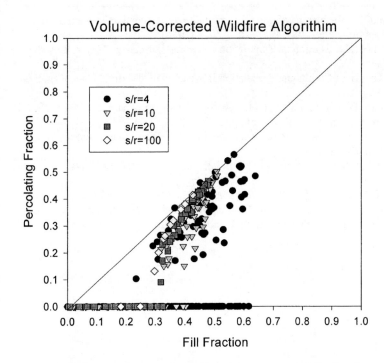

Figure 5. Wildfire Algorithm Results for various s/r ratios in 3-D. Note that theoretically predicted percolation at 0.3 is not obtained until s/r =100.

CONCLUSIONS

A series of models to describe the effects of particle size on percolation were generated. The models showed large scatter when the ratio of the inclusion size with respect to the sample space was large (i.e. when *s/r* was small). The model data was used to produce a probability function. This probability function was used in turn to scale the percolation models. The scaling of the models revealed that as the particles trend toward nanoparticle size, the probability of percolation function reduces from a sigmoidal to a step-like function.

ACKNOWLEDGEMENTS

The authors would like to acknowledge funding from the National Science Foundation under grant DMR-0076153.

REFERENCES

[1] I. Balberg, and N. Binenbaum, "Directed percolation in the two-dimensional continuum" Phys. Rev. B **32**, 527-529 (1985).

[2] I. Balberg and N. Binenbaum, "Direct determination of the conductivity exponent in directed percolation," Phys. Rev. B **33**, 2017-2019 (1986).

[3] A. Drory, "Theory of Continuum Percolation I. General Formalism," Phys. Rev. E **54**, 5992-6002 (1996).

[4] A. Drory, "Theory of Continuum Percolation II. Mean Field Theory," Phys. Rev. E **54**, 6003-6013 (1996).

[5] A. Drory, B. Berkowitz, G. Parisi and I. Balberg, "Theory of Continuum Percolation III. Low density expansion," Phys. Rev. E **56**, pp.1379-1395 (1997).

[6] D. Dhar, and S. S. Manna, "Inverse avalanches in the Abelian sandpile model," Phys. Rev. E. **49**, 2684-2687 (1994).

[7] D. Dhar, "Self-organized critical state of sandpile automaton models," Phys. Rev. Lett **64**, 1613-1616 (1990).

[8] P. Bak and K. Chen, "The Physics of Fractals," Physica D **38**, 5-12 (1989)

[9] Y.-B. Yi and A. M. Sastry, "Analytical approximation of the two-dimensional percolation threshold for fields of overlapping ellipses," Phys. Rev. E. 66, 066130-1 - 066130-8 (2002).

# EFFECTS OF THE GALLIUM MODIFICATION ON $BiFeO_3$-$PbTiO_3$ CRYSTALLINE SOLUTIONS

Jinrong Cheng, Nan Li and L. E. Cross
Materials Research Institute, The Pennsylvania State University,
University Park, PA 16802

## ABSTRACT

The gallium (Ga) substitution for iron in $Bi(Ga_xFe_{1-x})O_3$-$0.3PbTiO_3$ (BGF-0.3PT) crystalline solutions was investigated. X-ray diffraction analysis indicate that the tetragonal phase compete with rhombohedral phase forming a multiple perovskite cell in BGF-0.3PT with the increased gallium content. The great advantage of gallium substitution is its contribution to the reduced conductivity, which is one of major limitations for developing bismuth ferrite based solid solutions. The room temperature dielectric constant K and loss $\tan\delta$ of BGF-0.3PT for x=0.05 are of ~400 and 3% respectively. With increasing x, the loss $\tan\delta$ decreases, and Curie temperature (Tc) rises.

## INTRODUCTION

$BiFeO_3$ has been received great interest because of its simple perovskite structure and chemical composition, in which a combination of ferroelectric and antiferromagnetic properties has been found[1-3]. However, semiconductor nature of $BiFeO_3$ leads to high dielectric loss making difficulties in characterization and applications of the unique materials. Though other perovskites, such as $PbTiO_3$, $BaTiO_3$, $SrTiO_3$ and $Pb(Fe_{0.5}Nb_{0.5})O_3$ [4-7] have been utilized to form solid solutions with $BiFeO_3$ to make $BiFeO_3$ an insulator, the loss problem has not been effectively solved, and the dielectric measurement has to be conducted using a high measurement frequency in giga hertz. The conductivity is still a limitation to develop the multiferroics (ferroelectricity, ferromagnetism and ferroelasticity) in $BiFeO_3$ and its solid solutions.

In this paper, we aimed at reducing the conductivity of $BiFeO_3$-$PbTiO_3$ and controlling the low loss especially in lower frequencies. The amount of gallium substitutions for B-site iron cations were introduced to form $Bi(Ga_xFe_{1-x})O_3$-

Ceramic Materials and Multilayer Electronic Devices

0.3PbTiO$_3$ solid solutions. The effect of gallium modification on crystalline structures, dielectric and ferroelectric properties of BGF-PT were investigated.

## EXPERIMENTAL PROCEDURE

Mixed oxide ceramic processing had been utilized to synthesize BGF-PT solid solutions. Starting materials were commercial reagent-grade of Bi$_2$O$_3$, Ga$_2$O$_3$, Fe$_2$O$_3$, PbCO$_3$, and TiO$_2$ with 99%+ purity. The oxides were mixed by ball milling for 24 hours, and then calcined at 750°C for 4 hours. After calcination, the mixtures were vibratory milled for an additional 24 hours. Powders were uniaxially pressed into pellets with 12.7 mm in diameter and 1.5 mm in thickness. Pellets were sintered at 1000-1100 °C for 0.8 hours in a sealed crucible. The sintering weight loss was below 1%, and the shrinkage in diameter was ~18 % after sintering.

X-ray diffraction techniques (diffractometer, Sintag 2) were utilized to identify the structure and phase evolution. Fresh fracture surfaces of sintered pellets were observed using scanning electron microscopy (SEM, Hitachi S-3000H). Specimens were electroded using a post-fired silver paste (Dupont 6160). The room temperature and high temperature dielectric measurements were conducted by using a computer controlled HP4194A and HP4284 impedance analyzer respectively. Ferroelectric hysteresis loops were made using a modified Sawyer-Tower circuit. All specimens for electrical measurements were in disk form with ~10.4 mm in diameter and ~0.5 mm in thickness.

## RESULTS AND DISCUSSIONS

BiFeO$_3$-0.3PbTiO$_3$ (BF-PT) was investigated in this paper because it is known to be close to the morphotropic phase boundary (MPB)[8]. Figure 1 shows the XRD patterns of BGF-PT for x=0, 0.05 and 0.01 respectively.

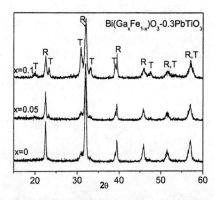

Figure 1. XRD patterns of BGF-PT crystalline solutions for different Ga contents

Ceramic Materials and Multilayer Electronic Devices

Stable perovskite phases were obtained for all investigated compositions. A multiple cell was formed with the coexistence of tetragonal and rhombohedral distortions, which was marked in the XRD patterns. Without gallium, strong rhombohedral diffraction peaks were observed with minor weak tetragonal peaks. With increasing Ga content, the fraction of tetragonal phase (T) increased, while rhombohedral phase (R) decreased. Gallium was dissolved in BF-PT solid solutions modifying the crystalline structures. According to XRD data, the tetragonal distortion of c/a ratio is as large as 1.16 of BGF-PT for x=0.1. This result is in agreement with the reference data of 1.18 for BF-PT near MPB[8]. It is the rhombohedral $BiFeO_3$ that strengthened the tetragonal distortion. We speculated that additional Ga content resulted in a single tetragonal symmetry of BGF-PT if the second phases would not appear with higher Ga content.

The dense ceramic is required to obtain the expected piezoelectric properties in BF-PT systems. Our processing made good ceramics with the relative density of higher than 98%. Figure 2(a), 2(b) and 2(c) display the SEM photos of BGF-PT for x=0, 0.05 and 0.1 respectively, which were taken from the fresh fracture surface.

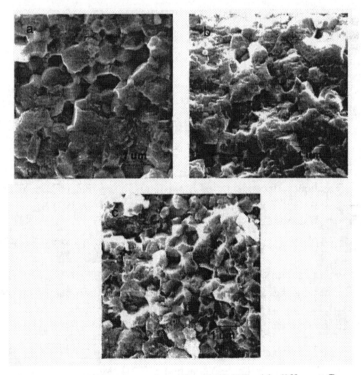

Figure 2. SEM photos of fracture surfaces for BGF-PT with different Ga content of (a) x=0, (b) x=0.05, and (c) x=0.1

It can be seen that the ceramics were densified without porosity. The fracture indicated the transgranular characteristics especially in the higher Ga compositions. The multiple cells with strong tetragonal distortion may be subject to the large internal stress, which prevented the fracture along grain boundaries. From SEM photos, the ceramics were observed to possess fine grains with ~1μm in diameter, and the grain size decreased with increasing Ga content.

The room temperature dielectric constant K and loss tanδ of BGF-PT were measured in the frequency range of 100Hz~1MHz as shown in Fig. 3(a) and 3(b). Specimens in Fig.3(a) has PT content of 30 at%. It can be seen that tanδ was greatly reduced in the lower measurement frequencies when using the $Ga^{3+}$ substitution for $Fe^{3+}$ cations. Conductivity is known a major contribution to the low frequency loss. It was the gallium that made BF-PT an insulator and caused to decrease the loss. In order to further check the effect of gallium on the loss control in BGF-PT, 5 at% Ga was used with different PT content. In Fig.3(b), tanδ is lower than 5% until 0.4 PT compositions, however, increased rapidly to 24% at 100 Hz when the PT content reached 60 at%.

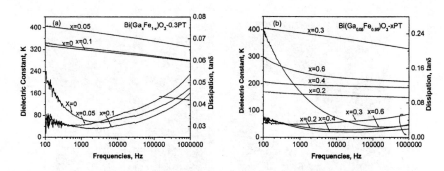

Figure 3. Frequency dependence of room temperature dielectric constant K and tanδ of (a) BGF-0.3PT with different Ga content, and (b) BGF-PT with 5% Ga and different PT content

According to Fig. 3(a) and 3(b), $Bi(Ga_{0.05}Fe_{0.95})O_3$-0.3PbTiO$_3$ was the best polable and insulation composition with the highest K of ~400 and the smallest tanδ of 3% at the frequency of lower than 1KHz. Combined with XRD and SEM results, we thought that using gallium substitutions for iron placed rhombohedral BF-PT with a strong tetragonal distortion forming a multiple cell of BGF-PT. The strong internal stress might be produced when two kinds of crystalline symmetry competed with each other for their equilibrium position. This state may help stabilize $Fe^{3+}$ and the stoicheiometry preventing BGF-PT from becoming conductive. When the PT content reached 60 at%, tetragonal PT controlled the structure of BGF-PT. The stress was partially released in the single-phase system. The effect of 5 at% gallium on the crystalline structure and conductivity was thus

Ceramic Materials and Multilayer Electronic Devices

weakened. In this situation, the additional amount of gallium was required to control the conductivity, which has been proved in our current work. In the BGF-PT system, gallium played an important role to reduce the conductivity, while PT was helpful to stabilize the perovskite state. Increasing either Ga or PT content would place BGF-PT in tetragonal symmetry resulting in the decrease of K.

Figure 4 shows the dielectric constant K and tanδ of BGF-PT for different Ga content measured at the temperature of 30-700 °C using the measurement frequency of 1 MHz. The existence maxima of the dielectric constant through temperatures reveals that the ferroelectric to paraelectric phase transition in BGF-PT. There is corresponding loss maxima observed at around 600 °C. All these revealed rather high Curie temperature (Tc) of BGF-PT. Tc was determined to be as high as ~650 °C rising up with increasing Ga content. The effect of Ga content on increasing Tc can be understood by its contribution to the formation of the tetragonal symmetry with the large c/a ratio. A shoulder in the curve of the dielectric constant vs temperature was observed at about 400~550 °C, which was corresponding to the onset temperatures of the rapid increase in loss. It is noticed that the shoulder became flatten coinciding with the reduced loss in high temperatures when increasing Ga content. Therefore, the high temperature conductivity caused the loss to rise up and the anomaly of the dielectric shoulder, but the gallium was also effective to reduce the conductivity in the high temperature.

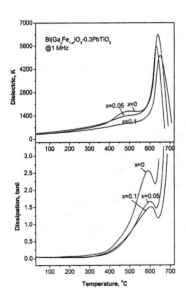

Figure 4. Dielectric constant K and tanδ vs temperature relationships of BGF-PT with different Ga content

Figure 5(a) and 5(b) present the ferroelectric hysteresis loops of BGF-PT with different Ga and PT content respectively. Two loops with the round corner were obtained for BF-0.3PT (without Ga) and BGF-PT with 5 at% Ga and 60 at% PT content indicating the conductivity of ceramics. Other compositions are less conductive, however, the hysteresis loops are not saturated even under the applied electrical field of higher than 100 kV/cm. These are in agreement with our dielectric data further proving the effect of gallium on conductivity control and its limitation in the high PT composition. The hysteresis loop of $Bi(Ga_{0.05}Fe_{0.95})O_3$-$0.3PbTiO_3$ shows the remnant polarization (Pr) of 2 $\mu C/cm^2$ in an unsaturated state. Unfortunately, the high Tc and coercive field made difficulties to pole these samples; therefore we are lack of piezoelectric properties for BGF-PT systems. The one interesting work is to make the insulator BGF-PT more polable. Our current work proved that it was realizable, which was presented in another paper[9].

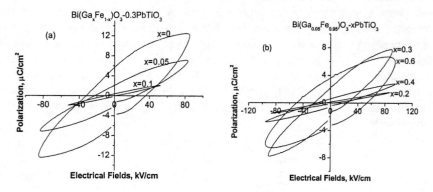

Figure 5. Ferroelectric hysteresis loops of (a) BGF-0.3PT for different Ga content, and (b) BGF-PT with 5 at% Ga and different PT content

## CONCLUSIONS

Dense and insulator ferroelectric ceramics of BGF-PT have been fabricated and characterized. Gallium was observed to play an important role on the conductivity control of BF-PT at both the room and high temperatures. A multiple cell with the coexistence of tetragonal and rhombohedral phase was formed with increasing the Ga substituent. The internal stress might contribute to stabilizing the stoicheiometry making BGF-PT an insulator. $Bi(Ga_{0.05}Fe_{0.95})O_3$-$0.3PbTiO_3$ is an insulator and more polable composition with the largest K of ~400 and an unsaturated Pr of 2 $\mu C/cm^2$.

## ACKNOWLEDGEMENT

We are pleased to acknowledge support from the office of Naval Research (ONR) under contract No. N00014-99-1-1011.

# REFERENCES

[1]R.Gerson, P.Chou and W.J.James, "Ferroelectric Properties of $ZrTiO_3$-$BiFeO_3$ Solid Solutions" J.Appl.Phys., **38**, 55 (1967).

[2]R.T.Smith, G.D.Achenbach, R.Gerson and W.J.James, "Dielectric Properties of Solid Solutions of $BiFeO_3$ with $Pb(Ti,Zr)O_3$ at High Temperature and High Frequency" J.Appl.Phys., **39**, 70 (1968).

[3]M. Mahesh Kumar and V.R. Palkar, "Ferroelectricity in a pure $BiFeO_3$ ceramics" Appl. Phys. Lett., **76**, 2764 (2000).

[4]M.M.Kumar, A.Srinivas, S.V.Suryanarayana and T.Bhimasankaram, "Dielectric and Impedance Studies on $BiFeO_3$-$BaTiO_3$ Solid Solutions," Phy. Stat. Sol., (a) **165**, 317 (1998).

[5]T.Kanai, S.Ohkoshi, A.Nakajima, T.Watanabe and K.Hashimoto, "A Ferroelectric Ferromagnet Composed of $(PLZT)_x(BiFeO_3)_{1-x}$ Solid Solution," Adv. Mater., **7**, 487 (2001).

[6]T.L.Ivanova and V.V.Gagulin, "Dielectric Properties in the Microwave Range of Solid Solutions in the $BiFeO_3$-$SrTiO_3$ System", Ferroelectrics, **265**, 241 (2002).

[7]M.Mahesh Kumar, A.Srinivas, and S.V.Suryanarayana, "Structure Properties Relations in $BiFeO_3$/$BaTiO_3$ Solid Solutions", J.Appl.Phys., **87**, 855 (2000).

[8]V.V.S.S.S.Sunder, A.Halliyal and A.M.Umarji, "Investigation of Tetragonal Distortion in the $PbTiO_3$-$BiFeO_3$ System by High-temperature x-ray Diffraction," J.Mater.Res., **10**, 1301 (1995).

[9]J. Cheng, R. Eitel, N. Li and L.E. Cross, "Structural evolutions, dielectric And piezoelectric properties of modified $BiFeO_3$-$PbTiO_3$ piezoelectrics", submitted to 105[th] Annual Meeting and Exposition of the American Ceamic Society.

# CHARACTERIZATION OF HYDROXYL CONTENT OF HYDROTHERMAL BARIUM TITANATE FILMS

Sandeep Patil,[1] Nipun Shah,[2] Frank D. Blum,[3] and Mohamed N. Rahaman[1]
[1]Department of Ceramic Engineering, [2]Materials Research Center, [3]Department of Chemistry, University of Missouri-Rolla, Rolla, MO 65409

ABSTRACT

$BaTiO_3$ films were deposited on single crystal $SrTiO_3$ substrates under hydrothermal conditions at 150 °C by reacting fine $TiO_2$ particles with an aqueous solution of $Ba(OH)_2$. The nature and concentration of hydroxyl groups incorporated into the films were investigated using X-ray photoelectron spectroscopy (XPS) and Fourier transform infrared spectroscopy (FTIR). The kinetics of exchange between hydrogen and deuterium (D) for OH incorporated into the film were measured following treatments with $D_2O$. FTIR data indicated a significant concentration of surface OH groups, but a sharply-defined peak that can be attributed to OH groups in the $BaTiO_3$ lattice was absent. The kinetics of the exchange reaction between OH and OD depends on the total reaction time as well as on the time interval for treatments of different durations. The concentration of OH groups replaced by OD decreases with time of reaction, but for a given reaction time, the rate of exchange is slower for short duration reactions and faster for longer duration runs.

INTRODUCTION

Barium titanate ($BaTiO_3$) thin films are of significant interest for several applications in the electronics industry because of their high dielectric constant and ferroelectric properties [1]. Conventional routes to the synthesis of $BaTiO_3$ films, such as sol-gel processing and vapor phase methods (e.g., metal-organic chemical vapor deposition, sputtering, and pulsed laser deposition), often require high synthesis temperatures or high vacuum conditions. There is interest in solution-based methods, such as hydrothermal and electrochemical techniques, because they can provide direct routes to the synthesis of epitaxial films at low temperatures.

The hydrothermal route to ceramic synthesis employs reactions in aqueous solutions at temperatures close to, or above, the boiling point of water to deposit inorganic materials in the form of epitaxial thin films on structurally similar single-crystal substrates. Epitaxial growth of $BaTiO_3$ films on single-crystal substrates of $SrTiO_3$ has been demonstrated by Chien et al. [2] and by Ciftci et al. [3].

Structural investigations of crystalline $BaTiO_3$ powders, precipitated under hydrothermal conditions similar to those used for the epitaxial films, indicate that defects and impurities such as Ba and Ti vacancies, $H_2O$, $OH^-$, and carbonate ions are incorporated into the crystal lattice during synthesis [4, 5]. The concentration of the species incorporated depends on the synthesis conditions, such as temperature, pH, Ba concentration, and time. Electrical characterization of epitaxial $BaTiO_3$ films, deposited hydrothermally on single crystal $SrTiO_3$ substrates at 90 °C, indicates that the incorporated $H_2O$ and $OH^-$ lead to high dielectric losses [6].

The location and nature of $H_2O$ and $OH^-$ incorporation in hydrothermal $BaTiO_3$ powders and epitaxial films have been studied, but a clear understanding of these phenomena is still lacking. The results indicate that the concentration of $OH^-$ and $H_2O$ can be significantly reduced by heat treatments in the range of 600–800 °C [5, 6]. The relationship between the heat treatment of powders and films and their electrical properties has also been examined. In addition, the use of deuterated water in the synthesis of $BaTiO_3$ powders and films has been employed to understand the mechanism of hydroxyl-group incorporation. Noma et al [7] studied the lattice hydroxyl group and proposed a role for lattice hydroxyl groups on the $O_6$ octahedra deformation mode. Fuenzalida et al [8] studied the surface adsorbed hydroxyl groups and found that surface hydroxyl groups are chemisorbed and are not desorbed, even under vacuum conditions.

In the present work, the nature of $H_2O$ and $OH^-$ groups incorporated into hydrothermal $BaTiO_3$ films has been examined by studying the exchange reaction between the incorporated OH groups and OD during treatment of the deposited film in $D_2O$ (deuterium oxide). The concentration of the OH and OD groups in the film and the kinetics of the exchange reaction between them were studied by X-ray photoelectron spectroscopy (XPS) and Fourier transform infrared spectroscopy (FTIR).

EXPERIMENTAL PROCEDURE

The starting materials and experimental procedure for the hydrothermal deposition of $BaTiO_3$ films on single crystal $SrTiO_3$ substrates are described in detail in earlier work [3]. Briefly, 4 g of Ba $(OH)_2 \cdot 8H_2O$ was added to 24 $cm^3$ of deionized water (previously boiled for 1 h to remove $CO_2$) in a Teflon-lined autoclave (45 ml; Parr Instrument Co., Moline IL) to give a 0.5 M $Ba(OH)_2$ solution. The system was purged with argon, sealed and heated for 3 h at 90 °C to dissolve the Ba $(OH)_2$. One gram of $TiO_2$ powder was added to the solution (pH =13.3) and a single crystal of (100) $SrTiO_3$ (polished on both sides) was suspended in the solution using Teflon thread. The autoclave was sealed and the system was heated to 150 °C in 8 minutes. After the required deposition time, the coated $SrTiO_3$ substrate was washed with deionized water in an ultrasonic bath and dried at ~80 °C.

The exchange reaction between the OH groups incorporated into the hydrothermal film and OD from a $D_2O$ medium was carried out by treating the coated substrate in $D_2O$ at 150 °C for the required time in a Teflon-lined autoclave. After submerging the coated substrate in 10 cm$^3$ $D_2O$, the system was sealed and heated to 150°C in 10 minutes and held at this temperature for the required time. The coated substrate was removed from the vessel and dried at 60 °C in a vacuum oven prior to analysis. One sample was subjected to three individual exchange reactions lasting 1 h each, followed by four individual reactions lasting 2 h each. Another sample was subjected to two individual exchange reactions lasting 5 h each.

The microstructure of the deposited films was examined using field-emission scanning electron microscopy, FESEM (Hitachi S4700). The presence of $H_2O$ and OH$^-$ in the deposited film was investigated using X-ray photoelectron spectroscopy, XPS (AXIS 165; KRATOS, UK). Scans of the O 1s spectrum in the region of 520–530 eV were performed on the surface of the BaTiO$_3$ film and at a point inside the film produced after 30 min of Ar ion sputtering. Deconvolution of the spectra into separate peaks was performed using a curve-fitting routine that assumed a Gaussian line shape and an S-shaped background.

The presence of OH groups in the BaTiO$_3$ film and the kinetics of the exchange reaction between OH groups in the film and OD from the $D_2O$ medium were investigated using Fourier transform infrared spectroscopy (FTIR) in the mid-IR range (Nicolet Magna-IR 750 Spectrometer). The FTIR scans were taken in transmittance mode. The concentrations were measured by integrating the area under the appropriate resonance.

RESULTS AND DISCUSSION

*(a) Characterization of the uncoated substrate and the hydrothermal film*

Figure 1 shows the SEM micrograph of a BaTiO$_3$ film on a single-crystal SrTiO$_3$ substrate after a deposition time of 12 h. The substrate is almost completely covered by the BaTiO$_3$ film, but a few pores and pinholes are visible.

The XPS spectra are shown in Fig. 2 for the O 1s peak at the surface of the deposited BaTiO$_3$ film and at a point within the film produced after 30 min of Ar sputtering. The best fit to the results is obtained by using two peaks: one at lower binding energy (529.3 eV), attributed to O from the BaTiO$_3$ structure, and the other at higher binding energy (531.1 eV), attributed to O from OH groups. After sputtering, the intensity of the higher energy peak (from the OH groups) decreases significantly, but does not disappear. The remaining higher energy peak in the sputtered film is often attributed to $H_2O$ and OH in the BaTiO$_3$ lattice, but its assignment is not certain.

Figure 3 shows FTIR spectra of the SrTiO$_3$ single crystal substrate (without a BaTiO$_3$ coating) and of the substrate after hydrothermal deposition of the BaTiO$_3$ coating. For the spectrum of the uncoated substrate, a sharp peak is observed at a frequency of 3496 cm$^{-1}$, along with two smaller peaks at 3381 cm$^{-1}$ and 3358 cm$^{-1}$. These resonances, associated with the substrate, are attributed to $H_2O$ incorporated into the single crystal substrate as a result of the aqueous polishing process used for producing the surface finish of the substrates.

Figure 1. SEM micrograph of BaTiO$_3$ thin film grown on single-crystal SrTiO$_3$ substrate, showing nearly complete coverage of the substrate.

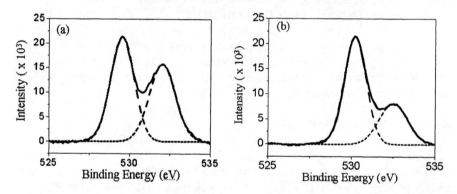

Figure 2. XPS spectra for the O 1s peak at the surface of the deposited BaTiO$_3$ film and at a point within the film produced after 30 min of Ar ion sputtering.

The spectrum for the BaTiO$_3$ film deposited on SrTiO$_3$ substrate (Fig. 3) shows a broad band in the frequency range of 3000–3600 cm$^{-1}$. It has been reported that OH groups adsorbed onto the *surface* of the BaTiO$_3$ film exhibit a broad band in this frequency range because of the availability of many different surface adsorption sites [7, 9]. For the spectrum of the coated substrate, it should be noted that the sharp absorption peak occurring at a frequency of ~3496 cm$^{-1}$ can be attributed to the OH groups in the SrTiO$_3$ substrate and not to OH groups associated with the BaTiO$_3$ film. However, in the case of hydrothermal BaTiO$_3$ powders, a relatively sharp peak occurring at a similar frequency (~3496 cm$^{-1}$) was observed by Noma *et al.* [7] and attributed to absorbance due to OH groups incorporated into the BaTiO$_3$ *lattice*. For the BaTiO$_3$ films deposited in the pre-

Ceramic Materials and Multilayer Electronic Devices

sent work, the absence of a sharp peak associated with OH groups in the lattice indicates that the concentration of OH groups in the film lattice is not significantly above the detection limits of the FTIR technique or that the OH environments are non-uniform.

*(b) Characterization of OH exchange in the BaTiO₃ film with OD*

Figure 4 shows the FTIR spectra for the substrate coated with the BaTiO₃ film after (i) three individual treatments of 1 h each in $D_2O$ (ii) five individual treatments lasting 1 h each in $D_2O$ and (iii) one treatment lasting 5 h. For comparison, the spectrum of the coated substrate without any treatment in $D_2O$ is also shown. The intensity of the broad OH band (3000–3600 cm$^{-1}$), taken as the area under the curve after subtracting the spectrum of the substrate, is found to decrease with increasing treatment time in $D_2O$, indicating replacement of the OH in the film by OD. Concurrent with the decrease in the OH intensity, a distinct band in the frequency range of 2450–2650 cm$^{-1}$, attributable to the OD groups that have replaced the OH groups in the film, develops in the spectra (Fig. 5). The intensity of the OD band increases with the time of $D_2O$ treatment.

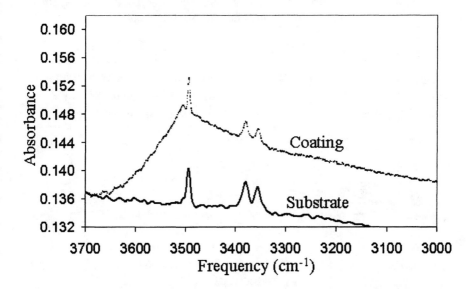

Figure 3. FTIR spectra of the uncoated SrTiO₃ single crystal substrate (bottom) and the substrate after hydrothermal deposition of a BaTiO₃ coating (top).

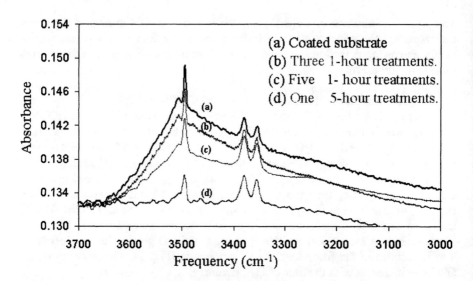

Figure 4. OH spectra prior to D₂O treatment, after three 1-h treatments; after five1-h treatments; after one 5-h treatment.

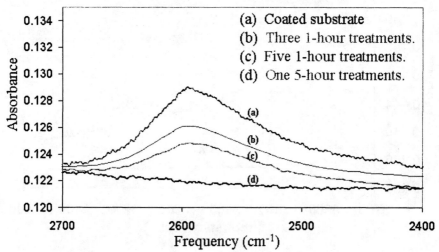

Figure 5. OD spectra prior to D₂O treatment, after five 1-h treatments; after three 1-h treatments; after one 5-h treatment.

An interesting feature of the FTIR data in Figs. 4 and 5 is that the kinetics of the exchange reaction between OH and OD depend on the duration of the individual treatments. For example, the intensity of the OH band for the sample treated in five individual runs lasting 1 h each is significantly higher than that for the sample

　　　　　　　　　Ceramic Materials and Multilayer Electronic Devices

treated in one run lasting 5 hours. To further investigate the influence of the duration of the individual runs on the exchange kinetics, coated substrates were treated in $D_2O$ for different time intervals and the FTIR spectra was measured after each run. As an example, Figs. 6 and 7 show the spectra for the OH and OD bands for samples treated in $D_2O$ when the duration of the individual runs was 2 h.

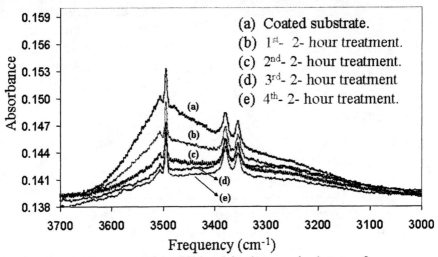

Figure 6. FTIR spectra of the OH band for the coated substrate after individual treatments in $D_2O$ lasting 2 h each.

The areas under the OH and OD bands were determined using standard software (FTIR spectrum V.200) and plotted as functions of the cumulative treatment time. Figures 8 (a) and (b) show the data for a coated substrate treated for 2 h intervals in $D_2O$. Corresponding data were obtained for individual $D_2O$ treatments of 1 h duration. For both treatment schedules, the decrease in the OH band intensity (area) and the increase in the OD band intensity can be fitted approximately by an exponential function of the form

$$y = A + B \exp\left(-t/\tau\right) \qquad (1)$$

where y is the intensity (area), t is the total time of treatment, $\tau$ is a characteristic decay time, and A and B are constants. Table 1 gives the values for A, B, and $\tau$ for the two treatments. For any time interval of the experiment, the decay time for the OD band intensity is 1.4–1.5 times the decay time for the OH band intensity. The decay times for the exchange reaction of 2 h duration are found to be 2 times the value for the treatment of 1 h duration. The significance of the kinetic parameters for the exchange reaction is unclear at present. Current work is aimed at developing a model for the exchange reaction between OH and OD in the film. We have also observed that there are some changes in the amounts of OH's exchanged when the samples are exposed to the atmosphere or left for more extended periods of time. The reasons for these changes are currently not known.

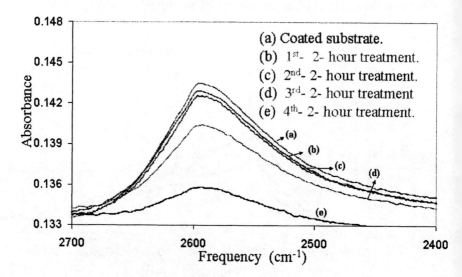

Figure 7. FTIR spectra of the OD band for the samples described in Fig. 6.

Table 1. Kinetic parameters for the exchange reaction between OH and OD.

| Treatment interval | Spectrum | A (Abs.cm$^{-1}$) | B (Abs.cm$^{-1}$) | $\tau$ (Hours) |
|---|---|---|---|---|
| 1 hour | OH | 2.82 | 0.46 | 0.94 |
|  | OD | 0.25 | 0.26 | 1.34 |
| 2 hours | OH | 1.25 | 1.56 | 1.92 |
|  | OD | 1.10 | 0.85 | 2.80 |

Ceramic Materials and Multilayer Electronic Devices

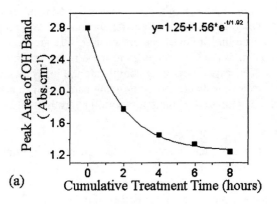

(a)

Figure 8 (a). Area of OH band as a function of $D_2O$ treatment time. The duration of the individual treatments was 2 h.

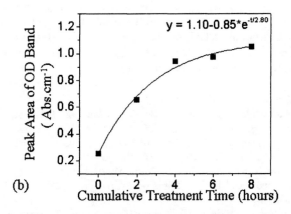

(b)

Figure 8 (b). Area of OD band as a function of $D_2O$ treatment time. The duration of the individual treatments was 2 h.

The data indicate that the rates at which OH species in the $BaTiO_3$ film are replaced by OD are very slow. Also, the rates for 2-hour treatments are faster than those for 1-hour treatments. This may indicate that the exchange reaction takes place in a diffusion-controlled regime, whereby the time of exposure of the sample to $D_2O$ affects the rate of exchange.

The XPS data indicate the presence of OH species, not only at the top surface of the film, but also incorporated within the $BaTiO_3$ lattice (Fig. 2). However, the absence of a sharp peak in the OH region of the FTIR spectra (Fig. 3) may indicate that either internal OH's are rare or the OH environments are non-uniform.

The different OH environments might give rise to a broad band of vibrational frequencies. Alternatively, the XPS peak attributable to OH groups in the bulk of film may not be a true indication of the presence of OH groups in the bulk. For example, the re-adsorption of OH groups on to the film surface during the sputtering process in the XPS experiment may complicate the interpretation of the XPS spectrum. Further experiments are currently being carried out to achieve a clearer understanding of the nature of OH incorporation in hydrothermal $BaTiO_3$ films.

SUMMARY AND CONCLUSIONS

Epitaxial barium titanate films were deposited on single crystal substrates of $\{100\}$ $SrTiO_3$ under hydrothermal conditions at 150 °C. The incorporation of $H_2O$ and OH groups in the film was investigated using XPS and FTIR spectroscopy. The XPS spectra show a significant peak that is often attributable to OH groups in the $BaTiO_3$ lattice. The FTIR spectrum shows a broad OH band, indicating the presence of a significant concentration of OH groups in the film, but there is no sharply-defined peak that can be unambiguously attributed to OH groups in the $BaTiO_3$ lattice. The kinetics of the exchange reaction between OH and OD were studied using FTIR spectroscopy. The rate of the exchange reactions depend on the total reaction time as well as on the time interval of the intermittent treatments. The concentration of OH groups replaced by OD decreases with time of reaction, but for a given reaction time, the rate of exchange is slower for short duration reactions and faster for longer duration runs.

REFERENCES

[1] R.E. Newnham, "Electroceramics," *Rept. Prog. Phys.*, **52** [2] 123-56 (1989).

[2] A.T. Chien, J.S. Speck, F.F. Lange, A.C. Daykin, and C.G. Levi, "Low Temperature/Low Pressure Hydrothermal Synthesis of Barium Titanate: Powder and Heteroepitaxial Thin Films," *J. Mater. Res.*, **10** [7] 1784-89 (1995).

[3] E. Ciftci, M.N. Rahaman, and F.D. Blum, "Hydrothermal Deposition and Characterization of Heteroepitaxial $BaTiO_3$ Films on $SrTiO_3$ and $LaAlO_3$ Single Crystals," *J. Mater. Sci.*, **37** 3361-67 (2002).

[4] R. Vivekanandan, S. Philip, and T. Kutty, "Hydrothermal Preparation of Barium Titanate Fine Powders," *Mater. Res. Bull.*, **22** [1] 99-108. (1987).

[5] D. Hennings and S. Shreinmacher, "Characterization of Hydrothermal $BaTiO_3$," *J. Eur. Ceram. Soc.*, **9** 41-46 (1992).

[6] A.T. Chien, L. Zhao, M. Colic, J.S. Speck, and F.F. Lange, "Electrical characterization of $BaTiO_3$ Heteroepitaxial Films by Hydrothermal Synthesis," *J. Mater. Res.*, **14** [8] 3330-39 (1999).

[7] T. Noma, S. Wada, M. Yano, and T. Suzuki, "Analysis of Lattice Vibration in Fine Particles of Barium Titanate Single Crystals Including Lattice Hydroxyl Group," *J. Appl. Phys.*, **80** 5223-5233 (1996).

[8] V. M. Fuenzalida, M. E. Pilleux, and I. Eisele, "Adsorbed Water on Hydrothermal $BaTiO_3$ Films: Work Function Measurements," *Vacuum,* **55** 81-83 (1999).

[9] S.Wada, Satoshi; T.Suzuki, T. Noma, "Preparation of Barium Titanate Fine Particles by Hydrothermal Method and their Characterization," *J. Ceram. Soc. Jpn.* **103** 1220-27 (1995).

# DISPERSION AND ULTRA-FINE GRINDING OF OXIDE POWDERS IN AN AQUEOUS SLURRY WITH A CONTROLLED VISCOSITY

D. Houivet and J.-M. Haussonne
Laboratoire Universitaire des Sciences Appliquées de Cherbourg
LUSAC EA2607
Site Universitaire, B.P. 78,
50130 Cherbourg Octeville – France

ABSTRACT:

When dispersing powders in slurries and grinding them by mechanical means, the first problem to be considered is to determine the accurate dispersion parameters of the particular powders to be processed. These parameters are closely related to the zeta potential values of the different constituents that are directly dependent on the pH of the slurry. If pH control is not possible, good dispersion may alternatively be obtained by the addition of an adequate dispersant.

During the process, as the surfaces of the materials increase due to the break-up of the different grains, surface reactions with the dispersion liquid occur and the pH and/or dispersant rate have thus to be continuously adjusted to be maintained at an adequate value. If not controlled, flocculation can occur and, consequently, viscosity increases with the consequence that the grinding efficiency is reduced.

One of our experimental supports has been the synthesis of $(Zr,Sn)TiO_4$ microwave dielectric compositions by solid state reaction of raw materials mixed and ground by attrition milling. Dispersing and mixing of powders have likewise to be considered as a grinding process. So, we also applied this concept of grinding slurries with a controlled rheological behavior to well known oxides: $TiO_2$ and $Al_2O_3$, using attrition milling with different 0.4 to 1.6 mm zircon or Y-$ZrO_2$ grinding balls. BET specific area measurements, X-ray diffraction analysis and electronic microscope observations pointed out the constant efficiency of the grinding behavior over time. Starting from approximately $10\ m^2g^{-1}$ powders, specific areas higher than $40\ m^2.g^{-1}$ and grain diameters much lower than 50 nm were thus obtained.

## INTRODUCTION

Many efforts are devoted today to the synthesis of ultra fine powders which have grain sizes that can be estimated in nanometers: they range typically from 10 or 20 to less than 100 nm. Most of the technologies therefore explored deal with chemical processes or sol-gel processes allowing a fine control of the size of grains, but being mostly very costly to be set up. One way of obtaining the size reduction of particles is to grind them. Yet, up to now, classical grinding processes have lead to only relatively large grain powders. It seems difficult, using these processes, to break down the grains of an oxide powder to a size lower than some hundreds of nanometers[1].

Another important problem for ceramists concerns the first step in synthesizing ceramic powders by the means of the calcination of precursors powders previously dispersed and ground. Because the precursor powders that must be ground together are different, they have different chemical and physical characteristics. The goal is to mix the powders via solid-state reactions induced by contact between the grains and processed by diffusion during the thermal cycle. Thus, the mixture of precursor powders must be extremely intimate and homogeneous, so that paths for further diffusion are as short as possible. An intimate mixture promotes easy reaction at lower temperatures and deters the formation of secondary phases, as established earlier for $BaTiO_3$ synthesis from $BaCO_3$ and $TiO_2$.[2,3].

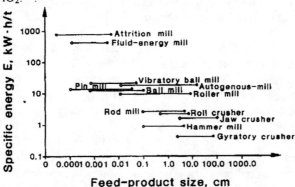

Figure 1: Average energy required for size-reduction equipment (from [4]).
O is typical product size; ✱ is typical feed size.

Both of these operations, grinding or mixing of powders, are processed using a mill in which the powders are submitted to shear and tensile stresses that make them break up and hence reduce in size. Considering the different types of mills, one can consider the average energy required for size-reduction as illustrated in Figure 1 reporting the energy required to grind a metric ton of material with the different types of mills. For the very smallest grind, the energy required can reach values as high as 1000 kWhr.ton[-1] for the most efficient mills. This energy is the sum of the energy required to move the machine, to move the material and to assure its plastic and elastic deformation together with internal friction and, finally, to break the material into smaller particles. This latter operation often accounts for less than 1% of the total energy needed to run the mill[4]. So, any progress permitting this "useful" energy ratio to be improved will allow the production of smaller and smaller grains. The aim of this paper is to present our first experimental results obtained when applying this philosophy that, as presented below, allowed us to get crushed alumina oxides with a mean diameter much lower than 50 nm.

It can be seen in Figure 1 that the smallest particles can be obtained using attrition milling. An attritor consists of a batch of small hard balls enclosed in a volume, that are mixed by arms moving into the batch. So, particles to be crushed are trapped between two adjacent balls during their movement, if the diameter of these balls is large enough and, therefore, crushed. On the other hand, if the balls are too small comparative to the diameter of the particles, they don't trap them and only erosion occurs (see Figure 2). Of course, if the milling balls are too large, crushing occurs but with fewer "crushing points" and, thus, the frequency of collisions is lowered with the consequence of only poor milling efficiency and, again, erosion that occurs between the milling balls. So, it seems evident that, for a correct attrition milling process, a careful choice of the diameter of the milling balls has to be made, taking into account the size of the particles to be ground.

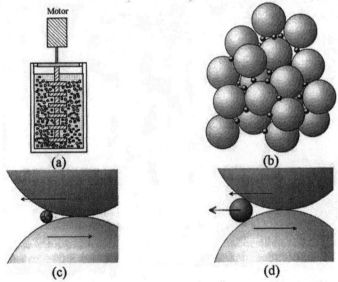

*Figure 2: (a) Principle of attrition milling; (b) grinding balls that are brassed will crush the small powder grains*
*(c) grinding balls large enough: powder grains are trapped between the grinding balls and crushed*
*(d) grinding balls not large enough: powder grains are not trapped and will not be crushed*

The powders to be crushed are dispersed into slurry generally composed of water with 20 to 60% weight (approximately 5 to 25 volume %) of powder dispersed in it. We consider here only fine grain powders that are well known to gather into flocs or agglomerates. **When agglomerates are present:** a part of the « grinding energy » is devoted to the destruction of the agglomerates. **When the slurry is viscous:** a part of the « grinding energy » is devoted to the liquid deformation and movement. **When the slurry is fluid and the particles well dispersed:** a maximum of the « grinding energy » is devoted to the crushing of the particles.

So, after recalling the principles of the dispersion of powders in liquids and rheological behavior, we shall expose how we determine the correct dispersion conditions and maintain them throughout the grinding process. We shall then present our first results concerning the grinding of 1/ a mix of $ZrO_2+SnO_2+TiO_2+La_2O_3+NiO$ powders, 2/ titanium oxide $TiO_2$, and 3/ alumina $Al_2O_3$.

## CONSIDERATIONS ON THE DISPERSION OF POWDERS AND ON THE RHEOLOGICAL BEHAVIOR OF SLURRIES[5]

Most solid surfaces are electrically charged. All of the links of a crystal are unsaturated, resulting in chemisorption, which entails the capture of foreign atoms, ions, or molecules on the surface. The surface electrical charge of particles dispersed in water or an electrolyte solution can be much more significant than that of particles in air. The electrical charges result from either dissolution of the solid into the liquid, ionization of surface groups (particularly $OH^-$), or substitution of ions belonging to the lattice of the solid. The charges are compensated by opposite-sign charges from the ions of the liquid, resulting in the formation of the so-called Helmholtz's double layer[6]. The potential at the Outer Helmholtz's Plane (OHP), which indicates the closest distance of approach of the hydrated ions in the solution, is assimilated into the zeta potential, $\zeta$ [7].

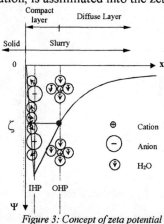

*Figure 3: Concept of zeta potential*

The principle of stabilization by electrostatic repulsion is described by the DLVO theory. Stabilization is possible only when repulsion forces are higher than attraction forces. The stabilization of electrostatic repulsion depends on both the radius of the particles and their surface potential, $\psi_0$. This latter parameter depends directly on the surface charges and is independent of the grain size of the powders. Consequently, the pH of the slurry, the concentration of the adsorbed ions and their nature are the main parameters to be taken into account. The value of the $\zeta$ potential depends directly on the concentration in the slurry of the ions determining the potential. As a consequence, it depends on the pH of the slurry and on the nature of these ions. The $\zeta$ potential 0 is the IsoElectric Point (IEP) (that is the same as the Zero Point of Charge, ZPC. We assume that there is no specific adsorption here). Table I gives examples of values of isoelectric points for some typical ceramic materials. As only low electrostatic repulsion forces are present, flocculation occurs. When $|\zeta|$ is high, higher electrostatic repulsion forces occur and the best dispersion state can then be obtained. It is generally admitted that the minimum value of $|\zeta|$ for a good dispersion to occur must be higher than 20 mV. When mixing different powders, the zeta potentials of all the mixed powders are to have the same sign.

Table I. typical values of isoelectric points of ceramic materials

| Material | IEP |
|---|---|
| $\alpha$-$Al_2O_3$ | 8-9 |
| $3Al_2O_3 \cdot 2SiO_2$ | 6-8 |
| $BaTiO_3$ | 5-6 |
| $CeO_2$ | 6.7 |
| $Cr_2O_3$ | 7 |
| $CuO$ | 9.5 |
| $Fe_3O_4$ | 6.5 |
| $La_2O_3$ | 10.4 |
| $MgO$ | 12.4 |
| $MnO_2$ | 4-4.5 |
| $NiO$ | 10-11 |
| $SiO_2$ (amorphous) | 2-3 |
| $Si_3N_4$ | 9 |
| $SnO_2$ | 7.3 |
| $TiO_2$ | 4-6 |
| $ZnO$ | 9 |
| $ZrO_2$ | 4-6 |

In the case of aqueous slurries of oxides, a surface reaction results in the formation of amphoteric hydroxide groups such as M–OH which can dissociate as weak acids or bases:

in basic slurries $\quad M-OH_{surface} \leftrightarrow M-O^-_{surface} + H^+ \quad$ (1)

in acid slurries $\quad M-OH_{surface} + H^+ \leftrightarrow M-OH_2^+{}_{surface} \quad$ (2)

It seems evident that when grinding powders new surfaces are created as a consequence of the breaking up of particles. These surfaces react with the liquid and thus make the value of pH change with a concomitant evolution of the Van der Waals forces. This has been well-known for years by traditional ceramics engineers who generally control the flocculation or deflocculation of clay slurries by regulating the amounts of basic compounds[1,8,9]. Recent studies have also been prompted by such considerations[10 to 14].

Newtonian liquids such as water or most solvents and oils are characterized by a viscosity independent of shear rate. A viscosity that increases with shear rate characterizes shear-thickening fluids. This seems to be characteristic of high-solid concentration suspensions[1,15,16]: they show shear thinning behavior at low shear rates and dilatant rheologies at high shear rates, typically higher than 50 s$^{-1}$. This behavior has been extensively studied. Although it is not yet completely understood, two different mechanisms have been proposed: order to disorder transition and hydrodynamic clustering[17,18]. On the other hand, viscosity that decreases with shear rate characterizes shear-thinning liquids. For flocculated slurries, this behavior can be related to the breaking of the links between particles gathered in the flocculates[1,9]. Thus, rheological measurements performed on slurries can reflect the flocculated or deflocculated state of the slurries.

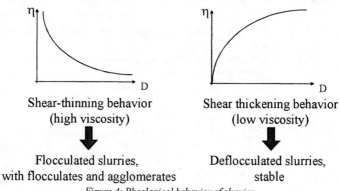

Shear-thinning behavior          Shear thickening behavior
(high viscosity)                 (low viscosity)

Flocculated slurries,            Deflocculated slurries,
with flocculates and agglomerates        stable

*Figure 4: Rheological behavior of slurries*

So, we can now present the process we set to work when grinding and or mixing fine particles. The first problem to be considered is to determine the accurate dispersion parameters of the particular powders to be processed. The absolute value of the zeta potential of each powder is supposed to be higher than 20 mV with all potentials having the same sign. The first characterization to be done is to determine for each powder to be processed its zeta potential versus pH. This allows us to ascertain the optimum pH of the slurry allowing a good dispersion of all the constituents. If pH control is not possible, good dispersion may alternatively be obtained by an adequate dispersant addition, but we shall not develop this here.

The surfaces of the materials increase during the dispersion and/or grinding process due to the break-up of the different grains. Surface reactions with the dispersion liquid occur and pH and/or dispersant rate have to be continuously adjusted to be maintained at an adequate value. These characteristics of the optimal processing conditions are closely correlated with the rheological behavior of the slurries, thus providing an analysis of the flocculated or deflocculated state. If zeta potential evolution as a consequence of the grinding process is not controlled, flocculation can occur and, consequently, viscosity increases. The danger is thus that the grinding efficiency will shrink. The slurry may then become as consistent as a solid. The target is thus to be able to maintain the deflocculated state of the slurries. So, after determination of the optimum dispersion parameters of powders in aqueous slurries by zeta potential measurements and rheological behavior determinations, the idea is to maintain the pH value (and/or the rate of dispersant addition) high enough during the whole grinding time to be coherent with a dispersed deflocculated state.

## EXPERIMENTAL SETUP

Measurements of $\zeta$ versus the pH of the dispersion medium were performed using a ZetaSizer 3000 (Malvern Instruments, Malvern, U.K.) coupled with an automatic titrator. Powders were first dispersed using an impeller mixer in deionized water and a drop of the upper part of this mixture was taken after some minutes of sedimentation and diluted into the ZetaSizer in such a concentration that the analyzed signal was correct. The pH of the dispersion was adjusted from this initial condition by the addition of hydrochloric acid or ammonia and measurements performed. When used later to adjust the pH value of the mixed slurries, these particular acid and base will not introduce any undesirable cations detrimental to the microwave characteristics of the ceramics. No inert electrolyte was used to fix the ionic strength in order to be as close as possible to the dispersion conditions in the ground slurries.

Rheograms were performed with a rheometer (Model No. Rheolab MC10, Physica Messtechnik, Stuttgart, Germany) using the Couette geometry (cell dimensions: $\phi = 48$ mm; height = 116 mm. cylinder dimensions: $\phi = 45$ mm; height = 68 mm. gap = 1.5 mm). Before any experimental evaluation of the rheological behavior, the time needed for the shear stress to stabilize under each shear must be determined. The time necessary for stabilization, independent of the shear rate, is for this particular rheometer ~ 2 s. Thus, when the rheograms of the different slurries were made, the shear rate was varied between 0 and 1000 s$^{-1}$, either increasing or decreasing with 50 measurements in each direction, and was applied 4 s before every measurement. Rheograms were immediately performed on samples just taken from the batches being ground.

Grinding and dispersion/mixing of the present powders were performed by attrition milling. The present dispersion medium was deionized water, the pH of which was adjusted by hydrochloric acid or ammonia additions. Fairly high-density slurries with a powder weight amount equal to 20wt%, 40wt%, 50wt% and 60wt% (that is to say ranging from approximately 5 to 25 % volume of solids in water, depending on the ground powders) were ground. Prior to grinding, the powders were pre-mixed in this dispersion medium using an impeller mixer. Balls (0.4 to 2.5 mm in diameter) of either zircon or Y-zirconia were used in a horizontal attrition mill (Dyno-Mill®, CB Mills, Gurnee, IL), which allowed high-energy grinding in a continuous process and recycling of the slurry. Batches of 0.5 to 3 kg were ground in this manner. The normalized grinding time, $t_N$, which represents the real grinding time, is defined as

$$t_N = \frac{t_A V_S}{V_T} \tag{3}$$

where $t_A$ is the total attrition time, $V_S$ the volume of slurry ground in the attrition chamber, and $V_T$ the total volume of the batch.

We characterized the powders during and after grinding by measuring their specific surfaces with the Brunauer–Emmet–Teller (BET) method using a Flowsorb II 2300 (Micromeritics Instrument Corp., Norcross, GA) using Heliofuit (mix of helium and 30 mol % nitrogen) as adsorption gas. Samples were desorbed at 250°C for 1 hour before measurements. The equivalent diameter of powders $\theta_{eq}$ was then deduced using the formula $\theta_{eq} = \frac{6}{S_{BET}.\rho}$ where $\rho$ is the specific weight, assuming that all particles are spherical and have the same diameter.

The equivalent diameter of powders was also estimated by X-ray diffraction: the shape of each diffraction peak depends on a convolution of the experimental peak (effect of the material) together with the «real» peak (effect of the material)[19]. So, after experimental correction using a quartz monocrystal, we analyzed the shapes of the peaks that depend on both the size of the crystallites and the rate of distortion. Two methods have been developed, the choice depending on the shape factor of the peaks: the Williamson and Hall and the Halder and Wagner methods. In our case, we used the Halder and Wagner method, making the estimation on five diffraction peaks with highly good correlation coefficients (see Figure 5 in the example of the $TiO_2$ powders). X-ray diffraction patterns were performed using a Siemens D5005 diffractometer and Cu $k_{\alpha 1}$ with the following recording conditions: 0.02° 2$\theta$ steps, 0.05 mm analysis slit and 100 s count time for each step.

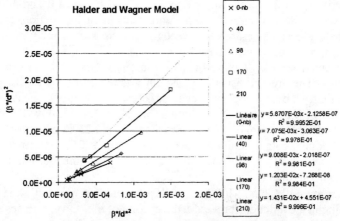

*Figure 5: X-ray diffraction peaks analysis using the Halder and Wagner model*

Ceramic Materials and Multilayer Electronic Devices

## RESULTS AND DISCUSSION

### Mix of $ZrO_2+SnO_2+TiO_2+La_2O_3+NiO$ powders

The experimental support is the synthesis of $(Zr,Sn)TiO_4$ microwave dielectric ceramics from $ZrO_2$, $SnO_2$, and $TiO_2$ powders with some NiO and $La_2O_3$ added as sintering aids (see Figure 6). These materials are processed to make microwave resonators. The performance of these components is quantified by their quality factor defined by the product $Q \times F$ ($Q = \dfrac{1}{tg\delta}$ is the inverse of the dielectric losses measured at the resonance frequency F) which value is, in a first approximation, constant with the frequency. Classically mixed in a ball mill, this composition leads only to ceramics characterized by much dispersed and relatively low values of the quality factor ranging typically from 30 000 to 45 000 GHz measured at 3 GHz. This can be attributed to the poor homogeneity and insufficient quality of dispersion and/or to the poor grinding effect obtained with this low energy mixing technique. Grinding and mixing these powders by attrition milling is hardly difficult in this particular case as the slurries, as will be discussed further, quickly become highly viscous with the progress of the grinding process.

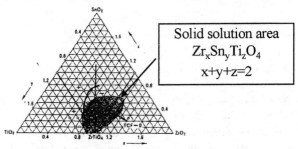

Solid solution area
$Zr_xSn_yTi_zO_4$
$x+y+z=2$

*Figure 6: Compositions to be mixed and ground together, with w% NiO and 2w% La$_2$O$_3$ additions*

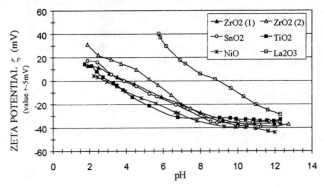

*Figure 7: Zeta potential of the different powders versus pH (from [5])*

Figure 7 shows zeta potential versus pH for each powder. The measured values of all the potentials, positive for low pH, decrease when pH goes up and are negative for a basic pH. That result is in agreement with the model for hydroxide groups adsorbed onto the surfaces of grains. The IEP values range from pH 3 for NiO to pH 9 for La$_2$O$_3$. For pH values ranging from 2 to 3, all of the potentials are positive but the absolute values are <20 mV for four of the different powders. Furthermore, La$_2$O$_3$ dissolves for pH <6 (pure dispersion cannot then be considered). These conditions are far from favorable to stable suspensions. A basic pH seems more favorable for stable and deflocculated slurries because all of the potentials are negative with all absolute values >20 mV when pH is >11.

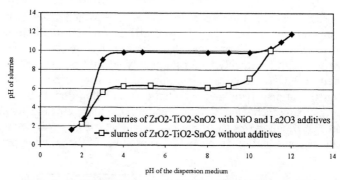

*Figure 8: pH of 40w% slurries versus pH of the dispersion medium (from [5])*

In addition, as already reported for other composition systems[10,20], it is noteworthy that the pH of the slurries are quite different from that of the liquid of the suspension (i.e. water plus acid or base additions): pH was dramatically modified by the powder additions as illustrated in Figure 8 in the case of a 40wt% slurry. Two remarks can be deduced from this observation: 1) to be able to assume that the pH of the slurry will be ≥ 11, the pH of the dispersion medium should be ≥ 11.6 in the case of this particular slurry concentration and 2) as the surface of the powders increases when grinding, further surface reaction will occur and the pH can then be expected to decrease. So, it may be necessary to adjust the pH of the slurry during the grinding operation, keeping its value ≥ 11 to be sure of avoiding further flocculation. We shall discuss further that particular point, which is one of the keys of the grinding principles we promote.

Figure 9 shows as evidence the high correlation between grinding efficiency and the viscosity of the slurries that, whatever the density of the slurry, the lower the viscosity for low shear rates, the higher the BET specific area of the ground batch. That can be easily correlated with the rheological behavior: all of the 60 wt% slurries, whatever their pH; the 50 wt% slurries with pH <10.5; and the 40 wt% slurries with pH values <10 are shear-thinning liquids and, therefore, flocculated slurries with high viscosities. As an example, Figure 10 shows the rheograms for 50 wt% slurries with different pH values. Conversely, the 40 wt% slurries with pH >10 and the 50 wt% slurries with pH >10.5 are shear-thickening liquids with low viscosities and, therefore, deflocculated stable slurries. Those viscosity values range from 6 to 7 mPa.s, not far from that of water (1 mPa.s).

Ceramic Materials and Multilayer Electronic Devices

Such low viscosities allow a high efficiency grinding and mixing of these high-density slurries by attrition milling.

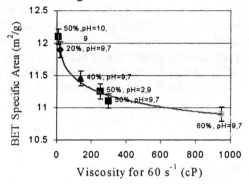

Figure 9: BET specific area versus viscosity for different slurries after 1 hour grinding time with 2.5 mm zirconia balls

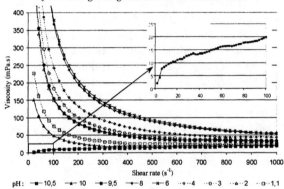

Figure 10: Rheogramm viscosity $v = f(\gamma)$ for 50w% slurries with different pH (from [5])

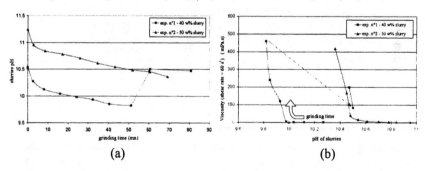

(a)                                            (b)

Figure 11: Evolution of (a) pH and (b) viscosity at 60 $s^{-1}$ shear rate versus time during the grinding process

The problem is now to keep this behavior constant throughout the grinding process. Figure 11 (a) shows that, effectively, pH evolves with time during the grinding process and Figure 11 (b) that, correlatively, viscosity at 60 $s^{-1}$ shear rate climbs dramatically when low viscosity values are attained. These two slurries were shear thickening and fluid at the beginning of grinding. They became highly viscous and shear thinning when pH was free to evolve at lower values as a consequence of the reactions between the new surfaces of the ground powders and the liquid. We adjusted the pH of slurry n°1 to the initial value after it fell to 9.8. Viscosity then effectively diminished drastically, but we failed to obtain again the initial low values and the behavior remained shear thinning: a slurry is very difficult to deflocculate after it has passed a certain level of flocculation. This is a general behavior that we observed every time we allowed any slurry to flocculate. It is thus of great importance to prevent it from occurring.

So, we ground two other slurries, respectively noted n°3 and n°4, continuously adjusting the pH to a value higher than 10.5, high enough to prevent flocculation. The diameter of the attrition balls was calibrated between 1.5 and 2.5 mm for slurry n°3, and between 0.8 and 1.25 mm for slurry n°4. Figure 12 shows the evolution of the specific areas of the different slurries versus grinding time. For slurries n°1 and 2, in which the pH was free to evolve during grinding, the specific area increased during the first 20 or 30 min of grinding and approached a limit. In contrast, for slurries n°3 and 4, the specific area increased continuously. In fact, the efficiency of the grinding process seemed closely related to low viscosities together with a deflocculated state. That theory is credible because all of the grinding energy in deflocculated slurries could be devoted to grinding and none was needed for crushing agglomerates or flocs. The slight increase of specific area in slurry n°1 after 50 min was related to the decrease in viscosity resulting from pH adjustment, but the effect was weak because the flocculated state remained.

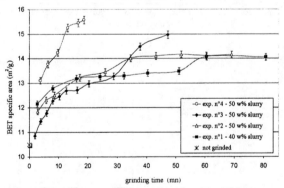

*Figure 12: Evolution of the specific area versus grinding time of the different experiments (from [5])*

The grinding process seems to have been highly efficient for the deflocculated slurries when the diameter of the grinding balls was small (1.5/2.5 mm for slurry n°3 versus 0.8/1.25 mm for slurry n°4). Under the most efficient grinding conditions—that is in the case of slurry n°4—the calculated diameter of the ground powder from its specific surface (assuming that all grains were spheres with the same diameter) was ~100 nm after only 18 min, compared with the mix of 0.3 to 10 μm diameter powders included into the slurry before grinding. We can notice that the grinding process was then interrupted, as shown in Figure 12, long before the specific area had approached a limit.

After shaping from slurry n°4 powders mixed for 20 minutes and sintering, the so-processed k37 resonators were characterized and possess a QxF factor higher than 60 000 GHz at 3 GHz. These performances are the best known today for this particular composition diagram.

Titanium oxide $TiO_2$

We ground anatase $TiO_2$ with a 8.6 $m^2.g^{-1}$ BET specific area (189 nm calculated equivalent diameter). The IEP of this particular $TiO_2$ powder is at pH = 3, and $\zeta$ is equal to –30 mV for pH 10. The density of the slurries that were attrition milled was 50w% (20.7 % volume of powder). The pH value was maintained at 10 throughout the process in order to keep the rheological behavior unchanged during the whole grinding process, as shown in Figure 13. In an attempt to evaluate the influence of the the diameter of the attrition balls on grinding efficiency, we used four different materials described in Table II.

Table II. Attrition balls used for the different grindings

| SEPR ER120S Zircon | | TOSOH YTZ Y-zirconia | |
|---|---|---|---|
| 1.25-1.6 mm | 0.8-1 mm | 0.8 mm | 0.4 mm |

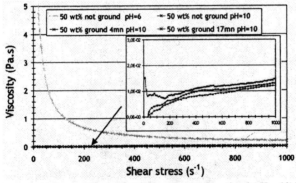

Figure 13: Rheological behavior of flocculated (pH = 6) and deflocculated (pH = 10) TiO₂ slurries

The evolution versus grinding time of the BET specific area of the powders issuing from these four batches is reported in Figure 14 (a). It is noteworthy that both grinding ball diameter and viscosity value effects are confirmed:

➤ Grinding efficiency remains constant throughout the process when the slurry is kept deflocculated by continuous adjustments of the pH value;

➤ The smaller the balls are, the more efficient the grinding process is.

Figure 14 (b) shows the evolution of the calculated equivalent diameter. The most significant effect is obtained with the 0.4 mm YZT balls that allow the production of a 32 $m^2g^{-1}$ BET specific area after 50 minutes grinding time. That corresponds to a calculated grain diameter equal to 48 nanometers. This is confirmed by the X-ray diffraction evaluation of the diameter of the particles, as shown Figure 15.

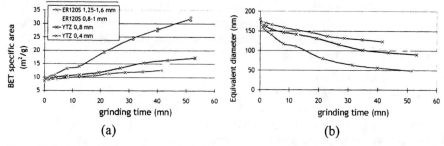

(a)                                           (b)

*Figure 14: Evolution of TiO₂ powder versus grinding time. (a): BET specific area; (b): equivalent diameter*

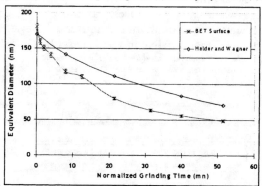

*Figure 15: Evolution of the diameter of the particles versus grinding time evaluated by BET specific area measurements and by X-ray diffraction with the Halder and Wagner method*

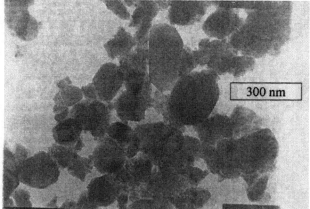

*Figure 16: TEM observation of the 32m².g⁻¹ TiO₂ powder**

* We thank Prof. Maryvonne HERVIEUX, from CRISMAT Laboratory (ENSI Caen, France) for the TEM observation of the TiO₂ powders.

Ceramic Materials and Multilayer Electronic Devices

TEM observations of the powders* confirm these evaluations, as the diameter of most of the grains lies between 50 and 80 nm. Some large grains remain. Their presence could be explained by the fact we have ground this particular powder directly with the 0.4 mm balls that were too small to crush these large grains. Thus, a correct schedule could be to process using grinding balls with decreasing diameters. On the other hand, grinding with larger balls (1.25 to 1.6 mm in the present case) seems much less efficient when considering the BET specific area evolution versus time, but is necessary as a first operation to reduce the diameter of the largest grains.

Alumina $Al_2O_3$

The isoelectric point of α-alumina is known to be around pH 8 or 9 and alumina slurries have long been known to be highly viscous for pH values ranging from 6 to 10. This behavior is confirmed Figure 17: shear-thickening deflocculated slurries are only obtained for highly basic pH $\geq$ 11 or acid pH $\leq$ 5.7.

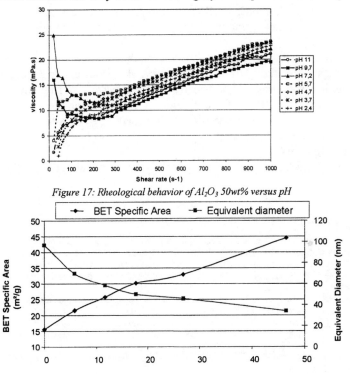

*Figure 17: Rheological behavior of $Al_2O_3$ 50wt% versus pH*

*Figure 18: Evolution versus time of the BET specific area and of the equivalent calculated diameter of particles for $Al_2O_3$ grounded with 0.4 mm grinding balls*

The α-alumina to be ground was characterized by a 15 $m^2.g^{-1}$ BET specific area. We chose to grind it with 0.4 mm balls in an acid slurry, maintaining the pH equal to 4 throughout the process. Figure 18 shows both the evolution of the BET specific area versus grinding time and the calculated equivalent diameter. After 50 minutes grinding time, BET specific area was as high as 44 $m^2.g^{-1}$. That corresponds to a calculated 34 nm equivalent particle diameter.

CONCLUSIONS

The experimental results presented here show that it is possible, using classical attrition milling material, to get nanometric powders. There are some conditions to be respected that allow this performance:

➤ The importance of maintaing at all times a low value of the viscosity of the slurry;

➤ This is closely correlated to the maintaining of a deflocculated state that can be characterized with a shear-thickening rheological comportment;

➤ These conditions have to be maintained during the whole grinding process, since any flocculation of the slurry is impossible to salvage;

➤ The importance of the diameter of the balls: large enough to allow the grinding of large grains, small enough to permit good efficiency. A "string of milling" using grinding balls with decreasing diameters may be implemented.

Much work has yet to be done to go further in this direction. It includes both a careful investigation of the rheological properties of slurries under different shear conditions with a modeling of the shear stresses occurring during the grinding process. Automatic regulation of the optimum grinding parameters will also be studied. Finally, similar prospective studies will be devoted to slurries deflocculated with steric dispersants.

**Acknowledgments**

Part of this work has been supported by the European Union (FEDER) and by TEMEX

REFERENCES
[1] James S. Reed, Principles of ceramic processing, John Wiley & Sons, second edition 1995.
[2] E. Bouteloup, C. Michel, J.M. Haussonne, P. Bourdois, O. Regreny, " Mixing of Powders: Main Parameter of Synthesis of a Material by Calcining ", Pp. 163-168 In Proceedings 14th Int. Conf. Science of Ceramics, Canterbury G.B. September 7-9th 1987, Edited By D. Taylor, The Institute of Ceramics Stoke on Trent G.B., 1988.
[3] J.C. Niepce and J.M. Haussonne, " BaTiO3: Matériau de Base pour le Diélectrique des Condensateurs Céramiques " ("BaTiO3, Base Material For Ceramic Capacitors"), Septima Paris, 1994.
[4] Terry A. Ring, Fundamentals of Ceramic Powder Processing and Synthesis, Academic Press, 1996
[5] D. Houivet, J. El Fallah, J.M. Haussonne, "Dispersion and Grinding of Oxide Powders into an Aqueous Slurry", J. Am. Ceram. Soc., 85, [2], pp.321-328, 2002.
[6] G.D. Parfitt, "Dispersion of Powders in Liquids with Special Reference to Pigments", Applied science Publishers, London,U.K., 1981
[7] R.J. Hunter, "Zeta Potential in Colloid Science, Principles and Applications", Academic Press, London, 1981.
[8] M. Haussonne, "Technologie Générale Céramique" ("Ceramic Technology"), Baillière Et Fils, Paris, 1954.
[9] C.A. Jouenne, "Traité des Céramiques et des Matériaux Minéraux" ("Introduction To Ceramics And Mineral Materials"), 2nd Edition, Septima, Paris, 1980.

Ceramic Materials and Multilayer Electronic Devices

[10] F.N. Shi, T.J. Napier-Munn, "Effects of slurry rheology on industrial grinding performance", Int. J. Miner. Process, 65, 125-140 (2002)

[11] S. Vallar, D. Houivet, J. El Fallah, D. Kervadec and J.M. Haussonne, "Oxide Slurries Stability and Powder Dispersion: Optimization with Zeta Potential and Rheological Measurements", J. Eur. Ceram. Soc., [19], 1017-21 (1999).

[12] C. Agrafiotis, A. Tsetsekou, I. Leon, "Effect of Slurry Rheological Properties on The Coating of Ceramic Honeycombs with Yttria-Stabilized-Zirconia Washcoats", J. Amer. Ceram. Soc., 83, [5], 1033-38 (2000).

[13] J. Jiyou Guo and Jennifer A. Lewis, "Effects of Ammonium Chloride on the Rheological Properties and Sedimentation Behavior of Aqueous Silica Suspensions", J. Amer. Ceram. Soc., 83, [2], 266-72 (2000).

[14] Jau-Ho Jean and Hong-Ren Wang, "Effects of Solids Loading, pH, and Polyelectrolyte Addition on the Stabilization of Concentrated Aqueous BaTiO$_3$ Suspensions", J. Amer. Ceram. Soc., 83, [2], 277-80 (2000).

[15] G.V. Franks, Z. Zhou, N.J. Duin and D.V. Boger, "Effect of Interparticle Forces on Shear Thickening of Oxide Suspensions", J. Rheol., 44, [4], 759-79 (2000).

[16] J. E. Funk & D. R. Dinger, "Predictive Process Control of Crowded Particulate Suspensions Applied to Ceramic Manufacturing", Kluwer Academic Publishers, Boston, Second printing 1997.

[17] R.L. Hoffmann, "Discontinuous and Dilatant Viscosity Behavior in Concentrate Suspensions. III: Necessary Conditions for their Occurrence in Viscometric Flows", Adv. Colloid Interfaces Sci., 17, 161-84, (1982).

[18] W.H. Boersma, J. Laven, H.N. Stein, "Computer Simulations of Shear Thickening of Concentrated Dispersions", J. Rheol., 39, [5], 841,60, (1995).

[19] N.C. Halder and C.N.J. Wagner, Act. Cryst., vol. 20, pp. 91-102, 1966

[20] E. Bouteloup, C. Michel, J.M. Haussonne, P. Bourdois and O. Regreny, "Mixing of powders, main parameter of synthesis of a paterial by calcining", in Proceedings of the 14$^{th}$ International Conference Science of Ceramics, D. Taylor Editor, Canterbury, Sept 1987, 163-68.

# PRODUCTION OF A SODA FELDSPAR-TiO$_2$ OZONIZER BY DIRECT EXTRUSION

Enrique Rocha, Martín Rodríguez*, Roberto Hernández, Alejandro Altamirano and José Hernández-Avila[+]
Departamento de Materiales, * Departamento de Ciencias Básicas, [+]Departamento de Energía
Universidad Autónoma Metropolitana
Av. San Pablo # 180, Col. Reynosa, México, D. F. 02200, México

ABSTRACT
Ceramic materials with good dielectric properties are frequently used in the construction of apparatus for the ozone production when is flowing oxygen or air through them. The present work describes the fabrication of a monolithic ceramic by the direct extrusion technique. The paste for the extrusion was prepared with 30 wt % of soda feldspar and 45 wt % of TiO$_2$, using distilled water and methocel as additive. The final product has tubular shape with 3 cm of external diameter and 1.4 cm of internal diameter. The obtained tube from the extrusion was sintered in air at 1080°C for different times (3, 6, 9 and 12 h). Density, shrinkage and hardness of the final product increases with increments of sintering time. Microstructure is homogeneous with two well defined phases that correspond to soda feldspar and TiO$_2$ respectively. Small and isolated porosity is also observed here. The produced monolithic present's good physical characteristics in order to develop good dielectric properties for its application in the production of ozone. Mayor processing details and the characterization of the dielectric properties of this monolithic are discussed in the text.

## INTRODUCTION
Ozone is the allotropic form of oxygen that has three oxygen atoms, its formula is O$_3$. It is a blue color gas with strong smell and highly poisonous. Ozone has an ebullition point of -192.5 °C and a density of 2.144 X 10$^{-3}$ g/cc. The liquid ozone is navy blue color and is strongly magnetic. Ozone is most active than ordinary oxygen and it is better as oxidizing agent. It is used for water purification and as air cleaner. On the other hand, its low level in the atmosphere, caused by the presence of nitrogen oxides and organic gases emitted by the automobiles and industries, is dangerous for the health because it is an important filter of the ultraviolet sun rays. The ozone is formed allowing medium frequency or high frequency waves to pass between ceramic discharge tube and electrode connection and by flowing dry air or oxygen. Commercial methods for obtaining

the ozone consists in pass an oxygen cold and dry flux through an electric discharge. In this way most ozone generators are dielectric materials and are commonly used bore silicates, SiC, glass or quartz tubes which have dielectric constant between 3.8 and 9.5 [1-7]. Moreover, ozone productivity in the discharge space is depending upon the temperature of the discharge tube and dielectrics of electrode itself. Ozone generation rate is constant proportion inductance rate or induced electricity. However, these generators are expensive and difficult for its fabrication. Therefore, some investigation looking for the used of cheap materials with high dielectric constant are important for the construction of ozonizers.

The aim of this study is the production of a soda feldespar-$TiO_2$ ceramic with both good physical characteristics and dielectric properties for its use as ozonizer.

## EXPERIMENTAL

The monolithic was prepared by the techniques combination of direct extrusion and sintering. The device used for the extrusion was designed for working in cold and consists of a container, ram, die and die holder, all these elements are made of 316 stainless steel. The device is assembled to a universal testing machine and then the direct extrusion is performed there. The ceramic paste was prepared using the next substances:

|  | Soda-feldespar | $TiO_2$ | Methocell | Distilled water |
|---|---|---|---|---|
| Quantity (wt %) | 30 | 45 | 6 | 19 |

(All chemicals were supply by Tecnomold S. A. Mexico)

The ceramic paste was prepared by hand mixing of components until a consistent mass has been formed. Then the container is filled with the paste and it is ready for the extrusion process. Conditions of extrusion are: 500 Kgf of stress at a speed of 200 mm/s. Tubular greens monolithic were obtained from this stage, they were dry at room temperature during 48 h. The next step is sintering of the greens in a high temperature electric furnace at 1080°C for different times (3, 6, 9 and 12 h). Characterization of fired samples was made as follows: Density and open porosity of fired samples were evaluated by the Archimedes's principle. Linear dimensional change in samples was measured by directed dimension of samples before and after sintering stage. The microstructural development was analyzed using optical and scanning electron microscopy (OP) and (SEM) respectively. Hardness was estimated using microscale Vickers.

## RESULTS AND DISCUSSION

Figure 1 shows a picture of the monolithic fabricated. The final product has tubular shape with 3 cm of external diameter and 1.4 cm of internal diameter, the length of the tube can be variable according to necessities. After processing, visual observations of the specimens let to conclude that through the combination techniques of direct extrusion and sintering the final shape is preserved.

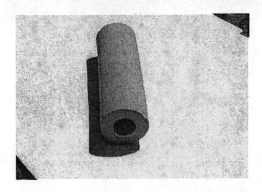

Figure 1. Picture of the tubular monolithic made of soda feldespar-TiO$_2$
ceramic. Sintered at 1080°C for 6 h.

Figure 2. Shows the weight changes of extruded sample during it's dried at
room temperature as a function of time. Sample presents a rapid loss weight
during the first two hours after it was extruded. This weight loss correspond to
evaporation of water used for prepare the ceramic paste and it was of 9.5 wt %.
For times bigger than two hours at room temperature samples still lossing weight
by evaporation of water however it is slowly and it is necessary wait during 46
hours more for get a ceramic completely dry.

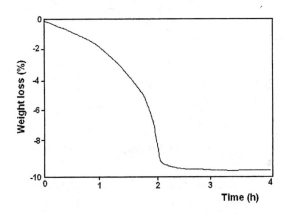

Figure 2. Weight loss of extruded sample during its dried
at room temperature as function of time.

Figure 3 shows the changes in density and open porosity in sintered samples
as a function of sintering time at 1080°C. For density there are small increments
in its value as the sintering time increases, whereas the open porosity diminish in
its values in the same way. These changes in both density and open porosity are
in good agreement with the sintering behavior of the samples shows in Figure 4
in where the shrinkage of the samples is major as the sintering time at 1080 °C is
higher. These is due to that with the increments in time there are major diffusion,
therefore the structure suffer major shrinkage, then free sites between particles
are reduce consequently densification occurs.

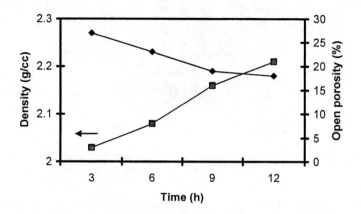

Figure 3. Density and open porosity of samples sintered
at 1080°C as a function of the sintering time.

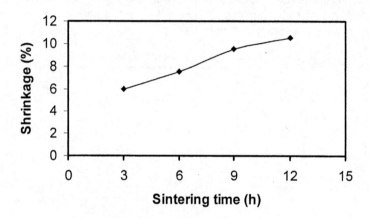

Figure 4. Shrinkage of samples sintered at
1080°C as a function of the sintering time.

The Figure 5 shows the microstructure of the transversal section in relation to the wall of the tubular sintered sample at 1080°C as a function of sintering time. Pictures where took using an optical microscopy. In general this micrographs show a homogeneous microstructure in where the presence of two phases are well defined, clear phase correspond to $TiO_2$, whereas the dark phase correspond to soda feldspar. Some isolated porosity regions and the sintering effects are observed in these pictures due to the neck formation between some particles principally in the $TiO_2$ phase. Grow microstructure and samples best densified are observed when the sintering time is bigger.

Ceramic Materials and Multilayer Electronic Devices

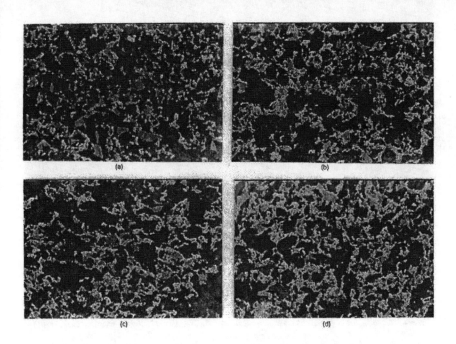

Figure 5. Optical micrographs of sintered samples at 1080°C for:
a) 3 h, b) 6h, c) 9h and d) 12 h.

The Figure 6 shows the SEM microstructures of the transversal section in relation to the wall of the tubular sintered sample at 1080°C as a function of sintering time: In these pictures it is possible observe big particles with size > 10 μm and the presence of cavities in all samples. In the way of sintering time increases the effect of diffusion is more evident because there are formation of necks between some particles. For the pictures corresponding to 3, 6 and 9 h of sintering time, there are not significant differences between their microstructure, this means that the size and shape of particles and the porosity are very similar in these samples. Whereas microstructure of sample sintered at 12 h is most homogeneous, with a regular distribution of porosity and phases, the microstructure here is dense and it is not observe the presence of big cavities that can be observed in samples sintered a lower times.

The results of hardness measurements are shown in Table 2. It can be observed the existence of important variations of hardness in the way of sintering time increases, because there are strong increments in hardness with this variable. This behavior is in good agreement with the density, open porosity and shrinkage in sample, as well as microstructure observations. Because, samples best consolidated where obtained at bigger sintering times.

Table 2. Hardness of sintered samples at 1080°C as a function of sintering time.

| 3 h | 6h | 9h | 12h |
|---|---|---|---|
| 1.85 GPa | 2.00 GPa | 5.10 GPa | 8.70 GPa |

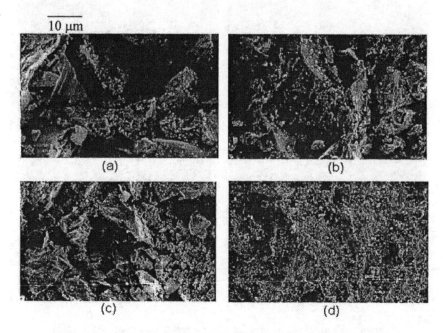

Figure 6. SEM micrographs of sintered samples at 1080°C for:
a) 3 h, b) 6h, c) 9h and d) 12 h.


Figure 7 shows the changes in dielectric strength in sintered samples as a function of sintering time at 1080°C. In this figure the dielectric strength increases with increments of sintering time. As it is knew high dilelectric strength implies high dielectric constant and the dielectric strength of materials is their ability to withstand large fields strengths without electrical breakdown. Values of dielectric strength of ceramic here produced are low compared with values of same property of other dielectric ceramic materials. Kingery et. al.[8] say that at low field strengths there is a certain dc conductivity corresponding to the movility of a limited number of charge carriers related to electronic or ionic imperfections. As the field strength is increased , this dc conduction increases, but also when some sufficiently large value of potential is reached, a field emission from the electrodes makes available sufficient electrons for a burst of current which produces breakdown channels, jagged holes, or metal dendrites bridging the dielectric and rendering it unusable. This is in good agrement with the behaviour of our material, because dielectric strenght increments with sintering time and in this experiments larger sintering time implicates materials best densified. However, final density reached for the best ceramic here produced is very low presenting enough porosity for the electrical breakdown at relative low dielectric strength. Therefore, it has to be necessary to review the process conditions here used for getting ceramics good densified in order to get ceramics with good dielectric properties.

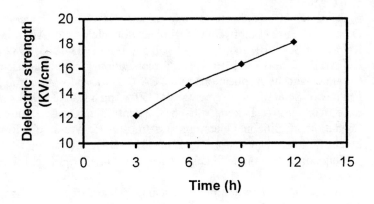

Figure 7. Dielectric strength of samples sintered
at 1080°C as a function of the sintering time.

## CONCLUSIONS

- Tubular ceramic samples for use as oxonizers can be fabricated by the techniques combination of direct extrusion and sintering here proposed.
- Long sintering times implicates samples best consolidated and microstructures more homogeneous, consequently best physical and mechanical properties.
- In this study density and dielectric strength of ceramics increases with sintering time, it means that are very important to produce well densified ceramics in order to get good dielectric properties.
- Due to the porosity presented by the ceramics here produced it is necessary to review the processing conditions for getting dense ceramics that present best dielectric properties.

## REFERENCES

1. E. J. Stone, J.R. Caldwell, C de Waal, J.J. Horvath, R. Pearson Jr. And D.H. Stedman, "Lightweight Ozonizer for Field and Airborne Use", Review of Scientific Instruments, Vol. 53, 2, pp 1903-1905, 1982

2. K. Asai, Simple and Reliable Preionization Technique Using SiC Ceramics and Its Applications to a TEA $CO_2$ Laser for Airborne DIAL", Review of Scientific Instruments, Vol. 59, 6, pp 880-882, 1988

3. K. Koike and T. Fukuda, "High Concentration Ozone Generator for Oxidation of Silicon Operating at Atmospheric Pressure", Review of Scientific Instruments, Vol. 71,11, pp 4182-4187, 2000

4. N. Nagamine, H. Itoh, H. Satake and A. Toriumi, Tech. Dig. Int. Electron Devices Meet. pp 847, 1998

5. K. Watanabe, S. Kimura and T. Tatsumi, Mater. Res. Soc. Symp. Proc. 567, pp. 268, 1999

6. S. Hosokawa and S. Ichimura, Rev. Sci. Instrum Vol 62, pp 1614, 1991

7. A. Kurokawa, K. Nakamura and S. Ichimura, Mater. Res. Soc. Symp. Proc. 513, pp 37, 1998

8. W. D. Kingery, H. K. Bowen and D. R. Uhlmann, "Introduction to Ceramics", Ed. John Wiley and Sons, pp. 930, USA, 1976

# CHARACTERIZATION OF BaTiO₃ POWDERS BY TRANSMISSION ELECTRON MICROSCOPY AND SCANNING TRANSMISSION ELECTRON MICROSCOPY

CHARACTERIZATION OF $BaTiO_3$ POWDERS BY TRANSMISSION ELECTRON MICROSCOPY AND SCANNING TRANSMISSION ELECTRON MICROSCOPY

Yoshinori Fujikawa, Fumikazu Yamane and Takeshi Nomura
Materials Research Center, TDK Corporation
570-2 Minamihadori Matsugashita Narita, Chiba, 286-8588, Japan

Yasuyuki Kitano
Department. Materials Science, Shimane Univ.
1060 Nishi-Kawatsu, Matsue, Shimane, 690-8504, Japan

ABSTRACT

Barium titanate ($BaTiO_3$) is the basic material of ceramic capacitors. Transmission Electron Microscopy (TEM) and Scanning Transmission Electron Microscopy (STEM) have been applied to investigate the microstructure of $BaTiO_3$ powders. Either a focused-ion-beam (FIB) cutting technique or a low angle Ar-ion beam milling technique has been successfully used to prepare TEM specimens of $BaTiO_3$ powder cross-sections. In this paper, examples of some observations have been shown. The mechanism of the solid state synthesis of fine $BaTiO_3$ powders has been studied. The reaction process can be observed as visual images. The surface modification of $BaTiO_3$ particles (0.2μm size) by leaching was also investigated. The leaching was performed using a hydrochloric acid solution (0.01N HCl) until a Ba/Ti ratio reached to 0.955. In this case, the formation of an amorphous Ti-O layer was confirmed by high-resolution electron microscopy (HRTEM). The surface modification, however, was found to have no significant influence on the overall crystallinity of the powders. In recent years the modifying techniques of the $BaTiO_3$ surface have made rapid progress and the TEM or STEM observations has been indispensable to investigate the surface structure.

INTRODUCTION

Barium titanate ($BaTiO_3$) is widely used as a ceramic dielectric or a ceramic semiconductor. It is the main component of the dielectric material of class 2 capacitors. In recent years the high-performance $BaTiO_3$ powder is in great demand with the rapid advance of multilayer ceramic capacitors (MLCCs). The requirements for higher capacitance and further miniaturization in MLCCs are driven by the down-sizing trend in electronics. Structurally it means reduced layer thickness and an increase in the number of layers in MLCCs (Fig.1).

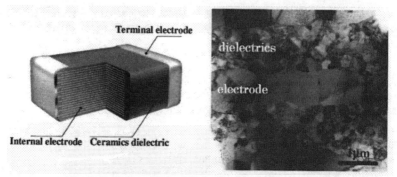

Fig.1 Structure of multilayer ceramic capacitor.

Therefore, the powder, which has even finer particle size, narrow distribution and even higher dielectric constant, is required. Recently, the X7R-MLCCs which has less than 1μm layer thickness are about to be produced. Since the grain-size of dielectric material used for this MLCCs is a few hundred nanometers, it means that only several grains exist along the dielectric layer thickness between internal electrodes. In such a case, the properties of each $BaTiO_3$ particles would have a direct influence on the performances of MLCCs. For that reason, it is desirable to know perfectly the mechanism and the influence on the synthesis of $BaTiO_3$ powders. It is important to control correctly the formation of $BaTiO_3$ powders.

Furthermore, it is important to confirm and control the properties of the $BaTiO_3$ surface. First, they have great effects on the sintering behavior[1]. Second, the surface of the raw powders becomes the grain boundary of the final ceramics in X7R-MLCCs, so the reactivity at the powder surface with additives is also notable. Finally, it is said that the absence of Ba ion or the existence of disordered lattices on the $BaTiO_3$ structure at powders surface causes pseudo-cubic structure[2,3]. Coating the powder surface with additives has also been developed actively for an improvement of additives distribution[4].

Therefore, how to control the properties of each powder particle is considered to be one of the keys for further reduction of layer thickness. These are the control technology in a nanometer order. Indeed, TEM or STEM is one of the most useful and effective instruments to investigate microstructures of $BaTiO_3$ powder particles. Nowadays the characterization of $BaTiO_3$ powders by TEM and STEM has been utilized not only for researches but also for quality control.

In general, most of these particles which have been used for MLCCs have a diameter on the order of sub-micrometer, and it is too thick for the 200-400keV which is usually applied by TEM to penetrate the specimens. So, it is necessary to prepare thin sectioned samples for TEM observation. In this paper, we introduce the easy methods about the thin sectioning and give some examples of observations.

## Thin Sectioning
### FIB cutting technique
In previous papers, we successfully applied the FIB cutting technique to powder particles[5,6]. This technique has previously been developed in the field of semiconductor-nanometer-fabrication[7]. Using this technique for the present study, a thin slice was cut off from powder particles, and thin specimens suitable for TEM observation were obtained. The example of adaptation of the FIB cutting technique to $BaTiO_3$ powder is introduced in Fig.2. The powder particles of $BaTiO_3$ were mixed with epoxy resin. After the curing, it was thinned to less than 100nm by the Ga focused ion beam.

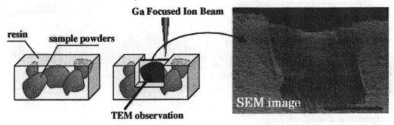

Fig.2 The procedure of sectioning way using FIB.

A low magnification TEM image of the specimen shown in Fig.2 is presented in Fig.3 (a). Fig.3 (b) is the magnified image of Fig.3 (a). Fig.3 (c) shows the image of the specimen using conventional method of direct particle observation. Each of these particles is the same $BaTiO_3$ powder. Compared Fig.3 (b) with Fig.3(c), it is found that the former is a clearer image than the latter.

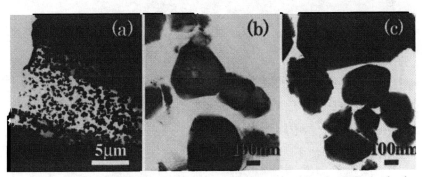

Fig.3 (a), (b) Example of the TEM specimen prepared by the FIB method.
(c) Specimen using conventional method.

However this method had some weak points. One of them is that the observable view is narrow. Another problem is that there is possibility that some damage is introduced to TEM specimens by the irradiation of $Ga^+$ ion[8].

*Ar-ion polishing technique*
There is another thin sectioning method; the Ar-ion polishing technique. This is simple and effective method to make a thin slice from $BaTiO_3$ powder particles as compared to the FIB method. The TEM specimens were suitable to be observed more widely and possible to be made more quickly.

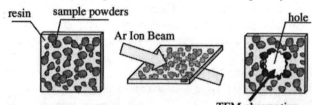

Fig.4 The procedure of sectioning way using Ar-ion polishing technique.

The procedure is shown in Fig.4. The powder particles of $BaTiO_3$ were mixed with epoxy resin. The slurry was applied thin on the plate. Several micrometers of the resin sheet were the best thickness for the next Ar-ion polishing progress and handling. After the curing, Ar ion beam was irradiated to the resin sheet until it had a hole.

Similarly to using FIB, the inner structures of $BaTiO_3$ were clearly observable. Example is given in Fig.5 (a). The TEM image using conventional method for the same $BaTiO_3$ powder is also shown (Fig.5(b)). This $BaTiO_3$ powder was synthesized by hydrothermal method. It is known that it can include some nano-sized pores[9]. The sectioned specimen showed the large and small pores more clearly.

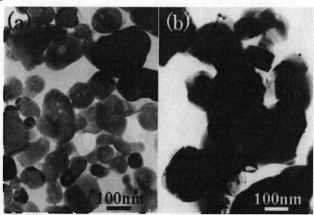

Fig.5 (a) Example of the TEM specimen prepared by Ar-ion polishing method. (b) Specimen using conventional method.

Ceramic Materials and Multilayer Electronic Devices

## The examples of observation

The examples of observation of $BaTiO_3$ powder by TEM or STEM are shown bellow.

### The solid-state reaction process of $BaCO_3$ and $TiO_2$

The solid state reaction between $BaCO_3$ and $TiO_2$ is still one of the main industrial ways to form $BaTiO_3$ powder. The microstructural change during the reaction was investigated to understand the reaction process and produce the fine $BaTiO_3$ powder for MLCCs.

Up to now, there have been many reports on this reaction process[10-14]. In general, the reaction process is explained as the following.

$$BaCO_3 + TiO_2 \rightarrow BaTiO_3 + CO_2\uparrow \qquad (1)$$
$$BaTiO_3 + BaCO_3 \rightarrow Ba_2TiO_4 + CO_2\uparrow \qquad (2)$$
$$Ba_2TiO_4 + TiO_2 \rightarrow 2BaTiO_3 \qquad (3)$$

The reaction process is illustrated in Fig.6. At the first stage, $BaTiO_3$ is produced at the surface of $TiO_2$ particle according to (1) (Fig.6(b)). After the surface of $TiO_2$ was covered with $BaTiO_3$ layer, $Ba_2TiO_4$ formation as the intermediate phase occurs according to (2) (fig.6(c)). After the disappearance of $BaCO_3$, the $Ba_2TiO_4$ reacts with $TiO_2$ to form $BaTiO_3$ according to the overall (3) (Fig.6(d)).

However, the model of this reaction process is mainly proposed on the basis of macroscopic analyses, such as X-ray diffraction and the apparent change, and there are also some still unknown points.

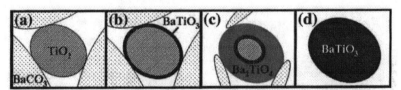

Fig.6 A schematic drawing for $BaTiO_3$ solid state reaction process.

In our investigation, $BaCO_3$ and $TiO_2$ which had about 0.3μm diameter and 0.1μm diameter respectively were used as starting materials. The equimolar mixture of $BaCO_3$ and $TiO_2$ was calcined in $N_2$ atmosphere at various temperatures. The obtained samples were observed by STEM. For STEM investigations, the specimens were prepared by the Ar-ion polishing technique as stated above.

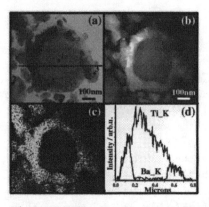

| position | BaO | TiO2 (wt.%) |
|----------|-----|------|
| 1 | 0 | 100 |
| 2 | 100 | 0 |
| 3 | 60 | 40 |
| 4 | 68 | 32 |
| 5 | 66 | 34 |
| BaTiO$_3$ | 66 | 34 |
| Ba$_2$TiO$_4$ | 79 | 21 |
| BaTi$_2$O$_5$ | 49 | 51 |

Fig.7 (a) STEM image of the typical particle in the first stage of this reaction, (b) Z-contrast image at same area, (c) Ba_K X-ray image at same area, (d) X-ray line spectrum along the line in (a), Table:composition estimated by EDS at respective points in (a).

The example of observation was shown in Fig.7. The STEM images showed that the layer of BaTiO$_3$ formed at the surface of TiO$_2$ particle in the first stage of this reaction.

Figure 8 shows the STEM images and the X-ray images of the sample powders obtained at respective calcined temperatures. The appeared phase was estimated by STEM-EDS. As the reaction progressed, the layer of BaTiO$_3$ thickened toward the center of TiO$_2$ particle without forming intermediate phase such as Ba$_2$TiO$_4$ (Fig.8).

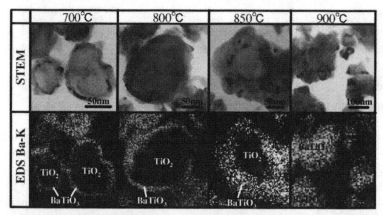

Fig.8 STEM images of the samples obtained at respective calcined temperatures. The upper side is blight field image. The lower side is X-Ray mapping image using Ba_K.

From these results, it is suggested that almost all BaTiO$_3$ was directly formed according to the equation (1) in this case with using fine $BaCO_3$ and $TiO_2$ powder as starting materials.

### The observation of surface modification of BaTiO3 particles

Fine $BaCO_3$ particles are often observed in fine $BaTiO_3$ powders. It is said that $CO_2$ reacts with $BaTiO_3$ to form $BaCO_3$ and Ba poor lattice at the surface of $BaTiO_3$ particles. It is known that the Ba ion leaching often happens from the surface of $BaTiO_3$ particles during the milling-mixing step with a solvent such as water[1,4]. On the other hand, it is said that the absence of Ba ion on the $BaTiO_3$ surface causes overall pseudo-cubic crystallization. Although the phenomenon of this pseudo-cubic crystallization has been greatly concerned industrially, it has had many unknown points until now.

So, in this research, the surface modification of $BaTiO_3$ particles (0.2μm size) by leaching was investigated. The leaching was performed using a hydrochloric acid solution (0.01N HCl). As a result, the powder which has a Ba/Ti ratio of 0.955 was obtained. Fig.9 shows the HRTEM images of the initial powder and HCl-treatment powder. At the surface layer, lattice fringe is not clear in latter case. But there is a possibility of the effect of sample thickness. So, taking sample thickness into consideration, multi-slice method simulations were performed[15]. They were shown in the frame in Fig.9 (b). At inner part of particle, simulated images were agreed with the observed image. At the surface, lattice fringe should be observed like the simulated image.

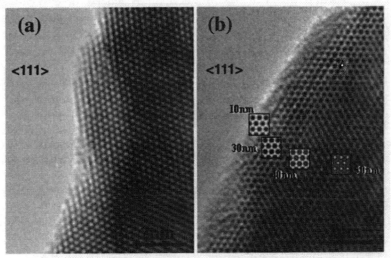

Fig.9 HRTEM image of $BaTiO_3$ particle. (a) before HCl-treatment, (b) after HCl-treatment.

Figure 10 shows the EDS spectra recorded along a line in perpendicular to the HCl-treatment particle surface. It revealed the existence of Ba poor layer of about 1nm in thickness. Observed amorphous-like layer at the surface is considered to be caused by Ba absence. The surface modification, however, was found to have no significant influence with the overall crystalinity of the powders. Fig.11 shows XRD profile of $BaTiO_3$ powder before and after treatment. The XRD profile shows hardly any change after HCl-treatment.

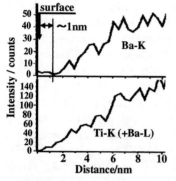

Fig.10 EDS-line profiles at the surface of HCl-treatment particle.

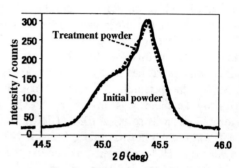

Fig.11 XRD profile of $BaTiO_3$ powder before and after treatment.

CONCLUSIONS

It is concluded that the thin sectioning technique enabled us to investigate detailed structures of powder particles. We successfully applied the FIB cutting technique and the Ar-ion polishing technique to $BaTiO_3$ powder particles. In the study of the solid state synthesis of fine $BaTiO_3$ powders, the reaction process was able to be observed as visual images. We studied the surface of leached $BaTiO_3$ powder and could observe the Ba poor layer as HRTEM image. It was found that the surface modification had no significant influence with the overall crystallinity.

REFERENCES

[1]H.-P.Abicht, D.Voltzke, A.Roeder, R.Schneider, and J.Woltersdorf, "The influence of the milling liquid on the properties of barium titanate powders and ceramics," J.Mater.Chem. 7 (1997) 487.

[2]T.Yamamoto, K.Urabe and H.Banno, "$BaTiO_3$ Particle-Size Dependence of Ferroelectricity in $BaTiO_3$/Polymer Composites," Jpn. J. Appl. Phys., 32 (1993) 4272.

[3]T.Yamamoto, H.Niori and H.Moriwake, "Particle-Size Dependence of Crystal Structure of $BaTiO_3$ Powder," Jpn. J. Appl. Phys., 39 (2000) 5683.

[4]D.Voltzke, H.-P.Abicht, J.Woltersdorf and E.Pippel, "Surface modification of pre-sintered BaTiO3 particles," Mater. Chem. Phys. 73 (2002) 274.

[5]Y.Kitano, Y.Fujikawa, T.Kamino, T.Yaguchi and H.Saka, "TEM observation of Micrometer-sized Ni Powder-Particles thinned by FIB Cutting

Technique," J. Electron Microsc., 44 (1995) 410.

[6]Y.Kitano, Y.Fujikawa, H.Takeshita, T.Kamino, T.Yaguchi, H.Matsumoto and H.Koike, "TEM Observation of Mechanically alloyed Powder Particles (MAPP) of Mg-Zn Alloy Thinned by the FIB Cutting Technique," J. Electron Microsc., 44 (1995) 376.

[7]E.C.G.Kirk, J.R.A.Cleaver and H.Ahmed, "Observation of voltage contrast in scanning ion microscopy of integrated circuits," Inst. Phys. Conf. Ser., 84 (1987) 691.

[8]K.Yamamoto, Y.Fujikawa, K.Ikeda, S.Orimo, H.Fujii and Y.Kitano, "Formation process of the amorphous MgNi by mechanical alloying," J. Electron Microsc., 47 (1998) 461.

[9]Y.Sakabe, N.Wada and Y.Hamaji, "Grain Size Effects on Dielectric Properties and Crystal Structure of Fine-grained $BaTiO_3$ Ceramics," J. Kore. Phys. Soc., 32 (1998) S260.

[10]L.K.Templeton and J.A.Pask, "Formation of $BaTiO_3$ from $BaCO_3$ and $TiO_2$ in Air and $CO_2$," J.Am Ceram. Soc., 42 (1959) 212.

[11]T.Kubo, M.Kato and T.Fujita, Kougyou kagakuzasshi, 70 (1976) 847.

[12]J.C.Niepce and G.Thomas, "About the mechanism of the solid-way synthesis of barium metatitanate. Industrial consequences," Solid State Ionics, 43 (1990) 69.

[13]C.Ando, N.Kohzu, H.Chazono and H.Kishi, "Effect of $CO_2$ Partial Pressure on Morphology and Growth of Particle of $BaTiO_3$ in Solid State Reaction Process," J.Japan Soc. Powd. And Powd. Met., 47 (2000) 916.

[14]C.Ando, Y.Iguchi, H.Kishi, R.Yanagawa and M.Senna, "Effects of Agitation Milling of a Starting Mixture on the Solid-State Synthesis and Properties of $BaTiO_3$," J. Japan Soc. Powd. And Powd. Met., 47 (2000) 1032.

[15]J.M.Cowley and A.F.Moodie, "The Scattering of Electrons by Atoms and Crystals" Acta Cryst., A263 (1957) 609.

# GROWTH BY PULSED LASER DEPOSITION AND FERROELECTRIC PROPERTY OF NATURAL-SUPERLATTICE-STRUCTURED FERROELECTRIC THIN FILMS OF $Bi_4Ti_3O_{12}$–$SrBi_4Ti_4O_{15}$ and $Bi_3TiNbO_9$–$Bi_4Ti_3O_{12}$

Masanori Okuyama, Akira Shibuya, and Minoru Noda

*Division of Advanced Electronics and Optical Science, Department of Systems Innovation, Graduate School of Engineering Science, Osaka University, 1-3 Machikaneyama-Cho, Toyonaka, Osaka 560-8531, Japan*

## ABSTRACT

$C$–axis oriented natural-superlattice-structure of $Bi_4Ti_3O_{12}$–$SrBi_4Ti_4O_{15}$ (BIT–SBTi) and $Bi_3TiNbO_9$–$Bi_4Ti_3O_{12}$ (BTN–BIT) epitaxial ferroelectric thin films have been grown by pulsed laser deposition method on MgO (001) and/or $SrTiO_3$ (001) substrates. The epitaxial growth of the natural-superlattice-structured the thin films was confirmed by X-ray diffraction $\theta$–$2\theta$ scan, pole figure plots and reciprocal space mappings. $C$ axis lattice constants of the BIT–SBTi thin films are very close to those of natural superlattices made up of regular stacking of one-halves of the unit cells of BIT and SBTi . The annealed BIT–SBTi thin film on $Pt/Ti/SiO_2/Si$ substrate exhibits superior ferroelectricity and the values of $2P_r$ and $2E_c$ are 32.0 $\mu C/cm^2$ and 190 kV/cm, respectively. The BIT-SBTi film shows that the degradation of switching charge after $1\times10^{10}$ switching cycles was 16.5%. $C$–axis lattice constant of BTN–BIT suggests that natural superlattice consisting of iteration of two unit cels of BTN and one unit cell of BIT. $2P_r$ of the BTN-BIT film are 50 $\mu C/cm^2$. This enhanced ferroelectric property is attributed to the structural stress through $Bi_2O_2$ layer induced by the differences of lattice parameters and chemical characters of the pseudo-perovskite structures.

# INTRODUCTION

In recent years, ferroelectric films have been intensively studied for their application to various devices such as nonvolatile ferroelectric random access memory (FeRAM), infrared sensor, piezoelectric actuator and optical modulator. Especially, research and development for the memory application has been extensively promoted. Bismuth-layer-structured ferroelectrics (BLSF) have attracted much attention due to their fatigue-free switching properties and low coercive field. The crystal structure of BLSFs is generally formulated as $(Bi_2O_2)^{2+} (A_{m-1}B_mO_{3m+1})^{2-}$, where A represents mono-, di-, or trivalent ions, B represents tetra-, penta-, or hexavalent ions with appropriate size and valency, and $m$ is the number of $BO_6$ octahedra in the perovskite blocks ($m$ = 1, 2, 3, 4, and 5). The perovskite blocks, $(A_{m-1}B_mO_{3m+1})^{2-}$, are sandwiched between bismuth oxide layers, $(Bi_2O_2)^{2+}$ along the $c$ axis. Ferroelectric $SrBi_2Ta_2O_9$ (SBT) and $Bi_4Ti_3O_{12}$ (BIT) films have been intensively studied among BLSF materials because of its low coercive field, low leakage current and excellent fatigue endurance even in the capacitor with Pt electrodes [1]. However, the remanent polarization ($P_r$) of SBT is not sufficient for high density integration of FeRAM and the ferroelectric properties of SBT exhibit a temperature drift [2] because of its low Curie temperature ($T_c$). Many efforts have been carried out to enhance remanent polarization. First effort is lanthanoid metal-doping to BIT. The prepared films show nice ferroelectric property and especially La-doped BIT[3] and Nd-doped BIT[4] have large remanent polarization and fatigue-free property. This enhancement is considered to be deformation of atomic position in the lattice. On the other hand, the other one is artificial superlattice which has stacked layers of different thin films deposited by pulse laser deposition (PLD)[5,6] and molecular beam epitaxy (MBE)[7]. However, remarkable polarization enhancement is not reported.

It was shown in the recent research of the bulk form that intergrowth $Bi_4Ti_3O_{12}$–$SrBi_4Ti_4O_{15}$ (BIT–SBTi) are able to overcome these drawbacks of SBT owing to the structural stress in the intergrowth structure[8]. The intergrowth BIT-SBTi is composed of two BLSFs, $Bi_4Ti_3O_{12}$ (BIT; $m$ = 3) and $SrBi_4Ti_4O_{15}$ (SBTi; $m$ = 4)[9]. The crystal structure shows an intergrowth made up of one-half of the unit cells of BIT and SBTi.[10] The perovskite blocks of BIT and SBTi are in turn sandwiched between $(Bi_2O_2)^{2+}$ layers, and the $BO_6$ octahedra in

BIT–SBTi are all $TiO_6$. Two Bi ions occupy the A-site of BIT blocks, while two Bi ions and one Sr ion compose that of SBTi blocks. Pseudo-perovskite layer of adjacent layer would be deformed through $(Bi_2O_2)^{2+}$ layer.

In this paper, we report the demonstration of making regular intergrowth of BIT–SBTi in the form of thin films on MgO (001), $SrTiO_3$ (001) and $Pt/Ti/SiO_2/Si$ substrates prepared by Pulsed Laser Deposition (PLD) method using a stoichiometric BIT–SBTi (1mol : 1mol) ceramic target. Moreover we report the preparation and characterization of a new natural-superlattice-structured BLSF thin film of $Bi_3TiNbO_9$-$Bi_4Ti_3O_{12}$ (BTN-BIT) with excellent ferroelectric properties and the superlattice structure different from BTN-BIT ceramics.

EXPERIMENTAL

The laser used for the PLD method was an ArF excimer laser with a wavelength of 193 nm. The laser beam was focused by a quartz lens onto the BIT, SBTi, BIT–SBTi (1 mol : 1 mol) and BTN–BIT (1mol : 1mol) ceramic targets rotating in a vacuum chamber while the oxygen pressure was 0.01 to 0.2 Torr. Laser repetition rate is 5 Hz, laser pulse energy density is 3.7 $J/cm^2$. The targets are BIT, SBTi, BIT–SBTi and BTN–BIT ceramic plates. The substrates (single crystal MgO (001), single crystal $SrTiO_3$ (001), $Pt/Ti/SiO_2/Si$ (100)) were heated at 400–550 °C. The thickness of deposited BIT, SBTi, BIT-SBTi and BTN-BIT films are about 400 nm. After the BIT–SBTi film was grown on $Pt/Ti/SiO_2/Si$, the film was post-annealed in oxygen atmosphere for 45 minutes at 700 °C, and cooled at the rate of 15 °C/min.

Finally, Pt top electrodes (0.18 mm in diameter) were deposited by sputtering method. The crystalline structures were investigated by X-ray diffraction (XRD). Polarization-electric filed ($P–E$) hysteresis loop, fatigue measurement and memory retention measurement were measured using a ferroelectric test system (Toyo-technica, FCE-1) at 60 Hz and 1kHz. Capacitance-Voltage ($C–V$) hysteresis was measured using precision impedance analyzer (Agilent 4294A).

## RESULTS AND DISCUSSION

### Deposition of BIT-SBTi thin films

*Crystalline structure*: Figure 1 shows the XRD patterns of BIT, SBTi and BIT–SBTi films deposited at 550 °C on MgO (001) substrates. Obviously, the peaks in BIT–SBTi thin film exist at different angles than those of BIT and SBTi films. While for BIT and SBTi, normal BLSFs, the peaks of 00$l$ with $l$ as an even number are observed because of the regular period of the $Bi_2O_2$ layer in the lattice, the BIT–SBTi thin film has the 00$l$ peaks not only with even number of $l$, but also with $l$ as an odd number, which is a distinguishing feature of intergrowth compounds [11]. Figure 2 shows the pole figure plot of BIT–SBTi thin film on MgO substrate, measured at $2\theta$ of 30.2 °. The XRD pole figure plot indicates that the BIT–SBTi thin film is in complete epitaxy with the substrate along $c$ axis and (001) in-plane direction of BIT–SBTi crystallites is 45 ° rotated from that of MgO crystallites. Lattice constant $c$ of BIT–SBTi film is 3.732 nm and is close to the value of intergrowth BIT–SBTi ceramics (3.692 nm), which becomes the average of those for BIT and SBTi. In addition, lattice constant $c$ (3.296 nm) of BIT film and lattice constant $c$ (4.189 nm) of SBTi film on MgO substrates are calculated from Fig.1; these average 3.742 nm, which is almost same to BIT–SBTi film on MgO substrate. These results of XRD analysis are

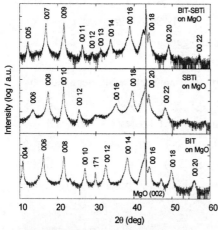

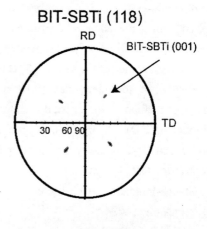

**BIT-SBTi (118)**

**Figure 1.** XRD θ-2θ scan patterns of BIT, SBTi and BIT–SBTi films on MgO (001) substrates.

**Figure 2.** XRD pole figure plot of the BIT–SBTi film on MgO (001) substrate.

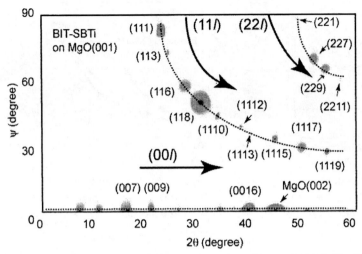

**Figure 3.** XRD reciprocal space mapping of the BIT–SBTi thin film on MgO (001) substrate.

quite reasonable from the viewpoint of their crystal structure, which is intergrowth structure. In the structure, in-plane stress is induced in $Bi_2O_2$ layer by the difference of lateral lattice parameters, and enhances the ferroelectricity by deformation of pseudo-perovskite layer.

Figure 3 shows the reciprocal space mapping of the BIT–SBTi thin film on MgO (001) substrate. These broken lines show interpolated curves of $(00l)$, $(11l)$ and $(22l)$ and clearly indicate that the BIT–SBTi thin film has exactly epitaxial BLSF structure along the $c$ axis, but not fluorite and pyrochlore structures. The peaks along $\Psi = 0$ give conventional $\theta$–$2\theta$ pattern and also support the film's $(00l)$ orientation. Lattice constants $a$ (0.547 nm) and $b$ (0.547 nm) obtained from Fig.3 are a little larger than those of the bulk BIT–SBTi ceramics [3]. This is attributed to the fact that the diagonal of MgO substrate in $a$-$b$ plane is 8.1% larger than the lattice constant $a$ of the BIT–SBTi film. We have also deposited BIT–SBTi on $SrTiO_3$ (STO) (001) substrates as well as on MgO substrates. The BIT–SBTi film on STO substrate is also in complete epitaxy with the substrate along $c$ axis. Lattice constants $a$, $b$ and $c$ of the BIT–SBTi on STO substrate are 0.549 nm, 0.549 nm and 3.715 nm, respectively. The diagonal of STO substrate in $a$-$b$ plane is 3.2 % larger than the lattice parameter $a$ of the BIT–SBTi film.

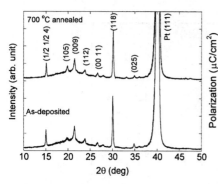

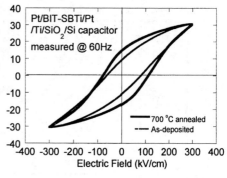

**Figure 4.** XRD θ-2θ scan patterns of BIT-SBTi films on Pt/Ti/SiO₂/Si substrates before and after oxygen annealing.

**Figure 5.** *P-E* hysteresis loop of BIT-SBTi films on Pt/Ti/SiO₂/Si substrates before and after oxygen annealing.

*Electrical property*: We have also made BIT–SBTi thin films on Pt/Ti/SiO₂/Si substrates by PLD method with the same conditions as on MgO and STO substrates. After the deposition, the BIT–SBTi thin film on Pt substrates was post-annealed in oxygen atmosphere for 45 minutes at 700 °C. Figure 4 shows the XRD pattern of BIT–SBTi film on Pt/Ti/SiO₂/Si substrate. We can identify some peaks as natural-superlattice-strucutured BIT–SBTi. There is almost no difference in crystalline property between the films before and after oxygen annealing and these films are polycrystalline. Figure 5 shows *P–E* hysteresis loops of the BIT–SBTi thin films before and after annealing measured at 60Hz. The twice values of remanent polarization ($2P_r$) and coercive field ($2E_c$) of the annealed BIT–SBTi film were 32 μC/cm² and 190 kV/cm, respectively, while $2P_r$ and $2E_c$ of as-deposited BIT–SBTi film were 20 μC/cm² and 145kV/cm, respectively. This enhanced ferroelectricity after annealing is attributed to decreased oxygen vacancies. The value of $2P_r$ of the annealed BIT–SBTi film is higher than conventional BIT and SBTi thin films. It is suggested that the natural superlattice structures enhance ferroelectric properties because of the structural stress induced through $Bi_2O_2$ layers by the difference of lattice parameters of the pseudo-perovskite structures.

Figure 6 shows *C-V* characteristics of BIT–SBTi films before and after oxygen annealing measured at 1 MHz while the scan rate is 50 kV/cm·sec. The coercive fields ($2E_c$) of BIT–SBTi in Fig. 5 correspond to the width between the

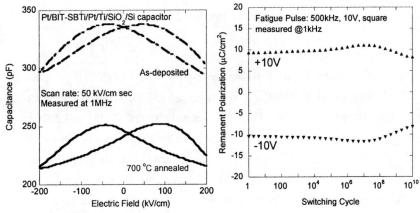

**Figure 6.** C-V characteristics of BIT-SBTi films on Pt/Ti/SiO₂/Si substrates before and after oxygen annealing.

**Figure 7.** Fatigue property of annealed BIT-SBTi film measured with 500kHz bipolar square pulses under 10 V.

points at maximal capacitance in Fig. 6 before and after annealing. This $C-V$ characteristics also suggest that the BIT–SBTi film has enhanced ferroelectricity after oxygen annealing. The relative dielectric constant and the dielectric loss of annealed BIT–SBTi film were 433 and 0.037 at room temperature, respectively, while those of as-deposited BIT-SBTi were 595 and 0.071 at a measuring frequency of 1MHz from Fig. 6. The reduction of dielectric loss after annealing may be attributed to decreasing oxygen vacancies in the bulk of BIT–SBTi film and the dielectric constant of BIT–SBTi film approaches to that of the ceramics after oxygen annealing.

Figure 7 shows the fatigue property of annealed BIT–SBTi film measured with 500 kHz bipolar square pulses under 10 V and −10 V. In Fig. 7, the remanent polarization shows slight rejuvenation around $10^7$ cycles. This may be due to the weak domain wall pinning and field-assisted unpinning that is seen in bismuth-layer-structured ferroelectric SBT film [12-14] and low oxygen vacancies concentration after oxygen annealing. The degradation of switching charge after $1\times10^{10}$ switching cycles was 16.5 %, which is much better compared with PZT films with Pt electrodes. But this fatigue property is expected to be improved. The relative dielectric constant of annealed BIT–SBTi after fatigue is 311. So this fatigue may be attributed to reduction of the field shared to ferroelectric due to growing passive layer during fatigue measurement. One of this fatigue mechanism might be the nearby-electrode injection of electrons [15].

Deposition of BTN-BIT thin films

*Crystalline property*: Figure 8 shows the x-ray diffraction (XRD) patterns of BTN–BIT films on Pt/TiO$_2$/SiO$_2$/Si substrates at 550 °C oxygen pressures ranging from 0.01 to 0.2 Torr and BTN–BIT ceramics target. BTN ($m = 2$) has the lattice parameter of $a = 0.540$ nm, $b = 0.545$ nm, and $c = 2.516$ nm in terms of orthorhombic structure, and similarly BIT ($m = 3$) has the lattice parameter of $a = 0.541$, nm, $b = 0.545$ nm, and $c = 3.284$ nm in terms of orthorhombic structure. $C$ lattice parameter of intergrowth BTN–BIT is estimated to be 2.900 nm that is average of BTN and BIT. Peaks of 002, 004 of BTN and 004 of BIT are observed in the XRD patterns of BTN–BIT films prepared at 0.2 and 0.1 Torr. Peaks different from BIT and BTN ones are observed below 16 ° in the film deposition at 0.07 Torr. All peaks below 16 ° are attributed to $c$ lattice

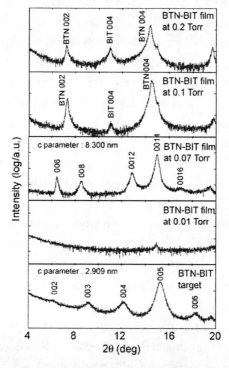

**Figure 8.** XRD $\theta$–$2\theta$ scan patterns of BTN–BIT ceramics target and BTN–BIT films on Pt/TiO$_2$/SiO$_2$/Si substrates at oxygen pressures ranging from 0.01 to 0.2 Torr.

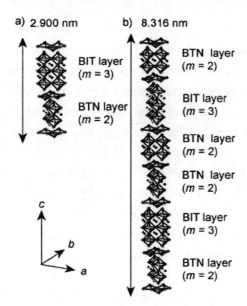

**Figure 9.** Schematic representation of a) 1–1 superlattice structure b) 2–1 superlattice structure of BTN–BIT.

parameter because these BLSFs have much longer $c$ lattice parameter (more than 2.516 nm of BTN) than $a$ and $b$ parameters (around 0.54 nm). BTN-BIT films prepared at 0.1 and 0.2 Torr consist of two phases of BTN and BIT. BTN–BIT films prepared at 0.07 Torr has single phase whose $c$ lattice parameter is estimated at 8.300 nm in consideration of periodicity of lattice structures. BTN–BIT target has also single phase whose $c$ lattice parameter is 2.909 nm. The BTN–BIT target has the 00$l$ peaks not only with even number of $l$ but also with odd number of $l$, which is a distinguishing feature of intergrowth compounds[11]. This different $c$ lattice parameters between BTN–BIT ceramics target and BTN–BIT film prepared at 0.07 Torr suggest that superlattice structures of BTN–BIT along $c$ axis are different each other. The former (2.909 nm) is very close to the value (2.900 nm) of superlattice structure consisting of one-half of the unit cells of BTN and BIT, that is 1–1 superlattice structure of BTN–BIT in Fig. 9 a) similar to $Bi_3Ti_{1.5}W_{0.5}O_9$–$Bi_4Ti_3O_{12}$ (m = 2-3) ceramics[16]. The latter (8.300 nm) is also very close to the value (8.316 nm) of that of two unit cells of BTN and one unit cell of BIT, that is 2–1 superlattice structure of BTN–BIT in Fig. 9 b). This situation is attributed to stability of natural superlattice structures. In the case of $m$ = 1-2 and $m$ = 2-3 natural superlattice BLSFs, there are two dielectric anomalies above room temperature[9,17], on the other hand, $m$= 3-4 natural superlattice BLSFs show only one dielectric anomaly[8,9] due to the strong ferroelectric interaction between them[18]. The 2–1 superlattice structure may be more stable than the 1–1 superlattice structure of BTN-BIT ($m$ = 2–3) especially in low deposition temperature such as 550 °C. It is also possible that oxygen pressure changes compositions of BTN–BIT films to form 2–1 superlattice in consideration of the strong effects of oxygen pressure shown in Fig. 8.

Figure 10 shows XRD patterns of BTN–BIT films on Pt/TiO$_2$/SiO$_2$/Si substrates at substrate temperatures ranging from 400 to 550 °C in oxygen of 0.07 Torr. The film deposited at 400 °C shows obviously pyrochlore phase, and the film deposited at 450 °C shows BLSFs phase. The natural superlattice peaks of 006 and 008 are observed in the film deposition above 500 °C.

*Electrical property*: Figure 11 shows polarization hystheresis loops of BTN–BIT films having 2–1 superlattice measured at 100 Hz using a ferroelectric test system (Toyo-technica, FCE–1). The twice values of remanent polarization (2$P_r$)

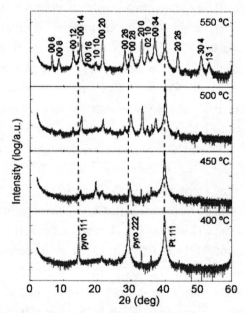

Figure 10. XRD $\theta$–2$\theta$ scan patterns of BTN–BIT films on Pt/TiO$_2$/SiO$_2$/Si substrates at temperatures ranging from 400 °C to 550 °C.

Ceramic Materials and Multilayer Electronic Devices

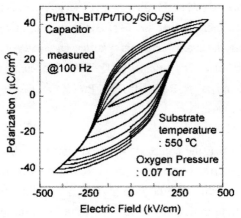

**Figure 11.** P–E hysteresis loop of the Pt/ BTN–BIT with 2–1 superlattice/Pt capacitor.

and coercive field ($2E_c$) are 50 $\mu$C/cm$^2$ and 350 kV/cm, respectively. This value of $2P_r$ of natural-superlattice-structured BTN-BIT film is much higher than 26.9 $\mu$C/cm$^2$ of 0.8SrBi$_2$Ta$_2$O$_9$–0.2Bi$_3$TiNbO$_9$ solid solution thin film [19] and 8 $\mu$C/cm$^2$ of Bi$_4$Ti$_3$O$_{12}$ along $c$ axis. This enhanced ferroelectric property is attributed to the structural stress induced through Bi$_2$O$_2$ layer by the difference of lattice parameters of the pseudo-perovskite structures as well as BIT–SBTi films[8,20]. The dielectric constant of this film is 350 at 1 MHz and the leakage current density is as low as 4.2×10$^{-7}$ A/cm$^2$ at 100 kV/cm.

Finally we have made BTN-BIT thin film on SrTiO$_3$ (STO) single crystal substrate by PLD with the same conditions as on the Pt/TiO$_2$/SiO$_2$/Si substrates. Figure 12 shows the XRD pattern of BTN–BIT film on STO substrate. We can identify all peaks as 2–1 superlattice structure of BTN–BIT along $c$ axis. Figure

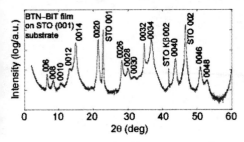

**Figure 12.** XRD $\theta$–$2\theta$ scan patterns of BTN–BIT film on STO (001) substrate.

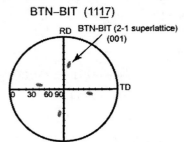

**Figure 13.** XRD pole figure plot of the BTN–BIT film on STO (001) substrate.

13 shows the pole figure of BTN-BIT film on STO substrate, measured at $2\theta =$ 29.55 °. Figs. 12 and 13 indicate that the BTN-BIT film is in complete epitaxy with the substrate along the $c$ axis, and this $c$ lattice parameter is estimated at 8.330 nm. Some peaks of $c$ axis oriented BTN-BIT film on STO substrates correspond to those of BTN-BIT film on $Pt/TiO_2/SiO_2/Si$ substrates.

CONCLUSIONS

(1) It is confirmed that the epitaxial BIT–SBTi intergrowth thin films by PLD have grown with alternative stacking structures along $c$ axis in the from of thin films. It was also shown from the $P$–$E$ hysteresis loop that the BIT–SBTi thin film on a Pt substrate has enhanced ferroelectricity that the values of $2P_r$ and $2E_c$ are 32.0 $\mu C/cm^2$ and 190 kV/cm, respectively.

(2) A new natural-superlattice structured BTN–BIT thin films has been prepared on $Pt/TiO_2/SiO_2/Si$ and STO substrates, consisting of iteration of two unit cells of BTN and one unit cell of BIT, which is 2-1 superlattice structure, by PLD at as low as 500 °C of deposition temperature. It was also shown from the $P$–$E$ hysteresis loop that the BTN–BIT thin film on $Pt/TiO_2/SiO_2/Si$ substrate prepared at 550 °C has an enhanced ferroelectricity that the value of $2P_r$ is 50 $\mu C/cm^2$.

ACKNOWLEDGMENT

The Authors would like to acknowledge Prof. Masaru Shimizu and Dr. Hironori Fujisawa of Himeji institute of technology for their helpful collaboration, Dr. Y. Noguchi of the University of Tokyo and Dr. K. Saito of Philips Japan, Ltd. for their helpful discussions. This work was partially supported by Grand-in-Aid No.12134205, STARC.

REFERENCES

[1] P. A. Paz de Araujo, J. D. Cuchiaro, L. D. Mcmillan, M. C. Scott, and J. F. Scott, Nature (London) **374**, 627 (1995)

[2] J. Lee, R. Ramesh, V. G. Keramidas, W. L. Warren, G. E. Pike, and J. T. Evans, Jr., *Appl. Phys. Lett.* **66**, 221 (1995)

[3] B. H. Park, B. S. Kang, S. D. Bu, T. W. Noh, J. Lee, and W. Joe, *Nature* (London) **401**, 682 (1999).

[4]T. Kojima, T. Sakai, T. Watanabe, H. Funakubo, K. Saito, M. Osada, *Appl. Phys. Lett.* **80**, 2746 (2002).

[5]H. Tabata, H. Tanaka, and T. Kawai, *Appl. Phys. Lett.* **65** 15 (1994).

[6]O. Nakagawara, T. Shimuta, T. Makino, S. Arai, H. Tabata, and T. Kawai, *Appl. Phys. Lett.* **77**, 20 (2000).

[7]S. O. Ferreira, E. Abramof, P. H. O. Rappl, A. Y. Ueta, H. Closs, C. Boschetti, P. Mtisuke, and I. N. Bandeira, *J. Appl. Phys.* **84**, 3650 (1998).

[8] Y. Noguchi, M. Miyayama, and T. Kudo, *Appl. Phys. Lett.* **77**, 22 (2000).

[9]T. Kikuchi, A. Arakawa, and K. Uchida, *Mater. Res. Bull.* **12**, 299 (1977).

[10]D. A. Jefferson, M. K. Uppl, and C. N. R. Rao, *Mater. Res. Bull.* **19**, 1403 (1984).

[11]Y. Noguchi, M. Miyayama, T. Kudo, *Trans. Mater. Res. Soc. Jpn.* **25**, 1 (2000).

[12]H.N. Al-Shareef, D. Dimos, T.J. Boyle, W.L. Warren and B.A. Tuttle, *Appl. Phys. Lett.* **68**, 690 (1996).

[13]D. Dimos, H.N. Al-shareef, W.L. Warren and B.A. Tuttle, *J. Appl. Phys.* **80**, 1682 (1996).

[14] D. Wu, A. Li, H. Ling, T. Yu, Z. Liu, and N. Ming, *Appl. Phys. Lett.* **76**, 2208 (2000).

[15] A.K. Tagantsev, I. Stolichnov, E.L. Colla, N. Setter, *J. Appl. Phys.* **90**, 1387 (2001).

[16] S. Luo, Y. Noguchi, M. Miyayama, and T. Kudo, *Mat. Res. Bull.* **36**, 531 (2001).

[17]Y. Noguchi, R. Satoh, M. Miyayama, and T. Kudo, *J. Ceram. Soc. Jpn.* **109**, 29 (2001).

[18] Y. Goshima, Y. Noguchi, and M. Miyayama, *Appl. Phys. Lett.* **81**, 2226 (2002).

[19]S. B. Desu, P. C. Joshi, X. Zhang, and S. O. Ryu, *Appl. Phys. Lett.* **71**, 1041 (1997).

[20]A. Shibuya, M. Noda, M. Okuyama, H. Fujisawa, and M. Shimizu, *Appl. Phys. Lett.* **82**, 784 (2003).

# SEEDED GROWTH OF STRONTIUM - DOPED LEAD ZIRCONATE TITANATE

I. Dutta and Raj N. Singh
Department of Chemical and Materials Engineering, University of Cincinnati,
Cincinnati, Ohio 45221–0012

## ABSTRACT

The growth of large grains of Strontium-modified Lead Zirconate Titanate (PZT) is investigated using a seeding approach. $SrTiO_3$ (111) single crystals are embedded into the polycrystalline Lead Strontium Zirconate Titanate (PSZT) using a tape lamination approach. The samples are then sintered and annealed at temperatures above $1300°C$ to promote crystal growth. The development of large grains (~15$\mu$m) adjacent to the single crystal is observed. However, development of very large grains > 40$\mu$m is hampered by the formation of a monoclinic $ZrO_2$ phase.

## INTRODUCTION

$PbZrO_3$-$PbTiO_3$ (PZT) ceramics have the perovskite structure of the form $ABO_3$. Pure $PbZrO_3$ is antiferroelectric (AFE) but PZT compositions are ferroelectric (FE) when the Zr:Ti ratio is < 95:5. Above the Curie temperature (Tc), the unit cell is cubic, but below Tc it is distorted to either tetragonal or rhombohedral. The boundary between these two phases is called morphotropic phase boundary (MPB).[1] For the same composition, an AFE form has a smaller lattice volume than that of the FE form.[2]

Conventional PZT materials which are used as electromechanical transducers and actuators, generally have compositions close to the MPB (Zr:Ti ≈ 52:48) because of high electromechanical coupling factor (typically $d_{33}$ ≈ 300pC/N and $k_{33}$ ≈ 0.5).[3] However interest has increased recently in the Zirconium-rich end of the PZT close to the AFE - FE phase boundary (Zr:Ti ≈ 95:5). This is because switching from the AFE to FE phase can be accomplished easily by the application of a suitable field, resulting in large strain.

Strontium is an antiferroelectric phase stabilizer. The phase diagram of the $PbTiO_3$ –$PbZrO_3$–$SrTiO_3$–$SrZrO_3$ system[4] (Fig.1) shows a long AFE–FE phase boundary suitable for the field-induced phase transition study. In the $A_T$ region, the compositions are energetically so close to those of the $F_R$ form that the switching between the $A_T/F_R$ form may be easily accomplished by an applied electric field. The compositions displaying field-induced AFE–FE phase transition were recently studied by polarization measurements.[5] It has been shown that compositions close to the MPB like $(Pb_{0.90}Sr_{0.10})(Zr_{0.86}Ti_{0.14})O_3$ shows polarization as high as $33\mu C/cm^2$ and field induced strain as high as $0.5\%$[5].

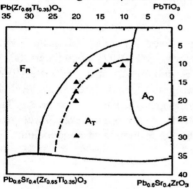

Figure 1: $PbTiO_3$–$PbZrO_3$–$SrTiO_3$–$SrZrO_3$ phase diagram (see Ref 4). The dotted line shows the modified $A_T$–$F_R$ phase boundary from our previous study (see Ref. 6). Compositions (solid triangles) close to the dotted line show field-induced AFE–FE phase transition, and those (open triangles) away from the dotted line are FE.

Improved electromechanical actuation can be achieved in single crystals oriented to optimize piezoelectric coefficients, in which the mechanical constraint of misaligned neighboring grains is absent. Consequently, a need exists to develop single crystals of different piezoelectric polycrystalline materials to enhance the electro-mechanical properties. But, materials that undergo incongruent melting or phase transitions when they are cooled cannot be grown easily as single crystals using flux techniques. Alternate routes to produce single crystals are needed to reduce cost and provide researchers with access to a wider range of single crystals.

Templated grain growth (TGG) is one approach for growing single crystals. TGG involves bringing a seed crystal and a sintered polycrystalline matrix into contact with each other and then heating the combination to produce a single crystal via sustained directional growth of the interface into the polycrystalline matrix. Early works have shown the growth of single crystal > 1mm in $BaTiO_3$ when heated at 1300°C for 20 hours.[7]

Seeded grain growth also has been used to produce single crystals. In these efforts, several large seed particles with a composition similar to that of the matrix are mixed with the powder before sintering. For a random distribution of the seed particles, the growth direction is not regulated. DeVries[8] was the first to take advantage of the exaggerated grain growth in $BaTiO_3$ to grow single crystals. He used a steep temperature gradient or the addition of seed crystals to grow grains much larger than those obtained using only exaggerated grain growth. More recently, seeded grain growth has been applied to the $Pb(Mg_{1/3}Nb_{2/3})O_3$–35mol% $PbTiO_3$ (PMN–PT) system.[9] In this work, one single crystal seed of PMN–PT was embedded in an unfired, PbO -excess polycrystalline powder compact and the compact was heated at 900°–1200°C. Growth from the initial ~1 mm seed was on the order of 1–2 mm after 140 h at 1150°C. Another recent work by the same group has shown that single crystal of the same material as that of the matrix can be used for substantial growth of single crystal.[10] They used fully dense hot pressed disks, each consisting of a single crystal (111) plate of the relaxor-based ferroelectric $Pb(Mg_{1/3}Nb_{2/3})O_3$–35 mol% $PbTiO_3$ (PMN–35PT) embedded in a $0.48 \pm 0.05\mu m$ grain size polycrystalline matrix of the same composition. It has been reported that when annealed for 10 h at 1150°C using $PbZrO_3$ sacrificial powder, the seed has shown a growth of 1.4mm along the (111) direction accompanied with a matrix grain coarsening of $13.3 \pm 0.3$ $\mu m$.

The objective of this present work was to examine the feasibility of growing single crystal of $(Pb_{0.90}Sr_{0.10})(Zr_{0.86}Ti_{0.14})O_3$ from polycrystalline precursor. The growth of the matrix grain was also studied at different annealing temperatures. X-ray diffraction and optical microscopy were used to study the phase assemblage and microstructure, paying particular attention on the surface decomposition and its effect on the relative permittivity ($\varepsilon_r$) and polarization.

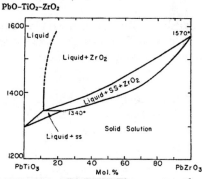

Figure 2: $PbTiO_3$-$PbZrO_3$ Phase Diagram. The congruently melting compound $PbTiO_3$ and the incongruently melting compound form a solid solution over the entire range of composition.

EXPERIMENTAL PROCEDURES

The composition was chosen from the earlier works of this group[5] and from the PSZT phase diagram (Fig.1) showing high polarization and electromechanical behavior. Polycrystalline PSZT ceramics were prepared by tape casting and sintering route.[6] The raw powders were obtained from Aldrich Chemical Company: PbO (99.91+ %,< 10 $\mu$m), TiO$_2$, ZrO$_2$ (99.1+ %,< 5 $\mu$m), and Sr(NO$_3$)$_2$ ACS reagent grade crystals (99+%). The powders were wet mixed, dried, and ball milled before calcinations at 850°C for 2 h. Polyvinyl butyral (Monsanto Company) was added to the tape casting slurry as a binder. Single crystal of SrTiO$_3$ [Alfa Aesar, <111> oriented] was used as the seed. The dried tapes were stacked with the single crystal inside and pressed under a laminating machine (Tetrahedron Associates Inc., CA). The crystal was oriented with the (111) plane parallel to the tape plane. Binder burnout was done at 350°C for 3 h and 600°C for 2 h. Sintering was conducted at 1320°C for 210 min in a lead-rich atmosphere provided by the PbZrO$_3$ sacrificial powder by using double crucible method. All the fired samples had relative densities around 97%, measured by the Archimedes method.

To see the growth of the single crystal as well as the growth of the matrix the sintered samples were annealed first at lower temperature (1300°C) for different duration. Subsequently, sintered samples were annealed at higher temperature with due considerations to phase diagram (Fig.2).

The rectangular sintered/annealed samples were ground and polished by silicon carbide and diamond polishing paste, respectively, to a thickness of 0.5 mm. The polished samples were chemically etched with HCl: HNO$_3$ solution containing a few drops of HF for several seconds to see a clear microstructure. Gold was sputtered as an electrode on to major surfaces for applying electric field across the thickness.

Sintered samples were analyzed using an X-ray diffractometer (Philips X'Pert $\theta$-$\theta$ powder diffractometer, 50mA 40KV) with Cu $K_\alpha$ radiation in the 2$\theta$ range of 20-60°. The Hanawalt search-and-match method was used to identify the phases present.

XRD peaks were indexed according to a pseudocubic perovskite cell. Using JCPDS cards nos. 33-0784 and 37-1484 (monoclinic ZrO2). The relative amounts of perovskite and second phase were quantified:

$$Pp\% = \frac{Ip}{Ip + Iz} \times 100$$

$$Pz\% = \frac{Iz}{Ip + Iz} \times 100$$

where, $Pp\%$ and $Pz\%$ are the volume percentages of perovskite and second phases formed, respectively, $Ip$ is the relative intensity of the major X-ray peak for the perovskite phase, which has a $d$-spacing of 0.287 nm, and $Iz$ is the relative intensity of the major X-ray peak for the second phase, which has a *d*-spacing of 0.316 nm.

The HP 4276A LCZ Meter was used to measure the sample capacitance as a function of temperature at 1 kHz. The ceramic samples were heated at a rate of about 3°C/min to about 300°C. Capacitance and loss tangent were recorded manually every 1–2°C. Capacitance was converted to dielectric constant using the sample geometry and permittivity of air.

The polarization ($P$) versus electric field ($E$) was measured using a modified Sawyer and Tower circuit.[11] The voltage was supplied using a high-voltage amplifier (Model 601C, Trek Incorporated). During testing, the samples were submerged into silicone oil (Aldrich Chemical Company, Inc.), which is an insulating oil, to prevent arcing of air.

RESULTS AND DISCUSSION

Figure 3 shows the XRD patterns of the PSZT ceramics sintered at 1320°C for 210 min and annealed at different temperatures. The degree of tetragonality increases with temperature, which is evident from the splitting of the (200) and (211) peaks. There is no formation of the second phase at the sintering temperature and time i.e. 1320°C/210min. But, the intensity of the $ZrO_2$ peak at ~27° (2θ) increases and further non perovskite reflections emerge as the temperature and time of annealing is increased. After 24 h at 1300°C sufficient $ZrO_2$ reflections are present to use the Hanawalt method for identification which is evident from the figure 4. All non-perovskite reflections fit the monoclinic $ZrO_2$. Fig. 4 gives the $ZrO_2$ (m) phase content as a function of temperature.

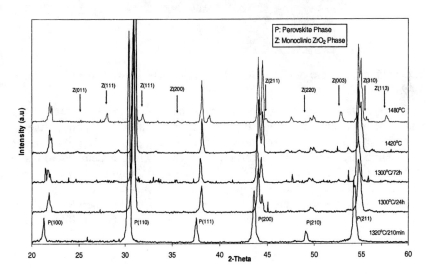

**Fig. 3.** XRD patterns of PSZT samples sintered and annealed at different temperatures.

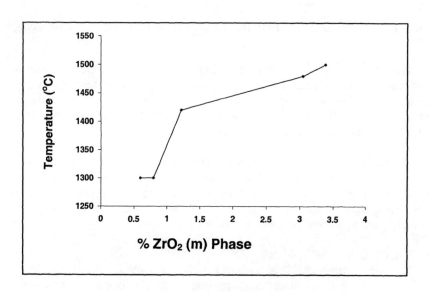

**Fig. 4.** Second phase formation with annealing time and temperature.

**Fig. 5.** Microstructure of $(Pb_{0.90}Sr_{0.10})(Zr_{0.86}Ti_{0.14})O_3$ sample sintered at $1320°C$ for 210min.

Figure 5 shows the etched optical microstructure of the as sintered PSZT sample. The microstructure shows that the uniformly distributed grains have an average size of ~3-5μm. Uniform growth of the matrix grain (~15μm) is visible with annealing at different temperatures and times which is evident from Figs. 6 (a,b,c,d). But it is also seen from these micrographs that, with the increase in the temperature there is a distinct change in the morphology. A second phase of monoclinic $ZrO_2$ starts to precipitate uniformly on the grains of the PSZT matrix, resulting in cracks. PbO loss is known to occur from the surface of PZT at high temperatures. As seen in the phase diagram (fig.2), this becomes increasingly significant as the temperature increases which leads into $ZrO_2$ and solid PZT phases.[12]

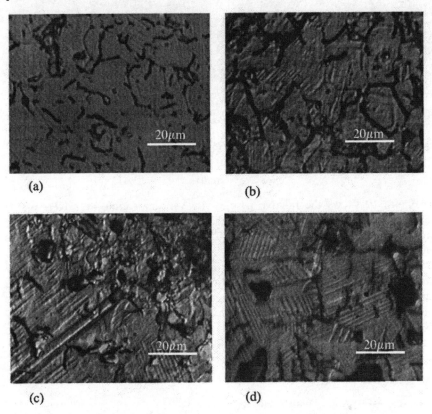

(a)

(b)

(c)

(d)

**Fig. 6.** $(Pb_{0.90}Sr_{0.10})(Zr_{0.86}Ti_{0.14})O_3$ annealed at (a) 1300°C for 24 h. (b) 1300°C for 72 h. (c) 1420°C for 2 h. (d) 1480°C for 2 h.

Figure 8 shows development of a few very large grains around the single crystal along the (111) plane. But the development of the single crystal is hampered due to the formation of cracks around the large grains. These cracks act as pinning points for the movement of the single crystal boundary. Another feature that is evident from fig 9 is the deep crack line between the seeded single crystal and the polycrystalline matrix. This is due to the fact that $SrTiO_3$ single crystal has a coefficient of thermal expansion ($\alpha$) of about 9 x $10^{-6}$/°C which is almost three times that of PZT ~3 x $10^{-6}$/°C. So, during cooling, the single crystal shrinks more than the matrix resulting in the deep crack along the boundary.

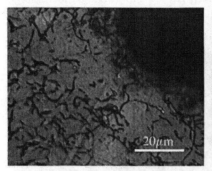 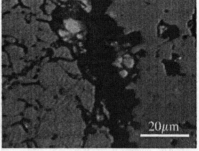

**Fig. 8.** Development of large grains around the single crystal seed.

**Fig. 9.** Development of a deep crack between seed and polycrystalline matrix.

Figure 10 shows the relative permittivity vs. temperature at 1 KHz of the PSZT samples sintered and annealed at different temperatures. It is seen that the Curie temperature (Tc) shifts from 210°C to 225°C with the increase in the annealing temperature and annealing time. This is due to the decrease in the Zr:Ti ratio as the Curie temperature generally increases with the $Ti^{4+}$ concentration.[14] Another factor that confirms the shifting of the material composition to the tetragonal side is the polarization. It is seen from fig 11 that the AFE- Fe phase transformation field is around 4KV/mm for the as sintered sample but increases to 5KV/mm for sample annealed at 1300°C for 24h. The samples eventually become anti-ferroelectric as the annealing time and temperature increases even more.

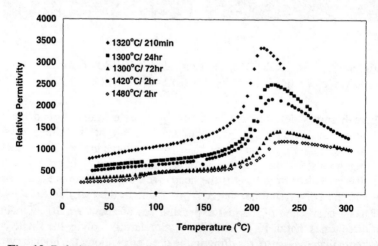

**Fig. 10.** Relative permittivity as a function of annealing temperature for PSZT.

Ceramic Materials and Multilayer Electronic Devices

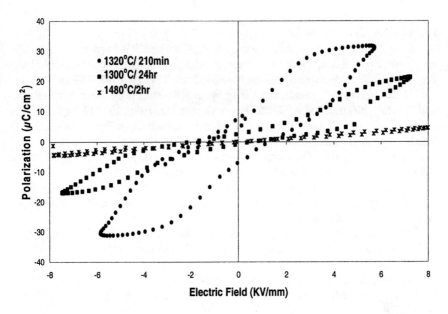

**Fig. 11.** Polarization behavior of PSZT at room temperature and 0.1 Hz frequency.

CONCLUSION

Annealing temperature and time has pronounced effect on the stability of the $(Pb_{0.90}Sr_{0.10})(Zr_{0.86}Ti_{0.14})O_3$ ceramic. High temperature and longer time favor the tetragonal over the rhombohedral phase.

As a result of the PbO loss from the sample, the formation of a monoclinic $ZrO_2$ phase takes place which is confirmed by the XRD and the dielectric measurements. This phase precipitates at the grain boundaries of the polycrystalline matrix creating cracks. Although some development of large grains is seen along the seeded single crystal the growth is hampered due to the formation of these cracks along the grain boundary.

The formation of the $ZrO_2$ is consistent with the shifting of the Curie temperature and the lowering of the maximum permittivity.

ACKNOWLEDGEMENT

This material is based upon work supported by the National Science Foundation. Any opinions, findings, and conclusions or recommendations expressed in this material are those of the authors and do not necessarily reflect the views of the National Science Foundation.

REFERENCES

[1]C.A. Randall, N. Kim, J.P. Kucara, W.W. Cao, and T.R.Shrout "Intrinsic and Extrinsic Size Effect in Fine Grained Morphotropic-Phase-Boundary Lead Zirconate Titanate Ceramics," *J. Am. Ceram. Soc.*, **81** [3] 677-88 (1998).

[2]D. Berlincourt, "Transducers Using Forced Transition Between Ferroelectric and Antiferroelectric States," *IEEE Trans. Sonics Ultrason.*, **13**, 116-24 (1966).

[3]L.X. He and C. Li., "Effects Of Addition Of MnO on Piezo Properties of Lead Zirconate Titanate," *J. Mater. Sci.*, **35**, 2477-80 (2000).

[4]T. Ikeda, "A Few Quartenary Systems of Perovskite Type $A^{2+}B^{4+}O_3$ Solid Solutions," *J. Phys. Soc. Jpn.*, **14** [10] 1286–94 (1959).

[5]Y.Yu and R. N. Singh, "Effect of composition and temperature on field-induced properties in the lead strontium zirconate titanate system," *J. Appl. Phys.*, **88** [12] 7249-57 (2000).

[6]Y.Yu, J. Tu and R.N. Singh, "Phase Stability and Ferroelectric Properties of Lead Strontium Zirconate ceramics," *J. Am. Ceram. Soc.*, **84** [2] 333-40 (2001).

[7]T.Yamamoto and T. Sakuma, "Fabrication of Barium Titanate Single Crystals by Solid-State Grain Growth," *J. Am. Ceram. Soc.*, **77** [4] 1107–109 (1994).

[8]R.C. DeVries, "Growth of Single Crystals of $BaTiO_3$ by Exaggerated Grain Growth," *J. Am. Ceram. Soc.*, **47** [3] 134–36 (1964).

[9]T. Li, A. M. Scotch, H. M. Chan, M. P. Harmer, S. Park, and T. R. Shrout, "Single Crystals of $Pb(Mg_{1/3}Nb_{2/3})O_3$–35 mol% $PbTiO_3$ from Polycrystalline Precursors," *J. Am. Ceram. Soc.*, **81** [1] 244–48 (1998).

[10]A. Khan, F.A. Meschke, T. Li, A.M. Scotch, H. M. Chan and M. P. Harmer, "Growth of $Pb(Mg_{1/3}Nb_{2/3})O_3$–35 mol% $PbTiO_3$ Single Crystals from (111) Substrates by Seeded Polycrystal Conversion," *J. Am. Ceram. Soc.*, **82** [11] 2958–62 (1999).

[11]Santanu Banerjee and Raj N. Singh, "Processing and Polarization Behavior of Sr-Containing Lead Zirconate Titanate," *Ferroelectrics*, **211** [1– 4] 89–110 (1998).

[12]S. Fushimi and T. Ikeda, "Phase Equilibrium in the System $PbO-TiO_2$-$ZrO_2$," *J. Am. Ceram. Soc.*, **50** [3] 129-132 (1966).

[13]H. Zheng, I. M. Reaney and W. E. Lee, "Surface Decomposition of Strontium-Doped $PbZrO_3$-$PbTiO_3$," *J. Am. Ceram. Soc.*, **85** [1] 207-12 (2002).

[14]B. Jaffe, W. R. Cook, and H. Jaffe, "Piezoelectric Ceramics"; p. 158 in *Non-metallic Solids*, Vol. 3. Academic Press, London, U.K., 1971.

# CHARACTERIZATION OF HIGH CURIE TEMPERATURE PIEZOCRYSTALS IN DOPED $Pb(Yb_{1/2}Nb_{1/2})O_3$-$PbTiO_3$ SYSTEM

Shujun Zhang, Clive A. Randall, Thomas R. Shrout
Material Research Institute
Pennsylvania State University
University Park, PA, 16802

## ABSTRACT

The industrial and scientific communities have expressed a real need for the capability of actuators and transducers at elevated temperatures. $Pb(Zn_{1/3}Nb_{2/3})O_3$-$PbTiO_3$ (PZNT) and $Pb(Mg_{1/3}Nb_{2/3})O_3$-$PbTiO_3$ (PMNT) single crystals attracted many attentions in the last two decades because of their ultrahigh piezoelectric and electromechanical properties compared to commercial $Pb(Zr_xTi_{1-x})O_3$ (PZT) ceramic, but the applications were limited owing to their low Curie temperature ($T_c$). In this work, attempts to grow high $T_c$ piezoelectric single crystals in the $Pb(Yb_{1/2}Nb_{1/2})O_3$-$PbTiO_3$ (PYNT) systems were explored. It was found that the zinc dope PYNT single crystals possess similar $T_c$ (~325°C) but much higher rhombohedral to tetragonal phase transition temperature ($T_{r-t}$) (~212°C) compared to the barium doped one (~160°C). The detailed dielectric and piezoelectric properties were reported for zinc doped PYNT single crystals and compared to the barium doped PYNT in this paper.

## INTRODUCTION

Since the development of PZT in the 1950s, these kinds of ceramics (including pure and doped PZT polycrystalline ceramics) have been the mainstay of transducer and actuator applications[1-3]. But demand for high performance and high frequency piezoelectric devices make ferroelectric single crystals increasing important for practical applications because of their high piezoelectric coefficient and high electromechanical coupling factor. A number of new relaxor-PT single crystals (such as PZNT and PMNT systems) have sparked interest in the last two decades because of their potential capability of improving device performance and extending application areas. PZNT and PMNT crystals show excellent piezoelectric coefficients up to ~2500pC/N with electromechanical coupling factors of ~93%, as compared to values of 200pC/N and 75% for soft PZT ceramic [4-10]. The applications of PZNT and PMNT single crystals are greatly limited by their low Curie temperature ($T_c$ – 150~180°C), which are further limited by ferroelectric phase transition temperature ($T_{r-t}$ – 70~120°C) because high temperature electronics is one of significant industrial importance, for example, environments of 150°C with repeated temperature cycles are at present considered as the automotive norm, and higher temperatures are expected in the future[11]. Of all the relaxor-PT based binary systems, the PYNT system has the highest Curie temperature near its MPB composition around 350°C for polycrystalline and single crystal form comparable to the undoped PZT ceramic[12-18]. The $T_c$ of barium doped PYNT single crystals near the morphotropic phase boundary (MPB) composition was found to be ~325°C while $T_{r-t}$ temperature around 160°C, with properties comparable to PZNT and PMNT single crystals, in which the high $T_{r-t}$ will expand the temperature operating range and make more temperature independent of properties[17,18]. Also the coercive fields of barium doped PYNT crystals (>10kV/cm) are significantly larger than that of the PZNT and PMNT single crystals (~2-3kV/cm), reflecting better domain stability and higher acoustic power[16].

In this work, zinc doped PYNT single crystals were grown using flux method and the dielectric and piezoelectric properties were characterized.

EXPERIMENTAL

The PYNT single crystals were grown using traditional high temperature solution technique with $Pb_3O_4$ as flux[14,16], because of instability of the perovskite phase for PYNT single crystals, $BaCO_3$ or $ZnO$ were selected as the doping to stabilize the perovskite phase. The samples for dielectric and piezoelectric measurements were oriented along the crystallographic directions <001>, <110> and <111> using a Real-time Laue orientation system (Multiwire Laboratories, Ltd) and polished to achieve flat and parallel surfaces onto which gold electrodes were sputtered. High temperature dielectric behavior was measured using a multi-frequency LCR meter (HP 4284A) with a computer controlled temperature chamber. High-field measurements at room temperature included polarization and strain hysteresis using a modified Sawyer-Tower circuit and linear variable differential transducer (LVDT) driven by a lock-in amplifier (Stanford Research Systems, Model SR830).

RESULTS AND DISCUSSION
Dielectric Properties

The dielectric permittivity for barium doped PYNT45 crystals at room temperature was found to be ~1700 while the value was 2600 for the zinc doped one, the dielectric loss for both crystals at room temperature was measured to be 1.5%. The dielectric permittivity and dielectric loss as a function of temperature for <001> oriented barium doped PYNT45 and zinc doped PYNT45 single crystals after poling are presented in Fig.1a and 1b, respectively. Two peaks are clearly shown at ~160°C and ~325°C for barium doped PYNT45 single crystals, while for zinc doped PYNT45, the dielectric anomaly occurred at around ~212°C and ~325°C. The first dielectric anomaly is believed to be associated with the breaking down of the metastable macro-domain structure and formation of the micro-domains on the scale of the local defect structure, which is the rhombohedral-tetragonal phase transition temperature ($T_{r-t}$), while the second large peak is the Curie temperature ($T_c$). It is found that the $T_{r-t}$ of the zinc doped PYNT single crystals is over 50°C higher than that of the barium doped one, while the $T_c$ is the same, indicating the application temperature range of the zinc doped crystals are much higher than the barium doped one. Temperature dependence of dielectric behavior $\partial\varepsilon\big/\partial T$ was 12/°C for barium doped crystal and 33/°C for zinc doped one in the range of [25, $T_{r-t}$], which is significantly low compared to that of the 0.7PMN-0.3PT ($\partial\varepsilon\big/\partial T = 445/°C$)[19,20].

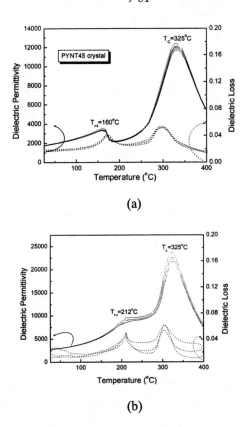

(a)

(b)

Fig.1 (a) The dielectric permittivity and loss as a function of temperature for barium doped PYNT45 crystals (after Ref.[20]) (b) the dielectric permittivity and loss as a function of temperature for zinc doped PYNT45 crystals showing that the ferroelectric phase transition temperature 50°C higher than barium doped one.

The dielectric permittivity and loss as a function of temperature for <110> and <111> oriented zinc doped PYNT single crystals were presented in Fig.2, in which the $T_{r-t}$ were found to be 190-210°C and $T_c$ around 330-340°C, both are much higher than those of the PZNT and PMNT single crystals. The dielectric losses were found to be about 1% for both directions at room temperature.

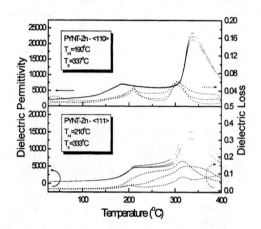

Fig.2 The dielectric permittivity and loss as a function of temperature for <110> and <111> oriented zinc doped PYNT45 single crystals after poling.

Piezoelectric Properties

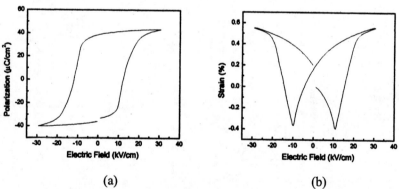

(a)                                    (b)

Fig.3 The bi-polarization of barium doped PYNT45 single crystals along <001> orientation (a) polarization versus electric field loop (b) strain versus electric field loop.

Barium doped PYNT45 single crystals were bi-polarized at room temperature along the <001> orientation using 1Hz and 30kV/cm field. A typical hysteresis loop and classical bipolar ferroelectric switching behavior, displaying a symmetric butterfly loop, were obtained, shown in Fig.3a and 3b. The remnant polarization ($P_r$) was found to be 33$\mu$C/cm$^2$ and the coercive field ($E_c$) was about 12kV/cm, which was significantly higher than that of PZNT and PMNT crystals ($E_c \sim$ 2-3kV/cm).

The same measurements were performed on zinc doped PYNT crystals along different orientations <001>, <110> and <111>, as given in Fig.4. The remnant polarizations of the samples were found to be 30 $\mu$C/cm$^2$, 40 $\mu$C/cm$^2$ and 41 $\mu$C/cm$^2$, and the coercive fields were around 10kV/cm, 14kV/cm and 17.3kV/cm, respectively. These orientation dependent values are very different from the barium doped PYNT40 single crystals[14], in which the properties along <110> was closer to that along <001> direction.

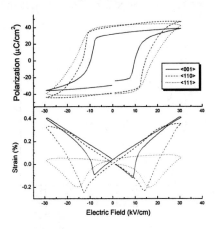

Fig.4 Polarization and strain versus electric field as a function of orientations for zinc doped PYNT45 single crystals.

Fig.5 presents the strain of <001> oriented barium doped PYNT46 single crystals measured as a function of electric fields. For a field up to ~20kV/cm, the strain was about 0.45% with low hysteresis, reaching 0.73% when the field was about 30kV/cm. This abrupt change in strain is probably associated with an electric field induced rhombohedral to tetragonal phase transition. The piezoelectric coefficient ~2250pC/N was calculated directly from the slope of strain versus electric field curve with minimal hysteresis (electric field lower than 20kV/cm). The strain became saturated when the field over 30kV/cm and the corresponding piezoelectric coefficient was found to be 550pC/N[16]. The strain of <001> oriented zinc doped PYNT45 crystals with electric fields were shown in Fig.6, the strain was found to be 0.35% when the field was 20kV/cm, with piezoelectric coefficient around 1750pC/N. The strain was 0.67% with electric field at 30kV/cm, the same tendency compared to barium doped crystals.

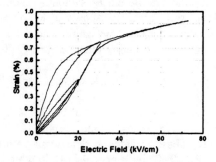

Fig.5 Strain-electric field curves at different electric fields for
<001> oriented barium doped PYNT46 crystals (after Ref.[16]).

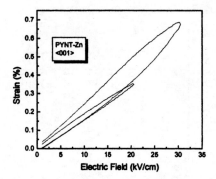

Fig.6 Strain-electric field curves at different electric fields for
<001> oriented zinc doped PYNT45 crystals.

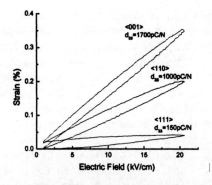

Fig.7 Strain-electric field curves as a function of orientations
for zinc doped PYNT45 crystals.

The unipolar strain versus electric field curves as a function of orientations for zinc doped PYNT45 single crystals were shown in Fig.7, in which the piezoelectric coefficients can be calculated according to the slope of the curves for <001>, <110> and <111> directions, and were found to be 1700pC/N, 1000pC/N and 150pC/N, respectively.

CONCLUSION

PYNT single crystals doped with barium and zinc were grown using high temperature solution technique. The Curie temperature of zinc doped PYNT crystals with compositions near the MPB was found to be ~325°C, while the rhombohedral to tetragonal phase transition temperature was found to be ~212°C, over 50°C higher than that of barium doped one(~160°C), and significantly higher than those of PZNT and PMNT crystals ($T_c$~ 150-180°C, $T_{r-t}$~ 70-120°C). The coercive field of <001> oriented zinc doped PYNT45 was found to be 10kV/cm, a little bit lower than the value of barium doped crystals (~12kV/cm), 3-5 times as those of PZNT and PMNT single crystals ($E_c$~2-3kV/cm). The piezoelectric coefficient of zinc doped PYNT45 crystal was around to be 1700pC/N, while the value was found to be around 2500pC/N for the barium doped crystals. All those excellent piezoelectric properties together with high Curie temperature and high coercive fields make PYNT single crystals promising new materials for the next generation high performance transducers and actuators.

ACKNOWLEDGMENT

This work was supported by DARPA, ONR and NIH. The authors would like to thank Ms. Ru Xia for the sample preparation.

REFERENCES
[1] B. Jaffe, "Properties of piezoelectric ceramics in the solid solution series PT, PZ, PSn and PHF" *J. Res. Nat. Bus. Stand.* **55** 239-48 (1955).
[2] B. Jaffe, W.R. Cook and H. Jaffe, *"Piezoelectric ceramic"* Academic Press Ltd, Reported by R.A.N Publisher, Marietta, Ohio, 1971.
[3] T.R. Shrout, R. Eitel, C.A. Randall, E. Alberta, P.W. Rehrig, "New high temperature morphotropic phase boundary piezoelectric ceramics" pp.277-80, in *proceedings of the 13th IEEE international symposium on applications of ferroelectrics*, Edited by Grady White and Takaaki Tsurumi. Piscataway, NJ, 2002.
[4] S.-E. Park, T.R. Shrout, "Relaxor based ferroelectric single crystals for electro-mechanical actuators" *J. Mater. Res. Innov.,* **1** 20-5 (1997).
[5] S. Shimanuki, S. Saito and Y. Yamashita, "Single crystal of the $Pb(Zn_{1/3}Nb_{2/3})O_3$-$PbTiO_3$ system grown by the vertical Bridgman method and its characterization" *Jpn. J. Appl. Phys.,* **37** 3382-5 (1998).
[6] M. Dong, Z.-G. Ye, "High-temperature solution growth and characterization of the piezo/ferroelectric $(1-x)Pb(Mg_{1/3}Nb_{2/3})O_3$-$xPbTiO_3$ [PMNT] single crystals" *J. Crys. Growth,* **209** 81-90 (2000).

[7] S.-E. Park, T.R. Shrout, "Ultrahigh strain and piezoelectric behavior in relaxor based ferroelectric single crystals" *J. Appl. Phys.*, **82** 1804-11 (1997).

[8] H.S. Luo, G.S. Xu, Z.W. Yin, "Compositional homogeneity and electrical properties of lead magnesium niobate titanate single crystals grown by a modified Bridgman technique" *Jpn. J. Appl. Phys.*, **39** 5581-5 (2000).

[9] R.C. Turner, P.A. Fuierer, R.E. Newnham and T.R. Shrout, "Materials for high temperature acoustic and vibration sensors: A Review", *Appl. Acoust.*, **41** 299-324 (1994).

[10] M. Naito, "Recent sensors for automotive applications", *Ceramic Engineering Science Proceedings,* **8** [9-10] 1106-19 (1987).

[11] T.R. Shrout, R. Eitel, C.A. Randall, "High performance, high temperature perovskite piezoelectric ceramics" pp.413-32. in *Piezoelectric Materials in Devices,* Edited by N. Setter, Switzerland, 2002.

[12] H. Lim, H.J. Kim, W.K. Choo, "X-ray and dielectric studies of the phase transitions in $Pb(Yb_{1/2}Nb_{1/2})O_3$-$PbTiO_3$ ceramic" *Jpn. J. Appl. Phys.*, **34** 5449-52 (1995).

[13] T. Yamamoto, S. Ohashi, "Dielectric and piezoelectric properties of $Pb(Yb_{1/2}Nb_{1/2})O_3$-$PbTiO_3$ solid solution system" *Jpn. J. Appl. Phys.*, **34** 5349-53 (1995).

[14] S.J. Zhang, P.W. Rehrig, C. A. Randall, T. R. Shrout, "Crystal growth and electrical properties of $Pb(Yb_{1/2}Nb_{1/2})O_3$-$PbTiO_3$ perovskite single crystals" *J. Crys. Growth*, **234** 415-20 (2002).

[15] N. Yasuda, H. Ohwa, M. Kume, Y. Hosono, Y. Yamashita, S. Ishino, H. Terauchi, M. Iwata and Y. Ishibashi, "Crystal growth and dielectric properties of solid solutions of $Pb(Yb_{1/2}Nb_{1/2})O_3$-$PbTiO_3$ with a high Curie temperature near a morphotropic phase boundary" *Jpn. J. Appl. Phys.*, **40** 5664-7 (2001).

[16] S.J. Zhang, S. Rhee, C. A. Randall, T. R. Shrout, "Dielectric and piezoelectric properties of high Curie temperature single crystals in the $Pb(Yb_{1/2}Nb_{1/2})O_3$-$PbTiO_3$ solid solution series" *Jpn. J. Appl. Phys.*, **41** 722-6 (2002).

[17] S.J. Zhang, L. Lebrun, S. Rhee, C.A. Randall, T.R. Shrout, "Shear-mode piezoelectric properties of $Pb(Yb_{1/2}Nb_{1/2})O_3$-$PbTiO_3$ single crystals" *Applied Phys. Lett.* **81** 892-4 (2002).

[18] S. J. Zhang, L. Laurent, S. Rhee, C.A. Randall, T.R. Shrout, "Dielectric and piezoelectric properties as a function of temperature for $Pb(Yb_{1/2}Nb_{1/2})O_3$-$PbTiO_3$ single crystals" pp.455-8 in *proceedings of the 13$^{th}$ IEEE international symposium on applications of ferroelectrics*, Edited by Grady White and Takaaki Tsurumi. Piscataway, NJ, 2002.

[19] D. Viehland, J. Powers, L. E. Cross, "Importance of random fields on the properties and ferroelectric phase stability of <001> oriented $0.7Pb(Mg_{1/3}Nb_{2/3})O_3$ -$0.3PbTiO_3$ crystals" *Appl. Phys. Lett.* **78** 3508-10 (2001).

[20] S.J. Zhang, S. Priya, E. Furman, T. R. Shrout, C. A. Randall, "A random-field model for polarization reversal in $Pb(Yb_{1/2}Nb_{1/2})O_3$-$PbTiO_3$ single crystals" *J. Appl. Phys.* **91** 6002-6 (2002).

# FACTORS DETERMINING CRYSTALLOGRAPHIC TEXTURE IN $Bi_{1/2}Na_{1/2}TiO_3$-BASED PIEZOELECTRIC CERAMICS MADE BY REACTIVE TEMPLATED GRAIN GROWTH METHOD

Toshio Kimura, Eiichiro Fukuchi and
Toru Takahashi
Faculty of Science and Technology
Keio University,
3-14-1 Hiyoshi, Kohokku-ku
Yokohama, 223-8522 Japan

Toshihiko Tani
Toyota Central Research &
Development Laboratories
41-1 Yokomichi, Nagakute-cho
Aichi-gun, Aichi, 480-1192 Japan

ABSTRACT

$Bi_{1/2}Na_{1/2}TiO_3$ (BNT)-based piezoelectric bulk ceramics with crystallographic texture were prepared by the reactive templated grain growth method. The effects of processing parameters including compositions were examined to obtain highly textured ceramics. The compacts after calcination were composed of template grains with specific crystallographic orientation and matrix grains with random orientation. The texture developed mainly by the growth of template grains at the expense of matrix grains, and the size difference between template and matrix grains must be maintained during the fabrication process. The direction of material transport during the formation of template grains was also important.

INTRODUCTION

The electrical properties of polycrystalline ceramics are determined not only by the composition and crystal structure of the phase present but also by the microstructure.[1] Therefore, the control of microstructure is very important to obtain ceramics with better performances. An introduction of crystallographic

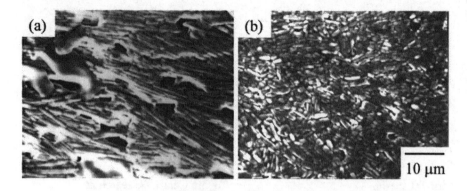

Fig. 1. Microstructures of sintered $Bi_4Ti_3O_{12}$ compacts. The green compacts were formed by uniaxial pressing of platelike particles prepared by the molten salt synthesis using (a) NaCl-KCl and (b) $Na_2SO_4$-$Li_2SO_4$.

texture to sintered ceramics is one of the techniques to control the microstructure. In a crystallographically textured ceramic, a specific crystal axis of individual grains is aligned in one direction, and high electrical properties are expected.[1]

Many techniques have been used to prepare crystallographically textured ceramics. This paper deals with the method to use template particles with an anisotropic shape. In the simplest method, the particles with shape anisotropy were tape-cast to prepare green sheets with aligned particles.[2, 3] Highly textured ceramics were easily obtained, but sometimes the density of the obtained ceramics was low because of the formation of large pores as shown in Fig. 1(a).[4] These large pores develop as a result of particle rearrangement during the early stage of sintering.[5] Kimura et al. obtained highly textured and dense $Bi_4Ti_3O_{12}$ ceramics by employing platelike particles with the small degree of particle rearrangement to avoid the formation of large pores (Fig. 1b).[6] Messing et al. proposed the templated grain growth method to prepare dense, highly textured ceramics by adding small, equiaxed particles to the particles with shape anisotropy to prevent the particle rearrangement.[7] These methods require particles with an anisotropic shape. Therefore, these methods are only applicable to the compounds with low symmetry.

Recently, Tani proposed the fabrication method of crystallographically textured ceramics with the perovskite structure and prepared $Bi_{1/2}(Na_{1-x}K_x)_{1/2}TiO_3$

Ceramic Materials and Multilayer Electronic Devices

(BNKT) with a high degree of orientation.[8] In this method, plate-like $Bi_4Ti_3O_{12}$ (BiT) was used as one of the starting materials, and BNKT was formed by *in situ* reaction between BiT and other starting materials ($Na_2CO_3$, $K_2CO_3$, and $TiO_2$). This method is called the reactive templated grain growth (RTGG) method.

This paper deals with the factor determining crystallographic texture in $Bi_{1/2}Na_{1/2}TiO_3$(BNT)-based perovskite ceramics made by the RTGG method. The systems dealt with in this paper are

1) $Bi_{1/2}Na_{1/2}TiO_3$- $Bi_{1/2}K_{1/2}TiO_3$ (BNT-BKT)
2) BNT-excess $Bi_2O_3$
3) BNT
4) BNT-$BaTiO_3$ (BNT-BT)

The results on the BNT-BKT system are shown first.[9] Then, the effects of excess $Bi_2O_3$ and the amount of template particles are examined in the BNT system. Finally, texture formation in the BNT-BT system is explained with the focus on the method of addition of BT ($BaCO_3$+$TiO_2$ or $BaTiO_3$).

Experimental Procedure

Chemically pure $Bi_2O_3$ (Kojundo Chemical Laboratory Co. Ltd., Saitama, Japan), $Na_2CO_3$ (Wako Pure Chemical Industries, Ltd., Osaka, Japan), $K_2CO_3$ (Wako Pure Chemical Industries, Ltd., Osaka, Japan), $TiO_2$ (Ishihara Sangyo Kaisha, Ltd., Osaka, Japan), $BaCO_3$ (Wako Pure Chemical Industries, Ltd., Osaka, Japan), and $BaTiO_3$ (BT-05, Sakai Chemical, Osaka, Japan) were used as raw materials. Platelike BiT particles were prepared from $Bi_2O_3$ and $TiO_2$ by molten salt synthesis using NaCl-KCl mixture in the molar ratio 1 : 1 (weight ratio of oxides to salt = 1 : 1).[10] The platelike BiT particles for systems 1) and 2) were prepared at 1050°C for 1 h and had an average diameter of 5 μm and a thickness less than 0.5 μm, and those for systems 3) and 4) were prepared at 1130°C for 1 h (an average diameter = 25 μm and a thickness = 0.5 μm). The platelike BiT particles were mixed with the raw materials. In the experiments for systems 1) and 2), the amount of platelike BiT was designed so that 20% of titanium and 53.3% of bismuth in final BN(K)T were supplied from platelike BiT. The overall reaction in the BNT case is shown in Eq. (1).

$$4Bi_4Ti_3O_{12}+7Bi_2O_3+15Na_2CO_3+48TiO_2 \rightarrow 60BNT+15CO_2 \qquad (1)$$

In systems 3) and 4), the amount of platelike BiT was designed so that50% of titanium and 100% of bismuth in final BNT were supplied from platelike BiT. The overall reaction is shown in Eq. (2).

$$Bi_4Ti_3O_{12}+2Na_2CO_3+5TiO_2 \rightarrow 8BNT+2CO_2 \qquad (2)$$

The powders were mixed with a solvent (60 vol% toluene-40%ethanol) in a ball mill for 20 h, and then poly(vinyl butyral) (binder) and di-$n$-butyl phthalate (plasticizer) were added and mixed for 1 h. The slurry was tape-cast to form a sheet with a thickness of about 0.1 mm. The sheet was cut, laminated, and pressed at 80°C and 10 MPa for 10 min to form green compacts with a thickness of about 2 mm. The compacts were further cut into small pieces (15 mm x 15 mm).

The green compacts were heated at 400°C for 3 h to remove organic ingredients, and then at 700°C for 2 h to form BNT-based perovskite (the heating rate was 50°C/h). A large fraction of perovskite formed at this stage as confirmed by X-ray diffraction analysis. The compacts were composed of grains with specific crystallographic orientation and grains with random orientation. These grains will be called "template" and "matrix" grains, respectively.

The heat-treated specimens were isostatically pressed at 140 MPa at room temperature, and then sintered at various temperatures between 800° and 1200°C for 0.1 ~ 10 h in a flowing $O_2$ atmosphere (the heating rate was 100°C/h). The maximum densities at 1200oC were more than 95% of theoretical for the specimens in systems 1) and 2) except pure BNT (86%) and more than 92% for the specimens in systems 3) and 4).

The crystalline phases and the degree of orientation were determined by X-ray diffraction (XRD: Model DX-GOP, JEOL, Tokyo, Japan) analysis using CuK$\alpha$ radiation on the major surface (the same as the sheet surface) of sintered compacts. The microstructure of sintered compacts was observed with a scanning electron microscope (SEM: Model JED-2110, JEOL) on fracture surfaces perpendicular to the major face.

RESULTS AND DISCUSSION

BNT-BKT System

Figure 2 shows the effect of potassium concentration on the degree of orientation in the BNT-BKT system. The degree of orientation was small in the specimens sintered at 1000°C irrespective of the potassium concentration, but increased as the sintering temperture increased for the specimens containing the

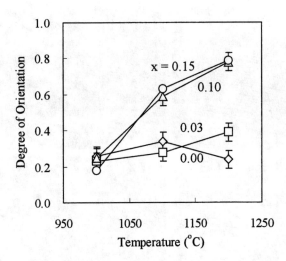

Fig. 2. Effect of potassium concentration on the texture development in (1-x)BNT-xBKT.

Fig. 3. Microstructure of 0.85BNT-0.15BKT sintered at 900°C for 2h.

high potassium concentration.

Figure 3 shows the typical microstructure of the specimen after the formation of BNKT solid solution. It was composed of two types of BNKT grains. One was platelike grains (template grains), which originated from platelike BiT. The other was fine, irregularly shaped grains (matrix grains), which were formed by the reaction between $Bi_2O_3$, $Na_2CO_3$, $K_2CO_3$, and $TiO_2$ particles.

Figure 4 shows the microstructures of specimens with various potassium

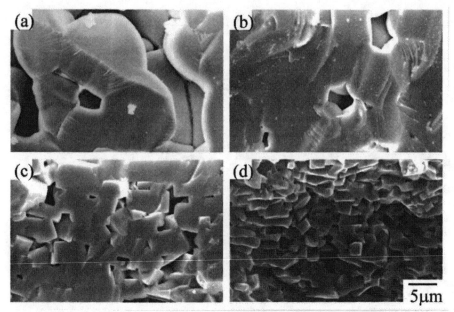

Fig. 4. Microstructures of the (1-x)BNT-xBKT specimens with x = (a) 0.00, (b) 0.03, (c) 0.10, and (d) 0.15 sintered at 1200°C for 2 h.

concentrations sintered at 1200°C for 2h. The grain size decreased as the potassium concentration increased. In the specimens with high potassium concentration, the grain growth rate was small and the size difference between the template and matrix grains was maintained, and the template grains grew at the expense of the matrix grains. This type of grain growth resulted in the increase in the degree of orientation (Fig. 2). In the specimens whit no or low potassium concentration, the grain growth rate was large, resulting in the elimination of size difference between the template and matrix grains, and no preferential growth of the template grains was possible. This type of grain growth did not contribute to the increase in the degree of orientation.

The formation of grains with a cubic shape in the specimen with high potassium concentration suggests that the change in the grain boundary structure is responsible for the reduction in the grain growth rate. The mobility of the boundary with atomically smooth (faceted) structure is less than that with atomically rough (defaceted) structure.[11]

BNT-excess $Bi_2O_3$ System

Table I shows the composition of starting mixture of the specimens containing excess $Bi_2O_3$. BNT-1 contained no excess $Bi_2O_3$ (BNT-1 is the same specimen as pure BNT in the BNT-BKT system ) and BNT-2 and 3 contained 0.0050 and 0.0205 mol of excess $Bi_2O_3$ to 1 mol of BNT, respectively. The chemical analysis by the inductively coupled plasma (ICP) spectroscopy indicated that the compositions of specimens sintered at $1200°C$ for 10h were $Bi_{0.500}Na_{0.500}TiO_{3.000}$ and $Bi_{0.513}Na_{0.494}TiO_{3.017}$ for BNT-2 and -3, respectively, indicating that a fairly large amount of excess $Bi_2O_3$ was eliminated during sintering. BNT-4 and -5 were used for examining the effect of excess $Bi_2O_3$ on the microstructure.

Figure 5 shows the degree of orientation of the specimens sintered at $1200°C$ for various durations. BNT-2 and -3 had larger degrees of orientation than BNT-1, indicating that the addition of excess $Bi_2O_3$ promoted the texture development.

Figure 6 shows the microstructures of the specimens sintered at $1200°C$ for 1 h. Excess $Bi_2O_3$ decreased the size of grains. Figure 7 shows the microstructures of BNT-4 and -5 (Table I), which were prepared by the conventional processing method at $1200°C$ for 2h. The microstructure of polished surface of BNT-5 (Fig.

Table I.   Composition of starting mixtures

| Name | Composition (mol) | | | | |
|------|------|------|------|------|------|
|      | BiT* | $Bi_2O_3$ | excess $Bi_2O_3$ | $TiO_2$ | $Na_2CO_3$ |
| BNT-1 | 0.20/3 | 0.25-0.40/3[+] | 0.0000 | 1.00-0.20[#] | 0.25 |
| BNT-2 | 0.20/3 | 0.25-0.40/3[+] | 0.0023 | 1.00-0.20[#] | 0.25 |
| BNT-3 | 0.20/3 | 0.25-0.40/3[+] | 0.0096 | 1.00-0.20[#] | 0.25 |
| BNT-4 | 0 | 0.25 | 0.0205 | 1.00 | 0.25 |
| BNT-5 | 0 | 0.25 | 0.074 | 1.00 | 0.25 |

*: plate-like $Bi_4Ti_3O_{12}$ powder.

[+]: 0.40/3 mols of $Bi_2O_3$ were supplied from BiT.

[#]:0.20 mols of $TiO_2$ were supplied from BiT.

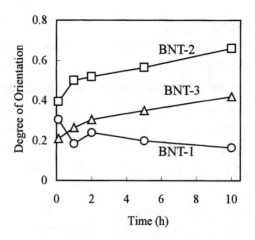

Fig. 5. Effect of excess $Bi_2O_3$ on the degree of orientation of the BNT specimens sintered at 1200°C.

7(a)) indicates the presence of liquid phase at sintering temperatures. In general, liquid phase promotes grain growth by enhanced material transport in liquid phase. In the present case, however, excess $Bi_2O_3$ reduced the grain growth rate. The microstructure of fracture surface of BNT-4 (Fig. 7(b)) indicates the presence of grains with a cubic shape. This implies that excess $Bi_2O_3$ forms liquid phase at the sintering temperatures and changes the boundary structure of BNT grains, as in the case of BNT-BKT. The faceted boundary has atomically smooth structure and its mobility is smaller than that of curved boundary with atomically rough structure.[11]

The low degree of orientation in BNT-1 was caused by a large grain growth rate. Excess $Bi_2O_3$ reduced the grain growth rate and maintained the size difference between the template and matrix grains, resulting in the preferential growth of template grains and the high degree of orientation.

BNT System

In the experiments in systems 1) and 2), the amount of platelike BiT particles was designed so that 20% of titanium and 53.3% of bismuth in final BNKT originated from platelike BiT. The calcined compacts were composed of template and matrix grains. The growth of template grains is responsible for development

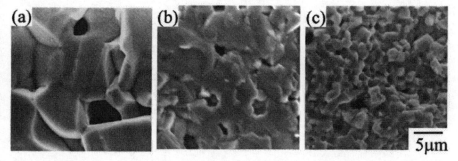

Fig. 6. Microstructures of the (a) BNT-1, (b) -2, and (c) -3 specimens sintered at 1200°C for 1 h.

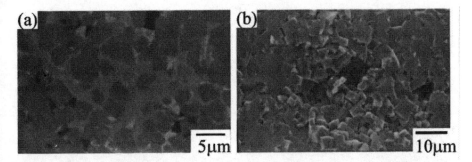

Fig. 7. Microstructures of the (a) BNT-5 and (b) -4 specimens sintered at 1200°C for 2 h.

of the crystallographic texture. The preferential growth of template grains may be enhanced by increasing the volume fraction of template grains. Therefore, the amount of platelike BiT particles was increased so that 50% of titanium and 100% of bismuth were supplied from platelike BiT to final BNT.

Figure 8 shows the degree of orientation of the BNT specimens in which the amount of platelike BiT particles was different. The percent of bismuth supplied from platelike BiT is indicated in parenthesis, as BNT(100). BNT(53.3) is the same as pure BNT in system 1). By increasing the platelike BiT particles, the sintered compacts with fairly high degree of orientation were obtained.

Figure 9 shows the microstructures of the BNT(100) and BNT(53.3) specimens sintered at 1000°C for 2h. The grains with platelike characteristics could be confirmed in the BNT specimens, but no such grains were lost in the

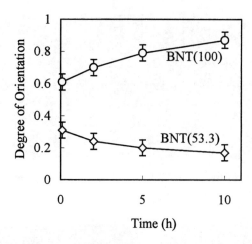

Fig. 8. Effect of the amount of platelike BiT on the degree of orientation in the specimens sintered at 1200°C.

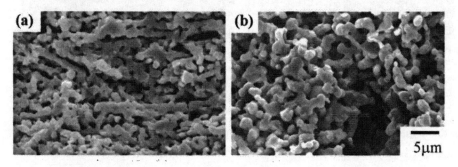

Fig. 9. Microstructures of (a) BNT(100) and (b) BNT(53.3) sintered at 1000°C for 2 h.

BNT(53.3) specimen. Furthermore, the grain size of BNT(53.3) was larger than that of the matrix grains of the BNT(100) specimen. A large volume fraction of matrix grains in BNT(53.3) may promote grain growth, and the size difference between the template and matrix grains, which was the driving force of the growth of template grains, is lost. Conversely, the growth of template grains is not hindered by the growth of matrix grains, because of a large volume fraction of template grains. Thus, crystallographic texture developed in BNT(100).

BNT-BaTiO$_3$ System

The composition was extended to 0.94BNT-0.06BT, because large piezoelectric coefficients were reported for a single crystal with this composition.[12] A large amount of platelike BiT as BNT(100) was used in the starting mixture. BaTiO$_3$ powder and powder mixture of BaCO$_3$ and TiO$_2$ were mixed to the starting mixture. The specimens will be abbreviated as BNT-BTC and BNT-BTR, respectively.

Figure 10 shows the degree of orientation of the BNT-BTC and BNT-BTR specimens as well as that of the BNT(100) specimen in system 3). Crystallographic texture developed in the BNT-BTC specimen but did not in the BNT-BTR specimen. The BNT formation reaction influenced the texture development as in the BNKT-PZT case [13]. In the NMT-BTC specimen, BNT formed at 800°C, and BNT and BT were present as separate phases at this stage. This implies that the template BNT particles formed in the BNT-BTC specimens. In the BNT-BTR specimen, on the other hand, the solid solution with the BNT-BT composition formed at 800°C. During the solid solution formation, Bi$_2$O$_3$ and TiO$_2$ diffuse out of platelike BiT particles and react with Na$_2$CO$_3$ and BaCO$_3$ in the matrix, resulting in the loss of template BNT particles. Thus, the direction of material transport during the formation of template grains was important for texture development.

CONCLUSIONS

In the BNT-based perovskite compounds, crystallographic texture develops by the growth of template grains at the expense of the matrix grains. The driving force is the size difference between the template and matrix grains. Therefore, the size difference must be maintained throughout processing. As the grain growth rate (dr/dt) is inversely proportional to grain size (r), it is necessary to reduce grain growth rate to maintain the size difference. In the BNT case, the substitution of K for Na and addition of excess Bi$_2$O$_3$ are effective to reduce the grain growth rate.

Because the growth of template and matrix grains is a competitive process, the larger volume fraction of template grains is more favorable for texture development. Therefore, highly textured BNT was obtained by use of a large amount of BiT.

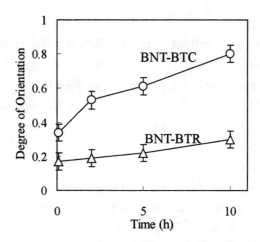

Fig. 10. Effect of mixing method of BT components to starting mixtuer on the degree of orientation in the specimens sintered at 1200°C.

The RTGG process involves the reaction between particle with shape anisotropy and raw materials, and the direction of material transport is important to obtain a large volume fraction of template BNT-based particles. In the BNT-BaTiO$_3$ system, the diffusion of Bi$_2$O$_3$ and TiO$_2$ out of BiT particles must be suppressed. Highly textured BNT-BT was obtained by use of BaTiO$_3$, instead of BaCO$_3$ + TiO$_2$, for raw materials.

REFERENCES

[1]T.Ota, J.Takahashi, and I.Yamai, "Effect of Microstructure on the Dielectric Property of Ceramics," *Key Engineering Materials,* **66 & 67**, 185-246 (1992).

[2]M. Granahan, M. Holmes, W.A. Shulze, and R.E. Newnham, "Grain-Oriented PbNb$_2$O$_6$ Ceramics," *Journal of the American Ceramic Society*, **64**[4] C-68-C-69 (1981).

[3]S. Swartz, W.A. Schulze, and J.V. Biggers, "Fabrication and Electrical Properties of Grain Oriented Bi$_4$Ti$_3$O$_{12}$ Ceramics," *Ferroelectrics*, **38**[1-4] 765-68 (1981).

[4]Y. Inoue, T. Kimura, and T. Yamaguchi, "Sintering of Plate-Like Bi$_4$Ti$_3$O$_{12}$ Powders," *American Ceramic Society Bulletin*, **62**[6] 704-710 (1983).

[5]T. Kimura, M.H. Holmes, and R.E. Newnham, "Fabrication of Grain-Oriented $Bi_2WO_6$ Ceramics," *Journal of the American Ceramic Society*, **65** [4] 223-226 (1982).

[6]H. Chazono, T. Kimura, and T. Yamaguchi, "Fabrication of Grain-Oriented $Bi_4Ti_3O_{12}$ Ceramics by Normal Sintering, I. Tapecasting and Sintering," *Yogyo Kyokai Shi*, **93** [9] 485-90 (1985).

[7]J. A. Horn, S.C. Zhang, U. Selvaraj, G.L. Messing, S. Trolier-McKinstry, and M. Yokoyama, "Fabrication of Textured $Bi_4Ti_3O_{12}$ by Templated Grain Growth"; pp. 943-46 in *Proceedings, The Tenth International Symposium on the Application of Ferroelectrics*, Vol. 2. Edited by B. M. Kulwicki, A. Amin, and A. Safari. Institute of Electrical And Electron Engineers, Piscataway, NJ, 1996.

[8]T. Tani, "Crystalline-Oriented Piezoelectric Bulk Ceramics with a Perovskite-Type Structure," *Journal of Korean Physical Society*, **32**, S1217-20 (1998).

[9]E. Fukuchi, T. Kimura, T. Tani, T. Takeuchi, and Y. Saito, "Effect of Potassium Concentration on the Grain Orientation in Bismuth Sodium Potassium Titanate," *Journal of the American Ceramic Society*, **85**[6] 1461-66 (2002).

[10]T. Kimura and T. Yamaguchi, "Fused Salt Synthesis of $Bi_4Ti_3O_{12}$," *Ceramics International*, **9** [1] 13-17 (1983).

[11]B.-K. Lee, S.-Y. Chung, and S.-J.L. Kang, "Grain Boundary Faceting and Abnormal Grain Growth in $BaTiO_3$," *Acta Materialia*, **48**[7] 1575-80 (2000).

[12]Y. M. Chiang, G. W. Farrey, and A. N. Soukhojak, "Lead-Free High-Strain Single-Crystal Piezoelectrics in the Alkaline-Bismuth-Titanate Perovskite Family," *Applied Physics Letter*, **73**[25] 3683-85 (1998).

[13]Y. Abe and T. Kimura, "Factors Determining Grain Orientation in Bismuth Sodium Potassium Titanate-Lead Zirconate Titanate Solid Solutions Made by the Reactive Templated Grain Growth Method," *Journal of the American Ceramic Society*, **85**[5] 1114-20 (2002).

# MID-PERMITTIVITY MICROWAVE DIELECTRIC CERAMICS BASED ON CaTiO$_3$–REAlO$_3$ (RE = La, Nd, Sm) PEROVSKITE SOLID SOLUTIONS

Bostjan Jancar, Danilo Suvorov, Matjaz Valant
Jožef Stefan Institute, Jamova 39, 1000 Ljubljana, Slovenia

ABSTRACT

Based on the CaTiO$_3$–REAlO$_3$ (RE = La, Nd, Sm) solid-solution systems we synthesized microwave dielectric ceramics with temperature-stable resonant frequencies ($\tau_f \approx 0$ ppm/K), that exhibit $\varepsilon_r > 40$ and Qxf $> 40000$ GHz. A more detailed study of the CaTiO$_3$–NdAlO$_3$-based ceramics revealed that the Q-value can be strongly influenced by the processing parameters. Using SEM and TEM analyses we found that during the solid-state reaction hexaluminate inclusions form as a transient phase. Their concentration in the microstructure of sintered ceramics depends on the thoroughness of the calcination process. In order to decrease the extrinsic dielectric losses (increase the Q-value) the amount of hexaluminate inclusions needs to be minimized. Apart from these inclusions the Q-value of the CaTiO$_3$–NdAlO$_3$ ceramics is influenced by the cooling rate after sintering. Slower cooling results in higher Q-value. When subjected to a thorough calcination (1300°C/30 hours with intermediate homogenization) and slow cooling after sintering (< 0.5 K/min), the 0.7CaTiO$_3$–0.3NdAlO$_3$ ceramics exhibit $\tau_f \approx 0$ ppm/K, $\varepsilon_r = 44$ and Qxf $= 44000$ GHz.

## INTRODUCTION

Dielectric materials with a near-zero temperature coefficient of resonant frequency ($\tau_f \approx 0$ ppm/K), which are extensively utilized as active components in microwave devices, are characterized either by a high permittivity ($\varepsilon_r > 80$) and a low quality factor (Qxf $< 10000$ GHz) or by a high quality factor (Qxf $> 100000$ GHz) and a low permittivity ($\varepsilon_r < 30$). The high-permittivity-class materials are suitable for applications where the need for miniaturization prevails over the need for effective usage of a certain frequency region. On the other hand, high-Q dielectrics are built into circuits where frequency selectivity is more important than the size of the device. Commercial high-permittivity materials are mostly covered by the so-called 114 solid solutions based on BaO-RE$_2$O$_3$-TiO$_2$[1] (RE =

Nd, Sm, Gd) systems, whereas high-Q materials are based on complex perovskites such as $Ba(Zn_{1/3}Ta_{2/3})O_3^2$ and $Ba(Mg_{1/3}Ta_{2/3})O_3^3$.

With the rapid development of wireless telecommunication technologies, however, the need for a new class of microwave dielectrics has emerged. These materials should exhibit $\varepsilon_r > 40$ and $Qxf > 40000$ GHz, which would provide a combination of a degree of miniaturization and a reasonable frequency selectivity. During the past ten years several researchers have described $CaTiO_3$-based systems as possible candidates for the synthesis of such materials.[4–9] $CaTiO_3$ was found to be a suitable base-material because of its high permittivity ($\varepsilon_r = 170$) combined with a reasonable Q-value (Qxf = 3500 GHz); a drawback is its highly positive temperature coefficient of resonant frequency ($\tau_f = +800$ ppm/K).[10] In all cases the objectives were to compensate $\tau_f$ while improving the Q-value and keeping $\varepsilon_r$ as high as possible. To accomplish this, solid solutions between $CaTiO_3$ and several complex perovskites were synthesized, from which the best results were obtained in the $(1-x)CaTiO_3-xLa(Zn_{1/2}Ti_{1/2})O_3$ system.[4] The ceramics based on the solid solution with $x = 0.5$ exhibit temperature-stable resonant frequency with permittivity $\varepsilon_r = 50$ and Qxf = 38.000 GHz.

In the scope of our investigations regarding the synthesis of mid-permittivity microwave ceramics we identified perovskite rare-earth aluminates as suitable candidates for tuning the dielectric properties of $CaTiO_3$. The reason being that majority of the known rare-earth aluminates exhibit a negative $\tau_f$, a high Q-value and a moderate permittivity.[11] We showed that ceramics with the temperature stable resonant frequency that exhibit $\varepsilon_r > 40$ and $Qxf > 40.000$ GHz can be synthesized in the $CaTiO_3-REAlO_3$ (RE = La, Nd, Sm) solid-solution systems.[12]

Following the initial synthesis of the $CaTiO_3 - REAlO_3$ based ceramics and measurements of their microwave dielectric properties we identified crucial features in the crystal structure and microstructure that control the microwave dielectric properties. The emphasis was on the investigation of the $CaTiO_3-NdAlO_3$ system.

EXPERIMENTAL PROCEDURE

$CaTiO_3-REAlO_3$ solid solutions were prepared by the solid-state reaction of commercial $CaCO_3$, $TiO_2$, $Nd_2O_3$, $Sm_2O_3$ and $La_2O_3$ powders. Stoichiometric amounts of powders were homogenized in an alcohol suspension with ytria-stabilized-zirconia (YSZ) balls. After removal of the alcohol in a rotary evaporator the powders were pelletized and calcined several times in the temperature range between 900 and 1300°C, with intermediate cooling crushing and repelletizing. The reaction mechanism leading to the formation of the solid solutions was followed with x-ray powder-diffraction analysis using a Philips PW 1710 diffractometer and $CuK\alpha$ radiation. The calcined powders were ball-milled under alcohol in a laboratory planetary ball-mill with YSZ balls. After the ball milling the powders were isostatically pressed at 700 MPa into disk-shaped samples and sintered in an air or oxygen atmosphere between 1300 and 1500°C.

The permittivities of the ceramic samples were calculated from the frequencies of the $TE_{01\delta}$ resonance modes using the Itoh-Rudokas model.[13] The Q-values were determined at the same resonance mode by analyzing the $S_{11}$ parameter as suggested by Kajfez and Hwan.[14] The temperature coefficients of the resonant frequencies were calculated from the resonance frequencies measured at 60 and 20°C.

The microstructural analyses were preformed with JEOL 840-JXA and JSM-5800 scanning electron microscopes (SEMs) and JEOL JEM-2000FX transmission electron microscope (TEM). For the SEM analysis the sample surfaces were ground and polished. Samples for the TEM were mechanically thinned to 20 μm and subsequently ion-beam milled with argon ions at 4 KV.

RESULTS AND DISCUSSION

The microwave dielectric properties of the ceramics based on $(1-x)CaTiO_3 - xREAlO_3$ (RE = La, Nd, Sm) solid solutions all exhibit a similar dependence on the value of x.[12] The concentration of aluminate required to completely compensate the positive temperature coefficient of $CaTiO_3$ was in all three cases, between 30 and 35 mol%. Furthermore, the ceramics with temperature-stable resonant frequencies exhibited comparable permittivities and Q-values (Table 1).

Table 1: Microwave dielectric properties of the ceramics with temperature-stable resonant frequencies based on $CaTiO_3 - REAlO_3$ (RE = La, Nd, Sm) solid solutions, sintered at 1350°C/10 hours and cooled at > 10 K/min.

|  | $\varepsilon_r$ | Qxf [GHz] | $\tau_f$ [ppm/K] |
|---|---|---|---|
| $0.65CaTiO_3 - 0.35LaAlO_3$ | 44 | 33000 | -3 |
| $0.7CaTiO_3 - 0.3NdAlO_3$ | 43 | 33000 | 0 |
| $0.7CaTiO_3 - 0.3SmAlO_3$ | 45 | 41000 | 3 |

Apart from having similar microwave dielectric properties the three solid solutions- $0.65CaTiO_3-0.35LaAlO_3$, $0.7CaTiO_3-0.3NdAlO_3$ and $0.7CaTiO_3-0.3SmAlO_3$ also exhibit similar crystal structures.[12] They belong to the family of orthorhombically distorted perovskites with the Pnma space group. The deviation of such a crystal structure from the ideal cubic $ABO_3$ perovskite structure can be readily described in terms of $[BO_6]$ octahedral tilting about the three fourfold pseudocubic axes. The orthorhombic distortion is characterized by two antiphase tilts of equal magnitude and an in-phase tilt of a different magnitude. In the Pnma setting, according to Glazer's notation[15], this is described by $a^-a^-b^+$.

The magnitude of the $[BO_6]$ octahedral tilts changed with an increase in x for the $(1-x)CaTiO_3-xREAlO_3$ solid solutions. From the x-ray diffraction spectra shown in Fig. 1 it can be observed that an increase in the $NdAlO_3$ concentration in the $CaTiO_3-NdAlO_3$ system results in a decrease in the intensity of the difference reflections. Lowering of the intensity of the 201, 102, 221 and 122 reflections indicates a decrease of the in-phase tilting angle, whereas a lowering of the

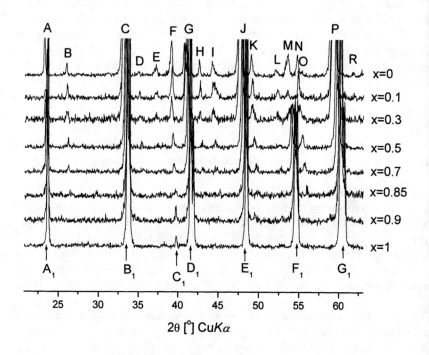

| *Pnma* | $R\bar{3}c$ |
|---|---|
| A...101; B...020; C...200, 121, 002 | $A_1$...012 |
| D...210; E...201, 102 | $B_1$...110, 104 |
| F...211, 031, 112; G...220, 022 | $C_1$...113 |
| H...131; I...221, 122 | $D_1$...200, 006 |
| J...202, 040; K...230, 212 | $E_1$...024 |
| L...231, 132, 013 | $F_1$...112, 116 |
| M...301, 222, 141, 103; N...311 | $G_1$...300, 214, 018 |
| O...113; P...321, 240, 042, 123 | |
| R...142, 203 | |

Fig.1: X-ray diffraction patterns of several compositions from the $(1-x)CaTiO_3 - xNdAlO_3$ tie line.

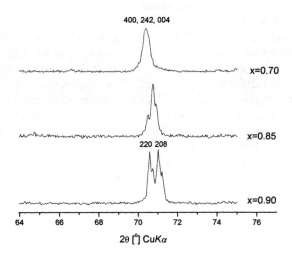

400, 242, 004

x=0.70

220 208

x=0.85

x=0.90

64    66    68    70    72    74    76

$2\theta$ [°] Cu$K\alpha$

Fig 2. Part of the x-ray diffraction patterns collected in the vicinity of the morphotropic phase boundary.

intensity of the 211, 031 and 112 reflections is a consequence of the decrease in the antiphase tilting angle. Therefore, the distortion of the perovskite structure, which is directly connected to the magnitude of [BO$_6$] octahedral tilting, decreases with an increase in the NdAlO$_3$ concentration. The decrease in the distortion is consistent with the increase in the tolerance factor. Furthermore, the x-ray diffraction analysis of the CaTiO$_3$–NdAlO$_3$ tie-line reveals a morphotropic phase transition from orthorhombic to trigonal symmetry (space group $R\overline{3}c$) which takes place between x = 0.85 and x = 0.90 (Fig. 2).

In the literature, the tilting of the [BO$_6$] octahedra is described as one of the crucial factors that influences the microwave dielectric properties, especially the temperature coefficient of resonant frequency, of materials with perovskite and perovskite-like crystal structures.[16, 17] Colla et al showed that the decrease in the tilt angles of the [BO$_6$] octahedra in the complex perovskites results in an increase in the $\tau_f$.[16] Such a dependence was also observed in the case of Ba$_{6-x}$RE$_{8+2x}$Ti$_{18}$O$_{54}$ (RE = La – Gd) solid-solution systems with the tungsten bronze structure.[17] In the (1-x)CaTiO$_3$–xNdAlO$_3$ system, however, the variation of the $\tau_f$ with the increase in x does not reflect the gradual increase of the octahedral tilting angle. Instead of increasing linearly with the increase of the NdAlO$_3$ concentration the dependence of the $\tau_f$ on x exhibits two distinct regions (Fig. 3a). From x = 0 to x = 0.4 the temperature coefficient of resonant frequency decreases from + 800 ppm/K to -50 ppm/K whereas between x = 0.4 and x = 0 it linearly approaches the $\tau_f$ value of pure NdAlO$_3$ (– 33 ppm/K). A similar trend is observed for the variation of permittivity with the increase of the NdAlO$_3$ concentration (Fig. 3b). After the initial increase from 170 to 35 with an increase in x from 0 to 0.4, the permittivity linearly decreases to 28 at x = 1.

The pronounced decrease of the $\tau_f$ and the $\varepsilon_r$ with the initial increase of the dopant concentration is also a characteristic of other solid-solution systems based on $CaTiO_3$[5, 6], as well as those based on $SrTiO_3$[18, 19]. Such behavior in these systems can be attributed to the effective suppression of the incipient ferroelectricity[20] of pure $CaTiO_3$ and $SrTiO_3$ with the small increase in the dopant concentration. The subsequent linear increase of the $\tau_f$ with the increase in x from 0.4 to 1 can be ascribed to the gradual decrease of the $[BO_6]$ octahedra-tilting angles which is consistent with the observation of Colla et al[16]. The linear decrease in the $\varepsilon_r$ between x = 0.4 and x = 1 is a consequence of the linear decrease of the molecular polarizability[21] of the solid solution with the increase in the $NdAlO_3$ concentration.

The Q-value of the ceramics based on the $(1-x)CaTiO_3-xNdAlO_3$ system was found to linearly increase with an increase in x (Fig. 3b). The peculiarity is its sensitivity to the processing parameters, especially the thoroughness of the calcinations prior to sintering, and the cooling rate after the sintering. By changing these two parameters the measured Qxf value of the $0.7CaTiO_3-0.3NdAlO_3$ ceramics varied from 27000 to 44000 GHz. In order to identify the possible reasons for such behavior a detailed microstructural analysis was preformed.

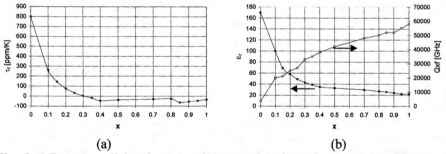

(a)            (b)

Fig. 3: Microwave dielectric properties as a function of x in $(1-x)CaTiO_3 - xNdAlO_3$: (a) $\tau_f$ vs. x, (b) $\varepsilon_r$ and Qxf vs. x.

Using the SEM and TEM we discovered three types of microstructural features as possible sources of the dielectric losses: Al-rich inclusions (Fig 4a), twin domains (Fig. 6a) and antiphase boundaries (Fig. 6b).[22] The selected-area electron-diffraction (SAED) analysis combined with the x-ray energy-dispersive (EDS) analysis showed that the Al-rich inclusions are solid solutions among hexaluminate $CaAl_{12}O_{19}$ and a $\beta$-$Al_2O_3$-type compound, $NdAl_{11}O_{18}$. These inclusions were found in the microstructure of the sintered ceramics regardless whether the starting material was a mixture of oxides and a carbonate or the pre-reacted perovskites $CaTiO_3$ and $NdAlO_3$. The analysis of the reaction mechanism for the formation of the solid solution, using x-ray diffraction, showed that the reaction between the two perovskites CaTiO$_3$ and NdAlO$_3$ is also the last step of the reaction sequence when oxide and carbonate powders are used as the starting materials. Therefore, we concluded that this step is the source of the hexaluminate-based inclusions. In order to study the reaction between CaTiO$_3$ and NdAlO$_3$ we prepared a diffusion couple.

As can be seen from the SEM micrograph shown in Fig. 4b the reaction layer of such a diffusion couple, after firing at 1350°C for six hours, consists of two distinct phases: a continuous phase in between the two perovskites, and the dark particles segregated along the NdAlO$_3$ side. The EDS analysis revealed that these particles are rich in Al, and contain some Ca and Nd. The EDS analysis consistently showed that the concentration of Nd in the continuous phase of the reaction layer was higher than the concentration of Al.

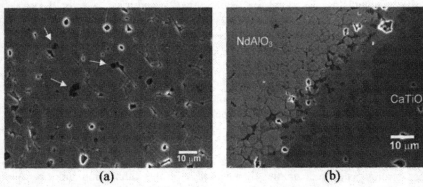

(a)                                        (b)

Fig. 4: (a) Microstructure of the 0.7CaTiO$_3$ – 0.3NdAlO$_3$ ceramics sintered at 1350°C/10 hours and thermally etched at 1300°C/10 minutes (arrows mark the hexaluminate inclusions) and (b) CaTiO$_3$ – NdAlO$_3$ diffusion couple, fired at 1350°C/10 hours.

From these results we concluded that during the reaction between CaTiO$_3$ and NdAlO$_3$ the Nd$^{3+}$ incorporates into the forming perovskite solid solution faster than the Al$^{3+}$, the consequence being the segregation of Al in the form of hexaluminate particles. Consequently, the perovskite solid solution needs to accommodate excess Nd, which can theoretically be accomplished in several different ways*:

1.) Excess Nd can incorporate into the perovskite interstitially

$$Nd_2O_3 \rightarrow 2Nd_i^{...} + 3O_i^{''}$$                (1)

---

* In order to account for the charge neutrality the incorporation of oxygen also has to be taken into consideration

2.) excess Nd can simultaneously occupy A and B sites in the perovskite structure

$$Nd_2O_3 \rightarrow Nd_A^x + Nd_B^x + 3O_O^x \qquad (2)$$

3.) excess Nd can incorporate solely on the A-site, thus creating B-site and oxygen sub-lattice vacancies

$$Nd_2O_3 \rightarrow 2Nd_A^x + 2V_B''' + 3O_O^x + 3V_O^{\cdot\cdot} \qquad (3)$$

Due to the close packing of the perovskite structure the formation energies of Frenkel defects are much higher than the formation energies of Shottky defects.[23] The mechanism described by equation (1) is thus unlikely to occur. On the other hand, the mechanisms described by equations (2) and (3) have both been described in the literature.[24, 25] The simultaneous incorporation of excess Nd on the A and B sites would force a large $Nd^{3+}$ ion into a six-fold coordination, which would increase the ionic radii difference on the B-site and thereby increase the distortion of the crystal lattice. The second possible mechanism of accommodating the excess Nd, where B-site and oxygen sub-lattice vacancies are formed, leads to the formation of a solid solution with a defect structure. Both of these mechanisms are possible sources of the extrinsic dielectric losses.

Further experiments have confirmed that the hexaluminate inclusions are a transient phase that forms during the solid-state reaction due to the kinetics. The concentration of inclusions in the microstructure of sintered $CaTiO_3$–$NdAlO_3$ ceramics strongly depends on the thoroughness of the calcination process. A comparison of Figs. 5a and 5b reveals that prolonging the calcination time, with intermediate crushing of the pellets, noticeably reduces the concentration of the hexaluminate inclusions in the microstructure.

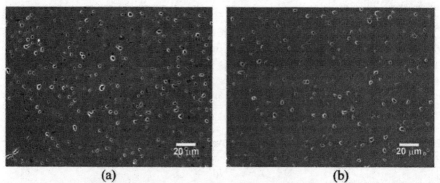

(a)  (b)

Fig. 5: Microstructures of the $0.7CaTiO_3$ – $0.3NdAlO_3$ ceramics sintered at $1350°C/10$ hours, calcined at (a) $1300°C/10$ hours and (b) $1300°C/30$ hours with intermediate homogenization.

By measuring the microwave dielectric properties of the sintered $0.7CaTiO_3$–$0.3NdAlO_3$ ceramic samples, that underwent different calcination conditions we substantiated the influence of hexaluminate inclusions on the dielectric losses. From table 2 it can be seen that the ceramics that underwent a more thorough calcination exhibit lower dielectric losses (higher Q value). From this we concluded that in order to optimize the dielectric properties of $CaTiO_3$–$NdAlO_3$-based ceramics the concentration of the hexaluminate inclusions needs to be minimized. This can be achieved by increasing the calcination time and the number of intermediate homogenizations.

Table 2: Microwave dielectric properties of the $0.7CaTiO_3$–$0.3NdAlO_3$ ceramics sintered at 1350°C/10 hours vs. calcination conditions

| Calcination conditions | $\varepsilon_r$ | Qxf [GHz] | $\tau_f$ [ppm/K] |
|---|---|---|---|
| 1300°C 10 hours | 44 | 27000 | +3 |
| 1300°C 30 hours | 44 | 35000 | +3 |

Apart from the thoroughness of the calcination the dielectric losses of the $CaTiO_3$–$NdAlO_3$ ceramics are influenced by the cooling rate after the sintering. As can be seen from table 3, slower cooling results in lower dielectric losses (higher Q value).

Table 3: Microwave dielectric properties of the $0.7CaTiO_3$–$0.3NdAlO_3$ ceramics sintered at 1350°C/10 hours vs. cooling rate

| Cooling rate K min | $\varepsilon_r$ | Qxf [GHz] | $\tau_f$ [ppm/K] |
|---|---|---|---|
| 10 | 44 | 33000 | +2 |
| 5 | 43 | 38000 | +2 |
| 0.5 | 44 | 44000 | +3 |

SEM and x-ray-diffraction analyses did not reveal any significant differences in the microstructure or the crystal structure between the samples cooled with different rates.[18] Therefore we preformed a detailed analysis of the individual grains of the matrix phase using the TEM.

We found that individual grains of the $0.7CaTiO_3$–$0.3NdAlO_3$ ceramics consist of elongated domains with average dimensions of 200 x 600 nm (Fig. 6a). These domains do not differ in chemical composition but exhibit a different orientation. Using SAED analysis we established that the domains are twin related across the (112) and (1$\bar{1}$2) crystallographic planes.[22] Such twins form as a consequence of a structural phase transition associated with the reduction of the point group order in cases where the lower symmetry phase is a subgroup of a higher symmetry one.[26] In the perovskite systems These types of structural phase transitions are most commonly cation order-disorder or $[BO_6]$ octahedral-tilting transitions. Since no cation order was detected in the $CaTiO_3$–$NdAlO_3$ system we concluded that the domain structure is a consequence of the octahedral-tilting transition, which occurs during the cooling from the sintering temperature.

Apart from the twin domains the grains of the $0.7CaTiO_3$–$0.3NdAlO_3$ ceramics contain curved features (Fig 6b), which we determined to be the antiphase boundaries. These antiphase boundaries separate the antiphase domains which in the perovskite systems form during the structural phase transition where the loss of translational symmetry occurs. Again, such a phase transition in the $CaTiO_3$–$NdAlO_3$ system can only be associated with the change of the octahedral-tilting regime.

A similar domain structure is also a characteristic of pure $CaTiO_3$, which during the heating/cooling cycle undergoes at least two different octahedral-tilting transitions.[27] One of these transitions is thermodynamically a second-order phase transition that involves a gradual decrease of the octahedral tilt angles over a certain temperature range. The similarity of the domain structure between pure $CaTiO_3$ and $0.7CaTiO_3$–$0.3NdAlO_3$ solid solution implies a similar sequence of structural phase transitions upon heating and cooling. Therefore, one of the phase transitions in the case of the $0.7CaTiO_3$ – $0.3NdAlO_3$ solid solution is of the second order, involving a gradual decrease of the $[BO_6]$-octahedra tilt angles. Strain formed in the crystal structure due to such a phase transition could depend on the cooling rate, which would thus influence the extrinsic dielectric losses of the system. However, a quantitative relationship has yet to be determined.

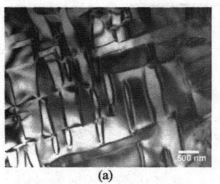 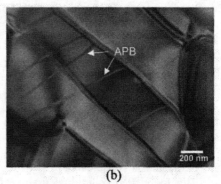

(a)                                                (b)

Fig. 6: (a) twin domains and (b) antiphase boundaries (APB) in the grains of $0.7CaTiO_3$ – $0.3NdAlO_3$ ceramics sintered at 1350°C/10 hours.

CONCLUSIONS

Mid-permittivity microwave dielectric ceramics can be synthesized by forming solid solutions with $CaTiO_3$ and $REAlO_3$ (RE = La, Nd, Sm). The amount of $REAlO_3$ required to compensate the highly positive temperature coefficient of resonant frequency of pure $CaTiO_3$ does not significantly depend on the RE. In all three cases the concentration of $REAlO_3$ that yields ceramics with a temperature-stable resonant frequency is between 30 and 35 mole%. A more detailed analysis of the $CaTiO_3$–$NdAlO_3$ system showed that the two perovskites form solid solutions across the entire compositional range. The crystal structure of the solid solutions is governed by the lowering of the [BO$_6$] octahedral-tilt angles as the concentration of NdAlO$_3$ increases. A microstructural investigation of the ceramics based on the 0.7CaTiO$_3$–0.3NdAlO$_3$ solid solution revealed the presence of three distinct microstructural features: hexaluminate inclusions, twin domains, and antiphase boundaries. Hexaluminate inclusions form during the calcination process due to the slower incorporation of the Al$^{3+}$ into the forming solid solution. The existence of twin domains and antiphase boundaries is a consequence of the symmetry-breaking structural phase transition, which occurs upon cooling from the sintering temperature. In order to optimize the microwave dielectric properties of the 0.7CaTiO$_3$–0.3NdAlO$_3$ ceramics, a thorough calcination at temperatures above 1300°C and slow cooling (< 0.5 K/min) after the sintering need to be applied. After such processing the ceramics based on the 0.7CaTiO$_3$–0.3NdAlO$_3$ solid solution exhibit $\varepsilon_r$ = 44, Qxf = 44000 GHz and $\tau_f \approx$ +3 ppm/K.

REFERENCES

[1]K. Wakino, K. Minai, H. Tamura, "Microwave Characteristics of (Zr,Sn)TiO$_4$ and BaO-PbO-Nd$_2$O$_3$-TiO$_2$ Dielectric Resonators," *J. Am. Ceram. Soc.*, **67** [4] 278-81 (1984).

[2]S. Kawashima, M. Nishida, I. Ueda, H. Ouchi, "Ba(Zn$_{1/3}$Ta$_{2/3}$)O$_3$ Ceramics with Low Dielectric Loss at Microwave Frequencies," *J. Am. Ceram. Soc.*, **66** [6] 421-23 (1983).

[3]K. Matsamuto, T. Hiuga, K. Takada, H. Ichimura, "Ba(M$_{1/3}$Ta$_{2/3}$)O$_3$ Ceramics with Ultra-Low Loss at Microwave Frequencies," *IEEE T Ultrason. Ferr.*, 33 [6] 802-02 (1986).

[4]IS. Kim, WH. Jung, Y. Inaguma, T. Nakamura, M. Itoh, "Dielectric Properties of A-Site Deficient Perovskite-Type Lanthanum-Calcium-Titanium Oxide Solid Solution System [(1-x)La$_{2/3}$TiO$_3$-xCaTiO$_3$ (0.1 ≤ x ≤ 0.96)]," *Mater. Res. Bull.*, **30** [3] 307-16 (1995).

[5]DH Yeo, JB Kim, JH Moon, SJ Yoon, HJ Kim, "Dielectric Properties of (1-x)CaTiO3 − xLa(Zn1/2Ti1/2)O3 Ceramics at Microwave Frequencies," *Jpn. J. Appl. Phys.*, **35** [2A] 663-67 (1996).

[6]S. Kucheiko, J-W. Choi, H-J. Kim, H-J. Jung, "Microwave Dielectric properties of CaTiO$_3$ − Ca(Al$_{1/2}$Ta$_{1/2}$)O$_3$ Ceramics," *J. Am. Ceram. Soc.*, **79** [10] 2739-43 (1996).

[7]JS. Kim, CI. Cheon, HJ. Kang, CH. Lee, KY. Kim, S. Nam, JD. Byun, "Crystal Structure and Microwave Dielectric Properties of CaTiO3-(Li$_{1/2}$Nd$_{1/2}$)TiO$_3$-(Ln$_{1/3}$Nd$_{1/3}$)TiO$_3$ (Ln = La, Dy) Ceramics," *Jpn. J. Appl. Phys.* **38** (9B) 5633-37 (1999).

[8]WS. Kim, KH. Yoon, ES. Kim, "Microwave Dielectric Properties and far-Infrared Reflectivity Characteristics of the CaTiO3 − Li(1/2)-3xSm(1/2)+xTiO3 Ceramics," *J. Am. Ceram. Soc.*, **83** [9] 2327-29 (2000).

[9]CL. Huang, RY. Yang, MH. Weng, "Dielectric Properties of CaTiO3 – Ca(Mg1/3Nb2/3)O3 Ceramic System at Microwave Frequency," *Jpn. J. Appl. Phys.* **39** (12A) 6608-11 (2000).

[10]R.C. Kell, A.C. Greenham, G.C.E. Olds, "High-Permittivity Temperature-Stable Ceramic Dielectrics with Low Microwave Loss," *J. Am. Ceram. Soc.*, **56** [7] 352-54 (1973).

[11]SY. Cho, IT. Kim, KS. Hong, "Microwave Dielectric Properties of Rare Earth Aluminates," *J. Mater. Res.*, **14** [1] 114-19 (1999).

[12]B. Jancar, D. Suvorov, M. Valant, "Microwave Dielectric Properties and Microstructural Characteristics of Aliovalently Doped Perovskite Ceramics Based on $CaTiO_3$," *Key. Eng. Mat.*, **206-2** 1289-92 (2002).

[13]T. Itoh, R.S. Rudokas, "New Method for Computing the Resonant Frequencies of Dielectric Resonator," *IEEE Trans. MTT.*, **MTT-8** [1] 52-54 (1977).

[14]D. Kajfez, E.J. Hwan, "Q-factor Measurements with Network Analyzer," *IEEE Trans. MTT.*, **MTT-32** [1] 666-70 (1984).

[15]A.M. Glazer, "The Classification of Tilted Octahedra in Perovskites," *Acta Cryst.*, **B28** 3384-92 (1972).

[16]E.L. Colla, I.M. Reaney, N. Setter, "Effect of Structural Changes in Complex Perovskites on the Temperature Coefficient of the Relative Permittivity," *J. Appl. Phys.*, **74** [5] 3414-25 (1993).

[17]M. Valant, D. Suvorov, C. J. Rawn, "Intrinsic Reasons for Variations in Dielectric Properties of $Ba_{6-3x}R_{8+2x}Ti_{18}O_{54}$ (R = La-Gd) Solid Solutions," *Jpn. J. Appl. Phys.*, **38** 2820-26 (1999).

[18]PH. Sun, T. Nakamura, YJ. Shan, Y. Inaguma, M. Itoh, T. Kitamura, "Dielectric Behavior of $(1-x)LaAlO_3-xSrTiO_3$ Solid Solution System at Microwave Frequencies," *Jpn. J. Appl. Phys.*, **37** [10] 5625-29 (1998).

[19]SY. Cho, HJ. Youn, HJ. Lee, KS. Hong, "Contribution of Structure to Temperature Dependence of Resonant Frequency in the $(1-x)La(Zn_{1/2}Ti_{1/2})O_3$-$xATiO_3$ (A = Ca, Sr) System," *J. Am. Ceram. Soc.*, **84** [4] 753-58 (2001).

[20]V. V. Lemanov, A. V. Sotnikov, E. P. Smirnova, M. Weihnacht, R. Kunze, "Perovskite CaTiO3 as an Incipient Ferroelctric," *Solid State Commun.*, **110** 611-614 (1999).

[21]R.D. Shannon, "Dielectric Polarizabilities of Ions in Oxides and Fluorides," *J. Appl. Phys.*, **73** [1] 348-66 (1993).

[22]B. Jancar, D. Suvorov, M. Valant, G. Drazic, "Characterization of $CaTiO_3$ – $NdAlO_3$ Dielectric Ceramics," *J. Europ. Ceram. Soc.*, **23** 1391-1400 (2003).

[23]G.V. Lewis, C.R.A. Catlow, "Defect Studies of Doped and Undoped Barium Titanate using Computer Simulation Techniques," *J. Phys. Chem. Solids*, **47** [1] 89-97 (1986).

[24]Y.H. Han, J.B. Appleby, D.M. Smyth, "Calcium as an Acceptor Impurity in $BaTiO_3$, " *J. Amer. Ceram. Soc.*, **70** [2] 96-100 (1987).

[25]N.G. Eror, D.M. Smith, "Nonstoichiometric Disorder in Single-Crystalline $BaTiO_3$ at Elevated Temperatures," *J. Solid State Chem.*, **24** [3-4] 235-44 (1978).

[26]H. Wondratschek, W. Jeitschko, "Twin Domains and Antiphase Domains," *Acta Cryst.*, **A32** 664-66 (1976).

[27]Y. Wang, R.C. Liebermann, "Electron Microscopy Study of Domain Structure due to Phase Transitions in Natural Perovskite," *Phys. Chem. Minerals.*, **20** 147-58 (1993).

# Microstructure and Properties of Materials

# MICROSTRUCTURAL EVOLUTION OF BULK COMPOSITE FERROELECTRICS AND ITS EFFECT ON THE MICROWAVE PROPERTIES

J. Synowczynski, S.G. Hirsch and B. L. Gersten
Weapons and Materials Research Directorate
Army Research Laboratory
APG, MD, 21005

R. Geyer
RF Technology Division
National Institute for Standards and Technology
Boulder, CO 80305

ABSTRACT

A study was conducted to determine the influence of the processing conditions on the microstructural evolution and subsequent microwave properties of $Ba_{0.55}Sr_{0.45}TiO_3$ (BST)/ MgO composites. The objective was to find the conditions necessary to maximize the permittivity while keeping the dielectric loss at a minimum. Experiments were designed to determine the effect of the processing at three different stages during the fabrication process: powder processing, green body densification, and sintering schedule. For the experiments, powders were processed using both conventional solid state calcinations (particle size ~ 1um) and wet chemical reactions (particle size ~25 – 100nm). These powders were then densified either colloidally (ie. Tape casting) or through uniaxial dry pressing. Geometric green density measurements revealed that the wet chemical powders compacted at a much lower green density than the calcined powders. These compacts were then sintered at three sintering temperatures (ie. $1250^{\circ}C$, $1350^{\circ}C$, and $1450^{\circ}C$) for 2 hours. SEM microscopy and BET analysis of the sintered compacts revealed the temperature onset for sintering as well as the grain growth kinetics. Archimedes density measurements determined that for wet chemically processed powders, the maximum density and minimum porosity were achieved at $1350^{\circ}C$ sintering temperature, whereas the solid state calcined powders did not reach full density until $1450^{\circ}C$. The effect of these results on the microwave properties will be discussed in further detail.

## INTRODUCTION

Recent efforts to reduce the weight, cost, and size of microwave devices such as electronic scanning antennas and voltage tunable filters, have created the need for low loss voltage-tunable ferroelectric materials. The critical materials parameters for many microwave device designs are [1] low dielectric constant for impedance matching ($\varepsilon_R$ ~100) [2] low dielectric loss tangent [3] high tunability (i.e. % change in dielectric constant with voltage) and [4] small temperature coefficient of permittivity. To meet these requirements several investigations have been published [1,2] describing an innovative approach which involves compositing the ferroelectric $BaSrTiO_3$ with a low-loss, temperature-stable dielectric such as MgO. Using this approach investigators at ARL have succeeded in producing voltage-tunable dielectric materials with dielectric constants in the range from 800 to 100 and loss tangents as low as 0.008 at 10GHz. After about 1 wt% MgO, the MgO separates out of the $BaSrTiO_3$ to form a pure MgO second phase. As more MgO is added, this second phase helps to reduce the dielectric constant and loss tangent as well as increase the temperature stability.

We seek to further improve the dielectric properties by carefully engineering the microstructure in the ferroelectric composite. Since ferroelectricity is a cooperative phenomenon, it can be influenced by boundary conditions and interfaces. Grain size is known to affect the domain size, domain configurations, and domain wall mobility. This is because the equilibrium domain size is determined by a balance of the domain wall energy $\omega_w$, the electric energy density $\omega_e$, and the mechanical energy density $\omega_m$. While investigating PZT, Cao[3] found that the domain size was proportional to the square root of the grain size for grain sizes between 1.0 and 10 micron but deviated for sizes less than 1 micron due to the higher domain densities resulting from inhomogeneous strain fields. Working with $BaTiO_3$, Luan[4] observed that decreasing the grain size reduced the dielectric loss tangent and dielectric constant. He concluded that the reduced dielectric constant resulted from an increased number of interfaces which strengthened the depolarization forces.

To date, there has been no systematic study of these effects in multiphase ceramics where the interface between the ferroelectric and dielectric filler phase can have a significant impact on the stress states as well as the depolarization fields. In a composite structure, as the ferroelectric phase goes through the ferroelectric phase transformation, a volume expansion occurs. This expansion is resisted by the non-ferroelectric phase, creating a compressive stress state at the interface. A compressive stress state can also result from the differences in the CTE between MgO and $BaSrTiO_3$. This compressive stress resists the gradual realignment of the atoms, thereby lowering the phase transformation temperature. Stress has also been shown to influence the order of the phase transition through higher order elastic coupling coefficients. The effect of the stress state on the domain configurations is grain size dependent. In the smallest grains, the polarization can be completely clamped, preventing domain reorientation in electric fields. For intermediate grains, the domains can still reverse. However, the phase transition occurs over a broader temperature range and the maximum dielectric constant is reduced. Large grains remain relatively unaffected by the stress state. Grain size also affects the electric field boundary conditions. Depolarization fields within the crystal are compensated for through either domain formation, surface charge, or polarization gradients within the crystal. For grains that are <0.1 micron, domain formation does not occur.[5] Therefore, the polarization at the center of the particles is different from the surface polarization.

In this investigation, we use this information to improve the dielectric properties of $BaSrTiO_3/MgO$ composites by evaluating the effect of the following three processing stages on the grain size and microwave properties: (1) powder synthesis – hydrothermal synthesis vs. solid state calcination (2) green body densification – uniaxial dry pressing vs. tape casting (3) sintering cycle –1250°C, 1350°C, and 1450°C.

EXPERIMENTAL

For this study, $Ba_{0.55}Sr_{0.45}TiO_3$ powders were produced either through solid state reaction of $BaTiO_3$ and $SrTiO_3$ at 1100°C in air for 2 hours or through hydrothermal synthesis. Hydrothermal synthesis is a method where chemical precursors for the powders are dispersed in water and then reacted in an autoclave at elevated temperatures (<100°C) to force a supersaturation condition and particle precipitation. The $Ba_{0.55}Sr_{0.45}TiO_3$ powders were then mixed with MgO in ethanol, ball milled for 24 hours, and finally dried under infrared heating lamps. After regrinding and sieving the powder mixture through a 425 micron sieve, the powder was either uniaxially pressed at 9000PSI or redispersed in a non-aqueous ethanol/xylenes tape casting system and cast. All samples were sintered in flowing air at 1250°C, 1350°C, or 1450°C for 2 hours. The sample key provided in table 1 identifies the composition and processing methods used for preparing the samples. Green density measurements were made geometrically whereas the percentage open porosity and sintered density were determined using the Archimedes method. The temperature onset for sintering was determined by BET analysis using a Micromeretics ASAP 2010 surface area analyzer. The samples were polished and thermally etched to expose the grain structure and then analyzed using a Jeol 840A Scanning Electron Microscope. The dielectric properties were measured using a coaxial reentrant cavity (Fig. 1)[6]. This cavity consists of a cylindrical cavity with a center conductor that allows insertion of a specimen for dielectric testing into an adjustable gap. Because the electric field in the sample is parallel to the sample's cylindrical axis, the permittivity is measured in that direction. This method is subject to depolarization effects in any air gaps between the sample and the center conductor posts. Hence the top and bottom surfaces of the sample under test must be metallized. Coaxial reentrant cavities may be used effectively over the frequency range between 100 MHz and 1 GHz depending on specimen and cavity dimensions and specimen permittivity. With proper sample preparation, real relative permittivities as high as 600 have been measured with this resonant system. An estimated upper limit on the uncertainty in dielectric loss tangent evaluation is approximately $5 \times 10^{-5}$.

Table I. Sample Code Key

| Sample Code | Weight %BaSrTiO$_3$ | Weight % MgO | Ba$_{0.55}$Sr$_{0.45}$TiO$_3$ Synthesis Method | MgO Synthesis Method |
|---|---|---|---|---|
| 5560 | 40 | 60 | Ferro – Solid Calcine | Alfa – Solid Calcine |
| H5560 | 40 | 60 | TPL - Hydrothermal | Alfa – Solid Calcine |
| 55H60 | 40 | 60 | Ferro – Solid Calcine | Nantek - Solgel |
| H55H60 | 40 | 60 | TPL - Hydrothermal | Nantek - Solgel |
| Tapecast | 40 | 60 | Ferro – Solid Calcine | Alfa – Solid Calcine |

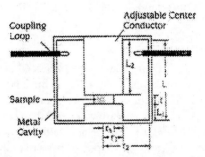

Fig. 1. Typical coaxial reentrant cavity for rf dielectric measurements. For a resonant frequency of 1 GHz, $r_1$=7.25 mm, $r_2$=25 mm, and L=60 mm.

RESULTS AND DISCUSSION

The results from the sintering studies are tabulated in Table 2. The surface area for the hydrothermally processed Ba$_{0.55}$Sr$_{0.45}$TiO$_3$ was more than double that of the solid-state calcined powder. However, the hydrothermal powder compacted to slightly lower green densities due to agglomeration and adsorbed water. The maximum sintered density for most samples in the study occurred at 1450°C. However, when both the Ba$_{0.55}$Sr$_{0.45}$TiO$_3$ and MgO powders were nanosized, the maximum sintered density increased and the sintering temperature reduced to 1350°C. Samples that were tape cast rather than dried press reached a 9.5% higher density with the same sintering profile. BET analysis revealed that most of the energy available due to the higher surface area in the nanosized powders was exhausted after about 1000°C. Figure 3 contains comparisons of the grain size distribution as a function of powder synthesis method and sintering temperature for different composites. The corresponding microstructures are shown in Figures 4 and 5. As is evident from the data, at 1250°C samples prepared with the higher surface area powder exhibited higher grain growth rates. The H55H60 and H5560 grain growth profiles nearly overlap for the BaSrTiO$_3$ although H55H60 has slightly lower overall MgO grain sizes. This trend holds true at 1350°C. By 1450°C, the solid-state calcined compacts begin to approach the grain size distributions of the higher surface area powders for the BaSrTiO$_3$ grains. However for the higher surface area compacts at this temperature, the MgO grain size increases significantly over the solid-state calcined compacts.

Table II. Sintering Study

| | Surface Area m$^2$/g | Green $\rho$ g/cm$^3$ | Sinter $\rho$ (%Open Porosity) | | |
|---|---|---|---|---|---|
| | | | 1250°C g/cm$^3$ | 1350°C g/cm$^3$ | 1450°C g/cm$^3$ |
| 5560 | 8.4 | 2.27 | 2.60 (32) | 3.62 (13) | 4.14 (0.1) |
| H5560 | 18.1 | 2.00 | 3.76 (11) | 3.70 (10) | 4.11 (0.1) |
| 55H60 | 3.1 | 2.16 | 2.55 (22) | 3.69 (6.1) | 4.11 (0.0) |
| H55H60 | 14.8 | 2.18 | 4.12 (5.9) | 4.52 (0.7) | 4.49 (0.3) |
| Tapecast | 8.4 | 2.16 | | | 4.50 (0.5) |

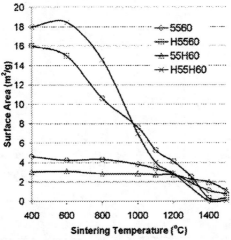

Fig. 2. BET Analysis of Compacts Sintered at Different Temperatures

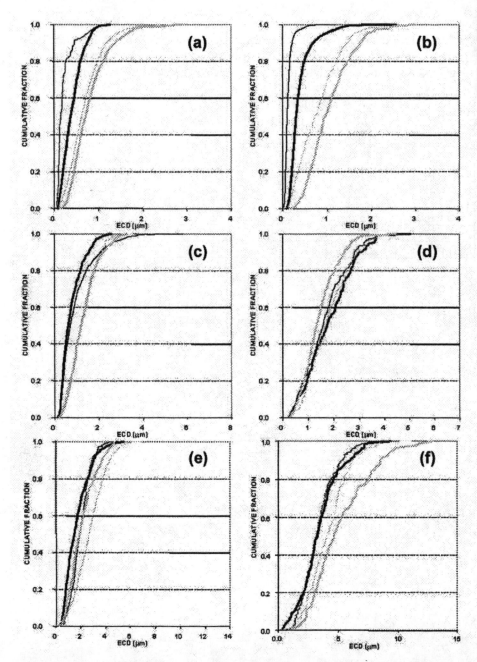

Fig. 3. BaSrTiO$_3$ and MgO Grain Size Distributions as a function of starting powder and sintering temperature. a) BST, 1250°C b) MgO, 1250°C c) BST, 1350°C (d) MgO, 1350°C e) BST, 1450°C f) MgO, 1450°C

——— 5560 ·········· H55H60 ═══ 55H60 ▓▓▓▓ H5560

Fig. 4. Microstructural evolution of 40 wt% $Ba_{0.55}Sr_{0.45}TiO_3$ / 60 wt% MgO composites prepared with solid-state calcined powders. Dark phase is MgO. Light phase is $BaSrTiO_3$

Fig. 5. Effect of starting powder on microstructural development at 1350°C

Table III. Coaxial Reentrant Cavity Measurements

| | Temp (°C) | $\rho$ (g/cc) | Grain Size BST/MgO (µm) | Frequency (MHz) | $\varepsilon_R$ | $\varepsilon_R/\rho$ | tan$\delta$ |
|---|---|---|---|---|---|---|---|
| 5560 | 1250 | 2.60 | 0.241 / 0.127 | 547 | 17 | 6.5 | 0.00507 |
| 5560 | 1350 | 3.62 | 1.001 / 1.700 | 453 | 29 | 8.0 | 0.00455 |
| 5560 | 1450 | 4.14 | 1.969 / 3.381 | 260 | 108 | 26 | 0.00217 |
| H5560 | 1250 | 3.76 | 0.801 / 1.052 | 330 | 67 | 18 | 0.00233 |
| H5560 | 1350 | 3.7 | 1.330 / 1.437 | 364 | 51 | 14 | 0.00162 |
| H5560 | 1450 | 4.11 | 2.081 / 5.343 | 261 | 105 | 26 | 0.00139 |
| 55H60 | 1250 | 2.55 | 0.420 / 0.381 | 526 | 20 | 8 | 0.00660 |
| 55H60 | 1350 | 3.69 | 0.775 / 1.834 | 458 | 30 | 8 | 0.00572 |
| 55H60 | 1450 | 4.11 | 1.669 / 3.454 | 272 | 103 | 25 | 0.00190 |
| H55H60 | 1250 | 4.12 | 0.701 / 0.796 | 184 | 228 | 55 | 0.00228 |
| H55H60 | 1350 | 4.52 | 1.277 / 1.788 | 148 | 353 | 79 | 0.00175 |
| H55H60 | 1450 | 4.49 | 2.750 / 4.213 | 147 | 356 | 79 | 0.00154 |

Correlating the microwave measurements listed in table III with the density and microstructure, two trends are clear. As expected from the dielectric mixing rules for air and dielectric, as the density increased, the permittivity also increased. However, after compensating for density it is clear that as the grain size decreases to less than 1 micron, the permittivity decreases dramatically. The second trend that is apparent is that as the grain size decreases, the dielectric loss increases. Dielectric loss is due to the delay in the polarization response and energy dissipation from conversion of momentum energy of charged carriers into heat during collisions with the polycrystalline matrix. Therefore, it is expected that as the grain size decreases, the polarization response and hence both the permittivity and dielectric loss become sensitive to the compressive stresses at the interface which resist the realignment of the ferroelectric dipoles. Because the differing nature of the powder processing methods resulted in different contamination levels, adsorbed species, and relative BaSrTiO3 / MgO grain size, it was not possible to draw any concrete conclusions from the microwave properties of compacts with approximately the same sintered density but differing grain size.

CONCLUSIONS

A processing study was conducted to determine the effect of using wet chemically processed powders in place of solid state calcined powder on the microstructural evolution at different temperatures during the sintering schedule. This information was correlated with coaxial reentrant microwave measurements to determine the structure-processing relationship. BET analysis showed that most of the free energy available due to the higher surface area was exhausted by 1100°C. This resulted in higher overall sintered densities and larger grain growth. The grain growth distribution curves showed that the higher surface area powders had significantly larger average BaSrTiO3 grain sizes until 1450°C at which point growth leveled off and the driving force for MgO grain growth increased. For compacts sintered at different temperatures from the same starting powders, it is clear that as the grain size decreases, the permittivity decreases and the dielectric loss increases. This is consistent with the literature and may be the result of interfacial stresses resisting the realignment of the ferroelectric dipoles.

REFERENCES
[1]J. Synowczynski, L. Sengupta, and L. Chiu, "Investigation of the Effect of Particle Size on the 10GHz Microwave Properties of $Ba_xSr_{1-x}TiO_3$ / MgO Composites," *J. of Integrated Ferroelectrics*, **22** 341-52 (1998).
[2] L. Sengupta, J. Synowczynski, and E. Ngo, "Fabrication and Characterization of Ferroelectric Composite Ceramics," *J. of Integrated Ferroelectrics*, **15** 181-190 (1997).
[3]W. Cao and C. Randall, "Grain Size and Domain Size Relations in Bulk Ceramic Ferroelectric Materials," *J. Phys. Chem. Solids*, **57** 1499-1505 (1996).
[4]W. Luan, L. Gao, and J. Guo, "Size Effect on Dielectric Properties of Fine-Grained BaTiO3 Ceramics," *Ceramics International*, **25** 727-729 (1999).
[5]G. Arlt, D. Hennings, and G. de With, "Dielectric Properties of Fine-Grained Barium Titanate Ceramics," *J. Appl. Phys.*, **58** (4) 1619–1625 (1985).

[6]R. G. Geyer, W. E. McKinzie, "RF Tunability Measurements of Ferroelectric Materials with a Coaxial Reentrant Cavity," *Dielectric Materials and Devices, Proc. American Ceramic Society*, 187-203 (2002).

# EFFECT OF Nb CONTENT ON THE STRUCTURE AND ELECTRICAL PROPERTIES OF Nb-DOPED BaTiO₃ CERAMICS

V.M.Mitic, Lj.M.Zivkovic and V.V.Paunovic
Faculty of Electronic Engineering, University of Nis,
Nis 18000,
Serbia and Montenegro

B.Jordovic
Technical Faculty, Cacak, University of Kragujevac,
Cacak 32000,
Serbia and Montenegro

ABSTRACT

$BaTiO_3$ ceramics doped with 0.5, 1.0 and 1.5wt% $Nb_2O_5$ were prepared and sintered at $1300^0C$ for two hours. The samples were previously pressed under different pressing pressure. The effects of Nb on $BaTiO_3$ microstructure and grain size distribution have been analyzed. The cumulative frequency curves showed a very narrow distribution for 1.0 and 1.5wt% $Nb_2O_5$ doped $BaTiO_3$ for pressing pressure of P=120MPa. In these samples grain size ranged from between 0.3-2μm. In 1.5 wt% $Nb_2O_5/BaTiO_3$ the regions reach in Nb have been detected. The measurements of capacitance and dielectric losses in function of frequency and temperature have been done in order to correlate the microstructure and dielectric properties of doped $BaTiO_3$ ceramics. It has been shown that the maximum capacitance has been noticed in 1.0 wt% $Nb_2O_5$ doped $BaTiO_3$ which is characterized by homogeneous microstructure. No change in capacitance vs. frequency, for frequency greater than 4kHz, has been detected in all of investigated samples. The Curie temperature is slightly shifted towards lower temperature than for undoped $BaTiO_3$. A relatively stable capacitance response in function of temperature has been noticed in 1.5wt% $Nb_2O_5/BaTiO_3$ samples.

## INTRODUCTION

A modified $BaTiO_3$ with different additives and dopants is the most extensively investigated dielectric material due to its attractive properties that can be used on a large scale of applications. The most commercial use is for multilayer capacitors, whereas $BaTiO_3$ with semiconducting properties is used widely in electronic devices such as thermistors, varistors and energy converting systems [1-3]. $BaTiO_3$ powder is usually mixed with additives in order to adjust the sintering parameters and electrical properties to the requirements of electronic devices. It has been found that the dielectric properties of polycrystalline $BaTiO_3$ depend in a great extent on the grain growth during sintering and on donor type and concentration [4-8]. The investigation of the grain growth is one of the most important subjects in $BaTiO_3$. To achieve a high dielectric constant a small-grained microstructure is needed, although a high PTC effect is noticed in bimodal microstructure. PTC effect also depends on grain size. According to B.K.Park at all [4] a coarse microstructure with grain size up to 55 μm exhibits a strong PTC effect and none is detected in small-grained microstructure with grain size around 1.5 μm. Stable dielectric properties, with a "flat" dielectric response in transition zone, could be obtained in suitable doped barium titanate ceramics with Nb and Bi that have a small grained microstructure. Among the additives, used to modify the dielectric and semiconducting properties, Nb has a special place because it can be incorporated in $BaTiO_3$ lattice as $Nb^{5+}$ at $Ti^{4+}$ site [8-12]. This substitution is charged compensated by a valence shift, providing a different donor levels in forbidden band, from which electrons can be exited into conduction band. A change of grain size and compensating defect mode, having different Nb-content, has been studied in Ref. 9. With a small amount of Nb, a defect mode of pure barium vacancies is more likely. With an increase of Nb-content another compensating defect mode, with a combination of titanium vacancies in grain interiors and barium vacancies at grain boundaries, can be used for explanation of semiconducting properties of $BaTiO_3$. The solubility of Nb depends on the sintering temperature and grain size. It has been reported that that up to solubility limit Nb makes a solid solution with $BaTiO_3$, above solubility limit Nb segregates at grain boundary regions [8]. Depending on the Nb-content and diffusion and reaction paths, nonequilibrium phases may be locally formed influencing densification and final microstructure. Moreover, the incorporation of Nb substituting titanium site may produce the titanium displacement out of grains, thus resulting the formation of liquid phase and change in microstructure.

The purpose of this paper was to analyze $BaTiO_3$ doped with various content of $Nb_2O_5$, previously pressed under different initial pressing pressure. The influence of dopant on the microstructure, capacitance and dielectric losses in function of frequency and temperature has been investigated.

## EXPERIMENTAL

Nb doped BaTiO₃ samples were prepared by conventional mixed oxides technology. Commercial grade $BaTiO_3$ and $Nb_2O_5$ powders were mixed in isopropyl alcohol, dried for several hours before being pressed into pellets under pressing pressure of P = 86, 105 and 120 MPa. The content of 0.5, 1.0 and 1.5 wt% $Nb_2O_5$ were used in this investigation. The pellets denote as IA1, IA2, IA3 refer to 0.5, 1.0, 1.5wt% $Nb_2O_3$ for pressing pressure of 86MPa. The pellets denote as IB1, IB2, IB3 and IC1, IC2, IC3 refer to pressing pressure of 105MPa and 120MPa. The pellets were sintered in air atmosphere in tunnel type furnace at $1300^0C$ for two hours. Microstructural analysis was performed using SEM JEOL 5300 equipped with energy dispersive spectrometer (EDS) system. The grain size distribution and porosity measurements were done by LEICA Q500 MC, Image Processing and Analysis system. The capacitance and loss tangent were measured using HP 4276 LCZ meter in frequency range 1-20 kHz. The variation of capacitance with temperature was measured at temperatures from $20^0C$ to $200^0C$.

## RESULTS AND DISCUSSION

Figure 1. shows the cumulative frequency vs. grain size for Nb/BaTiO₃ pressed under different initial pressure for 0.5-1.5wt%Nb₂O₅. At low pressing pressure no difference in grain size distribution can be observed in respect of Nb-content and grain size ranged from between 1-20μm (Fig.1a).

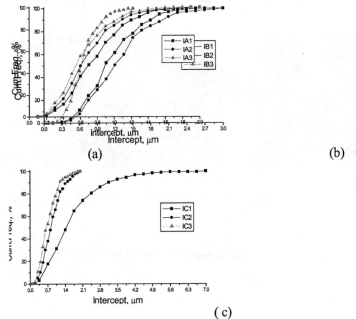

(a)                                    (b)

( c )

Figure 1. Cumulative frequency vs. grain size for Nb/BaTiO₃ for different pressing pressure a) 86MPa, b) 105MP, c) 120MPa.

Sintering density was very low up to 70% of theoretical density. The relatively low sintering temperature and short time of sintering was not enough to provoke a difference in grain size for various content of Nb. At higher pressing pressure and greater sintering density (75% of TD) the exaggerated grain growth is inhibited and generally small grain size can be obtained ranged from 0.3-3 μm ( Fig.1b). For pressing pressure of P=120MPa and sintering density of 80% TD, a narrow cumulative frequency vs. grain size for 1 and 1.5wt% of $Nb_2O_5$ with grain size up to 2 μm can be noticed (Fig 1c).

The microstructures of $BaTiO_3$ doped with 0.5, 1.0 and 1.5wt% $Nb_2O_5$ (P=120MPa) were shown in Fig.2. As can be seen, the microstructure reveals a high percentage of porosity. Two distinguish microstructural regions can be observed in samples with 1.5 wt% content of $Nb_2O_5$, (Fig.2c,2d).

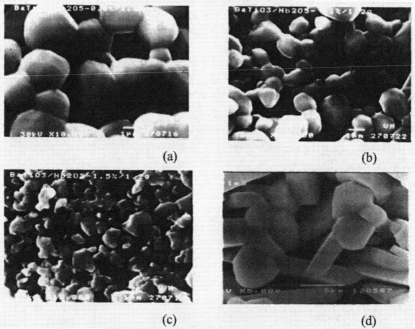

(a)          (b)

(c)          (d)

Figure 2. SEM microstructures of $BaTiO_3$ doped with (a) 0.5, (b) 1.0 and (c and d) 1.5wt% $Nb_2O_5$.

The first one, with a very fine small grained microstructure, with grain size from between 1-3 μm and the other one, with a rod like grains, with high aspect ratio such as 5. SEM microstructures given in Fig.2c and 2d were taken from the same sample.

The non uniform microstructure pointed out that the dopant was not homogeneously distributed among the particles of $BaTiO_3$. Two distinguish regions differ not only in grain size but as well as in phase composition. It is worth

Ceramic Materials and Multilayer Electronic Devices

to say that the concentration of Nb content less than 1 wt% could not be detected by energy dispersive spectrometer unless an inhomogeneous distribution and segregation of dopant is present. The EDS spectra taken from these two regions are presented in Fig.3.

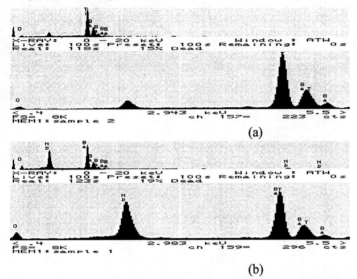

(a)

(b)

Figure 3. EDS spectrum of Nb-doped BaTiO$_3$, (a) taken from region given in Fig. 2c, (b) taken from region given in Fig. 2d

Nb reach region (Fig. 3b) is localized in area were rod like grains are present. In ceramics with content lower than 1.5 wt% Nb$_2$O$_5$, no considerable difference in EDS spectra along the specimen was detected. Bearing in mind that, in donor doped BaTiO$_3$, a diffusion of charged species and dissolution and precipitation occur simultaneously, it is for believe, that both of this processes affect in a great extent the microstructure.

One of the most important properties of BaTiO$_3$ is the permittivity. BaTiO$_3$ ceramics usually display a high dielectric constant at room temperature, but there is a variation, which is strongly dependent on microstructure, porosity, and dopant concentration and distribution. The microstructure analysis together with EDS analysis can be used to explain the capacitance and dielectric losses behavior.

The capacitance behavior in function of frequency (Fig.4) shows that, after insignificant low initial decrease in capacitance at low frequency, the capacitance became constant for frequency f= 4kHz. The highest value of capacitance has been obtained in 1 wt% Nb$_2$O$_5$/BaTiO$_3$ samples which are characterized by uniform microstructure in contrast to the other specimens with nonuniform microstructure.

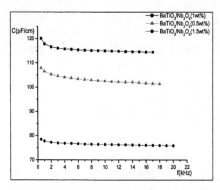

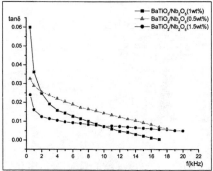

Figure 4. Capacitance vs. frequency   Figure 5. Dielectric losses vs. frequency

Regarding the dissipation losses, a liner decrease vs. frequency is measured for all investigated samples, although the greatest difference (Fig.5) is also detected in 1 wt% $Nb_2O_5/BaTiO_3$ sample. The corresponding curve for this sample could be separated into two regions with a change in linearity at f=4 kHz. The contribution from microstructure and corresponding Nb content on dielectric properties can be also analyzed through capacitance-temperature curves, (Fig.6).

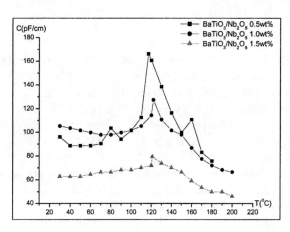

Figure 6. Capacitance vs. temperature

In 1.5 wt%Nb$_2$O$_5$/BaTiO$_3$ sample, where a chemically inhomogeneous system is formed, the overall dielectric behavior is governed by two different microstructural regions, thus leading to a temperature stable dielectric response (Fig.6). The "flatness" of this curve suggests that, besides the ferroelectric, the no ferroelectric regions are also present. Where a homogeneous material is formed the dielectric behavior is similar to that ones for polycrystalline BaTiO$_3$ ceramics with a shift of Curie temperature towards lower temperature.

CONCLUSION

In this paper the influence of different content of Nb$_2$O$_5$ on BaTiO$_3$ microstructure and dielectric properties has been done. The microstructure analysis showed the significant amount of porosity at sintering temperature of 1300$^0$C for two hours. With increasing of Nb$_2$O$_5$ content the exaggerated grains growth is inhibited, thus leading to relatively uniform microstructure. With 1.5wt% Nb$_2$O$_5$ two distinguish regions are formed, one with small grain size and second one with rod like grains reach in Nb. The change in capacitance with frequency, in the frequency region of 1-20 kHz, is negligible although a considerable change in tanδ in the same frequency region is observed. Due to different microstructure regions which differ not only in grain size but as well as in phase composition, a relatively stable capacitance response in function of temperature has been noticed in 1.5wt%Nb$_2$O$_5$/BaTiO$_3$ samples.

*Acknowledgements:* This research is the part of the project: "Synthesis of functional materials according to tetrad: synthesis-structure-properties-application" (No.1832). The authors gratefully acknowledge the financial support of Serbian Ministry for science technology and development for this work.

# REFERENCES

[1] W.Heywang, H.Thomann, "-Positive Temperature coefficient resistors", in *Electronic ceramics* London and New York,(1991).

[2] G.Artt, D.Hennings, G.de With, "Dielectric properties of fine grained barium titanate ceramics", *J.Appl. Phys.* 58 [4] pp.1619-1625 (1985).

[3] D.Hennings," Barium titanate based ceramics materials for dielectric use" *Int.J. High Technology Ceramics,* 3 pp.91-111 (1987).

[4] B.K.Park, J.H.Lee, D.Y.Kim, " Positive temperature coefficient of resistance effect in heavily niobium-doped barium titanate by the growth of the double – twinned seeds", *J.Am.Ceram.Soc,*84, pp.2707-2709 (2001).

[5] V.S.Tiwari,N.Singh, D.Pandey, "Structure and properties of (Ba,Ca)TiO₃ ceramics prepared using (Ba,Ca)CO₃ precursors: I, crystallographic and microstructural studies", *J.Am.Ceram.Soc,*77, pp.1205-1211,(1993).

[6] D.Markovec, N.Ule, M.Drofenik, " Positive temperature coefficient of resistivity effect in highly donor-doped barium titanate", *J.Am.Ceram.Soc,*84, pp.1273-1280,(2001).

[7] C.Metzmacher, K.Albertsen, " Microstructural investigation of barium titanate based material for base metal electrode ceramic multilayer capacitor", *J.Am.Ceram.Soc,*84, pp.821-826, (2001).

[8] K.Kowalski, M.Ijjaali, T.Bak, B.Dupre, J.Nowotny, M.Rekas, C.Sorrell, " Electrical properties of Nb-doped BaTiO₃", *Jour.of Phys. and Chem. of Solids* 62 pp. 543-551 (2001).

[9] T.B.Wu, J.N.Lin, "Transition of compensating defect mode in niobium doped barium titanate", *J.Am.Ceram.Soc,*77, pp.759-764, (1994).

[10] J.M.Wu, C.J.Chen, "Effect of powder characteristics on microstructures and dielectric properties of (Ba,Nb)- doped titanic ceramics", *J.Am.Ceram.Soc.* 73, pp.420-424, (1990).

[11] V.Mitic, I.Mitrovic, " The influence of Nb₂O₃ on BaTiO₃ ceramics dielectric properties", *Journal of the European Ceramic Society,* (2001).

[12] V.Mitic, I.Mitrovic, " The BaTiO₃ ceramics structure properties in function of Nb₂O₃ and CaZrO₃ additives", *Gordon Research Conference: Ceramics, Solid State Studies in Ceramics,* Kimball Union Academy, Meriden, New Hampshire, (2000).

# DIELECTRIC PROPERTIES OF NM-SIZED BARIUM TITANATE CRYSTALLITES WITH VARIOUS PARTICLE SIZES

Satoshi Wada, Hiroaki Yasuno, Takuya Hoshina, Song-Min Nam, Hirofumi Kakemoto and Takaaki Tsurumi
Tokyo Institute of Technology
Department of Metallurgy and Ceramics Science
2-12-1 Ookayama, Meguro, Tokyo 152-8552, JAPAN

## ABSTRACT

In this study, barium titanate ($BaTiO_3$) crystallites with various particle sizes from 17 nm to 100 nm were prepared by the 2-step thermal decomposition method of barium titanyl oxalate ($BaTiO(C_2O_4)_2 \cdot 4H_2O$). The crystal structure of these $BaTiO_3$ particles was assigned to cubic $m3m$ by a XRD measurement while that was assigned to tetragonal $4mm$ by a Raman scattering measurement. This difference was similar to a behavior observed just above Curie temperature for $BaTiO_3$ single crystals. Investigation of impurity in these particles using both TG-DTA and FT-IR measurements revealed that no impurity was detected in $BaTiO_3$ lattice while the hydroxyl and carbonate group were detected only on the surface of these particles. Moreover, Ba/Ti atomic ratio was almost 1.00 and these relative densities were over 97 % despite of particle sizes. The dielectric constants of these powders were measured using slurry by a modified powder dielectric measurement method. As a result, the dielectric constant of $BaTiO_3$ particles with a size around 70 nm exhibited a dielectric maximum over 15 000. This study revealed the existence of the size effect for $BaTiO_3$ particles, and $BaTiO_3$ particles with around 70 nm were the most desirable for a capacitor application.

## INTRODUCTION

Ferroelectric $BaTiO_3$ fine particles have been used as raw materials for electronic devices such as multilayered ceramic capacitors (MLCC). Recently, with the miniaturization of electronic devices, the down-sizing of MLCC has been

---

developed and accelerated. As a result, it is expected that the thickness of dielectric layers in MLCC will become less than 0.5 μm. Consequently, the particle size of the required $BaTiO_3$ raw materials will decrease from a few hundred nm to a few ten nm. However, in ferroelectric fine particles, it was known that ferroelectricity decreases with decreasing particle and grain sizes, and disappears below certain critical sizes; this is called the "size effect" in ferroelectrics.[1-7] Therefore, the size effect in ferroelectrics such as $BaTiO_3$ is one of the most important phenomena for an interest of the industry and science. To date, some researchers have estimated the critical size to be around 10~20 nm in $BaTiO_3$ fine particles.[7-9] This critical size is just an estimated value, and there is no experimental evidence on the critical size. Thus, it is very important to prepare $BaTiO_3$ ferroelectric crystals with sizes below the estimated critical size, and investigate their size effect. For this purpose, the following two solutions must be required. One is to develop a new preparation method for the impurity-free and nm-sized $BaTiO_3$ crystallites, and the other is to establish a new measurement method of the dielectric constants using the powders.

Recently, to prepare impurity-free and nm-sized $BaTiO_3$ crystallites, a new method was proposed.[10] This method was called as a 2-step thermal decomposition method of $BaTiO(C_2O_4)_2 \cdot 4H_2O$. This method was composed of the following two steps. The 1st step is the thermal treatment of $BaTiO(C_2O_4)_2 \cdot 4H_2O$ at around 400 °C for 1 hour under $O_2$ flow for the purpose of the removal of carbon species. The 2nd step is the formation of the fine $BaTiO_3$ crystallites by the thermal treatment at various temperatures over 600 °C in the vacuum. As a typical case, the fine $BaTiO_3$ crystallites with a size of about 16.5 nm were obtained by the treatment at 600 °C for 0.5 hour in the vacuum. Moreover, their characterization revealed that there was no impurity in the lattices of $BaTiO_3$ crystallites with 16.5 nm. If temperatures of the 2nd step will be changed from 600 °C to 1000 °C, we can easily control the particle sizes from 16.5 nm to 100 nm.

On the other hand, it is also known that it is too difficult to measure the dielectric constant of the powders. Wakino et al. reported the dielectric measurement of the powders using compact,[11] but after this, there has been few report about powder dielectric measurement. Recently, a new powder dielectric measurement method was proposed using a suspension (slurry).[12] This system was composed of two procedures i.e., (1) a dielectric measurement of slurry and (2) a calculation of a composite model by a finite element method (FEM). Using this method, the dielectric constant of tetragonal $BaTiO_3$ particles with a size of 500 nm was estimated as around 3 000 while that of cubic $SrTiO_3$ particles with a size of 300 nm was estimated as around 270. These values were almost consisted with the expected values of their single crystals. Thus, using this

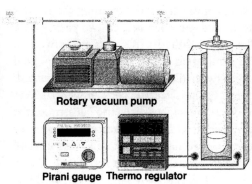

**Rotary vacuum pump**

**Pirani gauge** **Thermo regulator**

Fig. 1 A schematic diagram for the preparation system.

powder dielectric measurement method, the dielectric constants of BaTiO$_3$ particles with various particle sizes can be estimated.

In this study, the objective is to clear the particle size dependence of the dielectric constants of BaTiO$_3$ particles. For this objective, BaTiO$_3$ particles with various particle sizes from 17 nm to 100 nm were prepared by the 2-step thermal decomposition method, and the commercial BaTiO$_3$ powders were also used as samples. Moreover, the powder dielectric measurement method was modified to measure high dielectric constants over 10 000.

EXPERIMENTAL PROCEDURES

Sample Preparation and Characterization

BaTiO(C$_2$O$_4$) $_2$•4H$_2$O were prepared by Fuji Titanium Co., Ltd. Its Ba/Ti atomic ratio was 1.000 and the amount of the impurity was less than 0.02 %. The details were described elsewhere.[13] Using BaTiO(C$_2$O$_4$) $_2$•4H$_2$O powders, BaTiO$_3$ crystallites with various particle sizes were prepared by the 2-step thermal decomposition method. Figure 1 shows a schematic diagram for the preparation system. At first, the thermal decomposition at the 1$^{st}$ step was performed at 500 °C for 1 hour in air, and resulted in the formation of the intermediate compounds with almost amorphous structure. At the following 2$^{nd}$ step, this compound was calcined at various temperatures from 600 °C to 1000 °C in vacuum, and resulted in the formation of the white-colored BaTiO$_3$ powders. These powders were characterized using the following methods. The crystal structure of the products was investigated using a powder X-ray diffractometer (XRD) (RINT2000, Rigaku, Cu-k$\alpha$, 50 kV, 30 mA) and a laser Raman scattering spectrometer (Raman) (NRS-2100, Jusco, 514 nm, 100 mW). The average particle sizes and crystallite sizes were estimated using a transmission electron microscope (TEM) (CM300, Philips, 300 kV) and XRD. The impurity in the products was analyzed using a Fourier transform infrared spectrometer (FT-IR) (SYSTEM 2000 FT-IR, Perkin Elmer) and by differential thermal analysis with thermogravimetry (TG-DTA) (TG-DTA2000, Mac Science).

Powder Dielectric Measurement

Dielectric constant of the $BaTiO_3$ powders was measured by using the powder dielectric measurement method. This method was composed of two parts. One is the dielectric measurement using the slurry of the $BaTiO_3$ crystallites with an organic solvent, and the other is the simulation using the electrostatic field analysis of the FEM. In the previous powder dielectric measurement method, 1-propanol was used as a solvent.[12] However, its dielectric constant was 20.33 at 25.0 °C, and this value was too low to determine higher dielectric constant of the particles over 3 000. To estimate the dielectric constant of the particles over 10 000, a solvent with a dielectric constant over 50 must be required. As a result that new solvents with a dielectric constant over 50 were investigated, a new organic solvent was found. In this study, the 4-methyl-1,3-dioxol-2-one (propylene carbonate) was chosen as a organic solvent because of the following two reasons, i.e., (1) the dipolar non-HBD (Hydrogen-Bond Donor) solvent (this means that propylene carbonate is a harmless solvent for $BaTiO_3$ or $SrTiO_3$) and (2) the high dielectric constant of 66.50 at 20.0 °C. The $BaTiO_3$ crystallites were mixed with only propylene carbonate using the ball mill at a concentration of 10 vol%. After the mixing, this 10 vol% slurry was diluted to 4, 6 and 8 vol%. For the dielectric measurement using the slurry, a special attachment was designed and used. The dielectric property of the $BaTiO_3$ slurry was measured at 20.0 °C and 20 MHz using an impedance analyzer (Agilent, HP-4294A). On the other hand, for the simulation using the electrostatic field analysis of the FEM, the ANSYS/Emag3D software (ANSYS Inc., Revision 6.1) was used. At first, a schematic composite model for the $BaTiO_3$ slurry was considered. For the model, the following two assumptions were considered, i.e., (1) one sphere $BaTiO_3$ particle can be regarded as one semi-sphere made of a lot of tetrahedrons, and (2) one $BaTiO_3$ sphere must be surrounded by the propylene carbonate tetrahedrons (no contact between the $BaTiO_3$ spheres). Using these assumptions, the $BaTiO_3$ spheres were distributed randomly and homogeneously in the propylene carbonate matrix. In this model, a volume ratio of the $BaTiO_3$ spheres on the propylene carbonate tetrahedrons and a dielectric constant of the propylene carbonate tetrahedrons are the known values while only a dielectric constant of the $BaTiO_3$ spheres is the unknown value. Thus, we assume a certain value as a dielectric constant of the unknown $BaTiO_3$ spheres. Finally, the measured dielectric constant of the $BaTiO_3$ slurry was compared with the calculated dielectric constant of the $BaTiO_3$ slurry. When these two values becomes to same one, the dielectric constant of the $BaTiO_3$ crystallites can be determined. Through this manuscript, this method is called as a powder dielectric measurement method.

RESULTS AND DISCUSSION

Fig. 2   A TEM bright field image for A-1 sample.

Preparation and Characterization of BaTiO$_3$ Crystallites with Various Sizes

At first, we try to prepare impurity-free and nm-sized BaTiO$_3$ crystallites using the 2-step thermal decomposition method. At the 1$^{st}$ step, BaTiO(C$_2$O$_4$)$_2$•4H$_2$O was annealed at 500 °C for 1 hour in air, and then resulted in the formation of white-colored powders. These XRD showed that though several unknown broad peaks were observed, the most of the products were assigned to the amorphous phase. These unknown peaks can be assigned to (1) Ba$_2$Ti$_2$O$_5$•CO$_3$ phase reported by Kumar et al.[14] or (2) Ba$_2$Ti$_2$O$_5$ phase reported by Cho[15]. A weight loss at the 1$^{st}$ step was almost 38.3 % and this value supported that the unknown compound should be assigned to Ba$_2$Ti$_2$O$_5$•CO$_3$ phase. Using the intermediate compounds, the next thermal decomposition was performed under the vacuum. At the 2$^{nd}$ step, calcination temperatures were changed from 600 °C to 1 000 °C for 1 hour. The BaTiO$_3$ powders calcined at 660, 760, 840 and 860 °C under the vacuum were named as A-1, A-2, A-3 and A-4, respectively. On the other hands, the BaTiO$_3$ powders calcined at 860 °C in air were named as A-5. Moreover, we also prepared the BaTiO$_3$ powders by a normal thermal decomposition of BaTiO(C$_2$O$_4$)$_2$•4H$_2$O over 1 000 °C, and named as B-1.

Figure 2 shows a TEM bright field image for A-1 sample. This TEM observation revealed that an average particle size of A-1 was around 17.0 nm, and one particle was also a single crystal. Moreover, its selected area electron diffraction (SAED) pattern revealed that its crystal structure was assigned to cubic BaTiO$_3$ phase. Similar TEM observation was performed for A-2, A-3, A-4, A-5 and B-1 samples. As a result, their average particle sizes were estimated at 33.0, 59.0, 68.0, 102 and 400 nm, respectively.

Figure 3 shows the XRD patterns of these powders. As described in the previous report[10], in the XRD pattern for the products calcined below 700 °C, a trace of hexagonal BaTiO$_3$ phase was observed as the 2$^{nd}$ phase while most of the products were cubic BaTiO$_3$ phase. On the other hands, the XRD patterns for

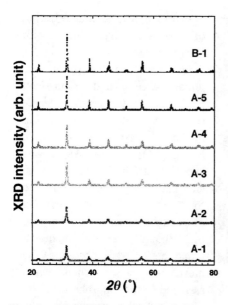

Fig. 3 The XRD patterns of these BaTiO₃ powders.

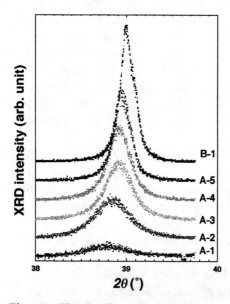

Fig. 4 The BaTiO₃ (111) plane of these BaTiO₃ powders.

the products calcined above 700 °C revealed that there was a cubic BaTiO₃ single phase. However, at present, it is not clear that this cubic phase is true cubic *m-3m* symmetry or tetragonal *4mm* symmetry with a *c/a* ratio closed to 1.00. These crystallite sizes ($d_{111}$) and lattice constants (*a*-axis) were also estimated from the FWHM and peak position of BaTiO₃ (111) plane. Figure 4 indicates the BaTiO₃ (111) plane for these BaTiO₃ powders. The FWHM of BaTiO₃ (111) plane decreased and the peak top of BaTiO₃ (111) plane shifted to higher angles with increasing calcination temperatures. This means that the $d_{111}$ increased from 17.4 nm to 56.2 nm and the *a*-axis shrank from 402.3 pm to 400.6 pm with increasing calcination temperatures from 660 to 860 °C. In this study, we also used some commercial BaTiO₃ powders from Sakai Chemical Industry Co., Ltd., *i.e.*, BT-03 (BaTiO₃ powders with 300 nm) and BT-05 powders (BaTiO₃ powders with 500 nm). Figure 5 shows the particle size dependence of the *a*-axis and *c*-axis. This result suggests that the average and static crystal symmetry below 150 nm becomes to cubic *m-3m* while that over 150 nm becomes to tetragonal *4mm*.

Figure 6 exhibits the Raman scattering spectra for these BaTiO₃ powders. Raman scattering measurement can clear the local and dynamic symmetry. Despite of calcination temperature, the local

Ceramic Materials and Multilayer Electronic Devices

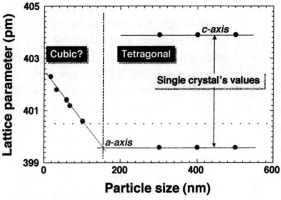

Fig. 5 The particle size dependence of the *a*-axis and *c*-axis for the BaTiO$_3$ powders.

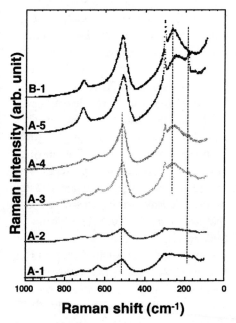

Fig. 6 The Raman scattering spectra of these BaTiO$_3$ powders.

symmetries of these BaTiO$_3$ powders were assigned to tetragonal *4mm* symmetry. However, in the BaTiO$_3$ powders calcined below 860 °C, one peak was observed at around 640 cm$^{-1}$, and assigned to hexagonal BaTiO$_3$ phase. In this study, for the BaTiO$_3$ powders below 100 nm, an average crystal structure was assigned to cubic phase by XRD while the local structure was also assigned to tetragonal by Raman. This difference was similar to a behavior observed just above Curie temperature (133 °C) for BaTiO$_3$ single crystals.[16] This similarity suggests that the size effect of BaTiO$_3$ crystallites can be one of the ferroelectric phase transitions.

For the BaTiO$_3$ fine particles, it is known that the effects of defect structure and impurity on the crystal structures and properties were very significant. Thus, it is very important to investigate the impurity in these particles using FT-IR and TG- DTA measurements. Figure 7 shows the FT-IR spectra of these BaTiO$_3$ powders. Just two kinds of impurities were observed, *i.e.*, the hydroxyl group (OH$^-$) and carbonate group (CO$_3^-$), and the amount of OH$^-$ and CO$_3^-$ groups decreased with increasing particle sizes. On the other hands, TG-DTA measurement for A-1 sample indicated the weight loss of 5.4 % up to 800 °C, but when this measurement was stopped at 600 °C and the same measurement was repeated after cooling in air, the almost same weight loss was

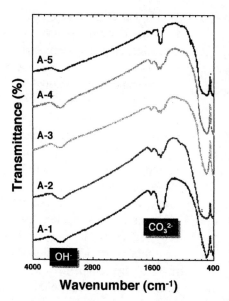

**Fig. 7** The FT-IR spectra of these BaTiO₃ powders.

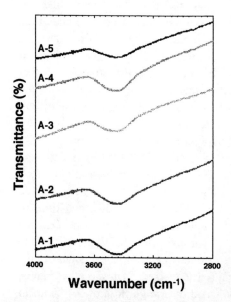

**Fig. 8** The FT-IR spectra of the OH⁻ group for these BaTiO₃ powders.

observed. This suggests that this weight loss was caused by desorption of the adsorbed species. Figure 8 exhibits the FT-IR spectra of the OH⁻ group for these BaTiO₃ powders. If there is a lattice OH⁻ group in the BaTiO₃ lattices, a sharp absorption band of the lattice OH⁻ group must appear at around 3 500 cm⁻¹. In the hydrothermal BaTiO₃ powders, a sharp band was always observed at 3 500 cm⁻¹. However, in Fig. 8, there was no sharp band around 3 500 cm⁻¹. This supported the TG-DTA results which there was just adsorbed species such as surface OH⁻ and surface CO₃⁻ groups. Now, we believe that the 2-step thermal decomposition method is enough effective to prepare nm-sized and impurity-free BaTiO₃ particles.

We also measured the density and a Ba/Ti atomic ratio for the BaTiO₃ particles prepared in this study. Table I shows these results. The absolute density of the BaTiO₃ powders was measured using a pycnometer, and the relative density was calculated using a theoretical density estimated from *a*-axis by the XRD measurement. The relative density of all BaTiO₃ particles was over 97 %, and this revealed that there was few physical defects such as voids. On the other hands, the Ba/Ti atomic ratios for the BaTiO₃ particles were determined by using the X-ray fluorescence analysis. Their Ba/Ti ratio was always 1.00, and these results suggest that these BaTiO₃ particles may be defect-free materials.

Up to date, it has been considered

Table I. The density and a Ba/Ti atomic ratio for the BaTiO$_3$ particles prepared in this study.

|  | A-1 | A-2 | A-3 | A-4 | A-5 | B-1 |
|---|---|---|---|---|---|---|
| $d$ (g/cm³) | 5.78 | 5.85 | 5.90 | 5.91 | 5.88 | 5.91 |
| Relative $d$ (%) | 97.3 | 97.9 | 98.6 | 98.5 | 97.6 | 98.2 |
| Ba/Ti ratio | 1.00 | 1.00 | 1.00 | 1.00 | 1.00 | 1.00 |

that it is too difficult to prepare nm-sized, impurity-free and defect-free BaTiO$_3$ particles. However, the BaTiO$_3$ particles prepared by the 2-step thermal decomposition method of BaTiO(C$_2$O$_4$) $_2$•4H$_2$O have very excellent properties such as nm-sized, impurity-free and defect-free.
Therefore, this means that we can obtain the desirable materials for the investigation of the size effect.

Modification of the Powder Dielectric Measurement

The previous powder dielectric measurement was modified to determine the higher dielectric constants of the BaTiO$_3$ crystallites over 10 000. In the previous powder dielectric measurement method, 1-propanol was used as a solvent, but in this study, propylene carbonate with the high dielectric constant of 66.50 at 20.0 °C was used as a solvent. At first, to confirm the validity of the modified powder dielectric measurement, the ST-03 (SrTiO$_3$ powder with 300 nm) and the BT-05 powders (Sakai Chemical Co.) were used as the references. The average dielectric constant of an ideal paraelectric SrTiO$_3$ single crystal and ideal ferroelectric BaTiO$_3$ single crystal is expected as 310 and 2,980 (= $(2\varepsilon_a + \varepsilon_c)/2$, $\varepsilon_a$=4 400, $\varepsilon_c$=129)[17], respectively. Figure 9 indicates the frequency dependence of the capacitance of the BT-05 slurry with various powder contents from 0 to 10 vol%. The extremely large peaks

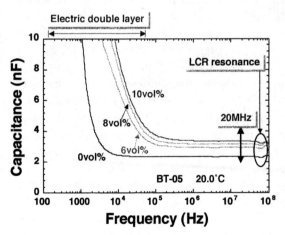

Fig. 9 The frequency dependence of the capacitance of the BT-05 slurry with various powder contents from 0 to 10 vol%.

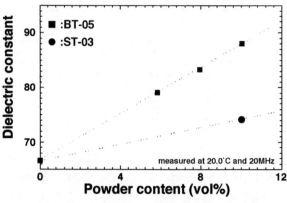

Fig. 10 The dielectric measurement results using their slurry of ST-03 and BT-05.

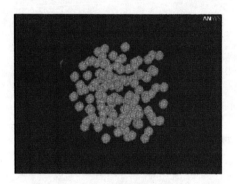

Fig. 11 The optimized model made of BaTiO₃ tetrahedrons.

below 100 kHz were assigned to the electric double layer while the resonance peaks above 40 MHz were assigned to the electric LCR resonance of the measurement system itself. Thus, the dielectric constants of the slurry were estimated using the capacitance measured at 20 MHz. Moreover, the control of a measurement temperature is also very important to measure an accurate capacitance. In this study, the measurement was always done in the thermostatic bath kept at 20.0 °C.

Figure 10 shows the dielectric measurement results using their slurry of ST-03 and BT-05. The slope of the lines in Fig. 10 is proportional to the dielectric constant. These results must be fitted by the FEM calculation using the optimized model as described in the experimental procedure. For example, Fig. 11 exhibits the optimized model made of tetrahedron. In this model, 140 BaTiO₃ spheres made of a lot of tetrahedrons were distributed homogeneously and randomly. Using this model, the relation of dielectric constants between slurry and powder was estimated as shown in Fig. 12. This result suggests that using the modified powder dielectric measurement, we can estimate the dielectric constants of the powders up to 30 000.

As the result that the FEM was applied for the result of Fig. 10, the dielectric constants of ST-03 and BT-05 powders were determined at 183±1 and 3 320±10, respectively. The dielectric constant for ST-03 powders was a little lower value than the expected one while that for BT-05 powders was the almost same as the expected one. Therefore, it is clear that the powder dielectric measurement modified in this study is very effective to determine the higher dielectric constants

Ceramic Materials and Multilayer Electronic Devices

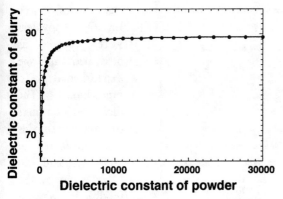

**Dielectric constant of powder**

Fig. 12 The relation of dielectric constants between slurry and powder calculated by FEM using the model (Fig. 11).

of the $BaTiO_3$ powders.

Particle Size Dependence of Dielectric Constants of the $BaTiO_3$ Crystallites

First of all, Table II summarizes the characterization results for the $BaTiO_3$ powders prepared in this study and the commercial powders such as BT-03 and BT-05. It should be noted that all $BaTiO_3$ powders in Table II are almost defect-free and impurity-free particles. The

Table II. The characterization results of the $BaTiO_3$ particles prepared in this study and the commercial $BaTiO_3$ particles.

| Sample No. | Symmetry | Composition | Density | Size | Impurity |
|---|---|---|---|---|---|
| A-1 | XRD: $Pm\bar{3}m$<br>Raman: $P4mm$ | Ba/Ti: 1.00 | 5.78 g/cm$^{-3}$<br>>97.3 % | 17.0nm | lattice: negligible<br>surface: OH$^-$, CO$_3^{2-}$ |
| A-2 | XRD: $Pm\bar{3}m$<br>Raman: $P4mm$ | Ba/Ti: 1.00 | 5.85 g/cm$^{-3}$<br>>97.9 % | 33.0nm | lattice: negligible<br>surface: OH$^-$, CO$_3^{2-}$ |
| A-3 | XRD: $Pm\bar{3}m$<br>Raman: $P4mm$ | Ba/Ti: 1.00 | 5.90 g/cm$^{-3}$<br>>98.6 % | 59.0nm | lattice: negligible<br>surface: OH$^-$, CO$_3^{2-}$ |
| A-4 | XRD: $Pm\bar{3}m$<br>Raman: $P4mm$ | Ba/Ti: 1.00 | 5.91 g/cm$^{-3}$<br>>98.5 % | 68.0nm | lattice: negligible<br>surface: OH$^-$, CO$_3^{2-}$ |
| A-5 | XRD: $Pm\bar{3}m$<br>Raman: $P4mm$ | Ba/Ti: 1.00 | 5.88 g/cm$^{-3}$<br>>97.6 % | 102nm | lattice: negligible<br>surface: OH$^-$, CO$_3^{2-}$ |
| BT-03 | XRD: $P4mm$<br>Raman: $P4mm$ | Ba/Ti: 1.00 | 5.92 g/cm$^{-3}$<br>>98.5 % | 300nm | lattice: negligible<br>surface: OH$^-$, CO$_3^{2-}$ |
| BT-05 | XRD: $P4mm$<br>Raman: $P4mm$ | Ba/Ti: 1.00 | 5.94 g/cm$^{-3}$<br>>98.9 % | 500nm | lattice: negligible<br>surface: OH$^-$, CO$_3^{2-}$ |
| B-1 | XRD: $P4mm$<br>Raman: $P4mm$ | Ba/Ti: 1.00 | 5.91 g/cm$^{-3}$<br>>98.2 % | 400nm | lattice: negligible<br>surface: OH$^-$, CO$_3^{2-}$ |

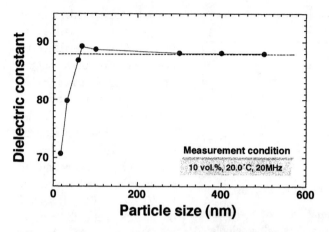

Fig. 13 The dielectric measurement results of these slurries.

slurries of these BaTiO$_3$ powders were prepared as described in the experimental procedure. The dielectric constants of these slurries were measured at 20.0 °C and 20 MHz using by the modified powder dielectric measurement method.

Figure 13 shows the dielectric measurement results of these slurries. This result indicated that the dielectric constants of BaTiO$_3$ slurries with sizes over 300 nm were almost constant at around 88.0 while the dielectric constants of BaTiO$_3$ slurries with sizes below 200 nm increased with decreasing particle sizes down to 70 nm. Moreover, the dielectric constants of BaTiO$_3$ slurries with sizes below 70 nm rapidly decreased with decreasing particle sizes. This result revealed that the BaTiO$_3$ slurry with a size around 70 nm possessed a maximum dielectric constant. This is a phenomenon found for the first time in the dielectric powders. Moreover, this result also suggests that the dielectric layer thickness for the future MLCC will be much thinner down to 100 nm using the BaTiO$_3$ powders with 50 ~ 80 nm.

The dielectric constants of these BaTiO$_3$ powders were estimated by the FEM calculation using the measured dielectric constants of BaTiO$_3$ slurries as shown in Fig. 13. Figure 14 exhibits the particle size dependence of the dielectric constants of these BaTiO$_3$ powders. This result indicated that the dielectric constants of BaTiO$_3$ powders with sizes over 300 nm were almost constant at around 3 300 while the dielectric constants of BaTiO$_3$ powders with sizes below 200 nm drastically increased with decreasing particle sizes down to 70 nm. The dielectric constant of BaTiO$_3$ particles with a size around 70 nm was a very high value around 15 000. Moreover, the dielectric constants of BaTiO$_3$ powders with sizes below 70 nm rapidly decreased with decreasing particle sizes. The high dielectric constant of 15 000 is strongly dependence of the used model. Therefore, the value of 15 000 itself may be no meaning, but as described in the previous section, it is fact that the maximum dielectric constant was obtained at a

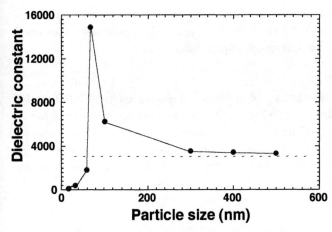

Fig. 14   The particle size dependence of the dielectric constants of these BaTiO₃ powders.

particle size around 70 nm. Now, it is very difficult to explain this reason. However, this study revealed the existence of the size effect for BaTiO₃ particles, and BaTiO₃ particles with a size around 70 nm were most desirable as capacitor materials. As the next step, this origin of the higher dielectric constants will be investigated as a function of frequency and temperature.

CONCLUSION

In this study, BaTiO₃ crystallites with various particle sizes from 17 nm to 100 nm were prepared by the 2-step decomposition method of BaTiO(C₂O₄)₂•4H₂O. The crystal structure of these BaTiO₃ particles was assigned to cubic *m3m* by a conventional XRD measurement while that was assigned to tetragonal *4mm* by a Raman scattering measurement. This difference was similar to a behavior observed just above Curie temperature for BaTiO₃ single crystals. Investigation of impurity in these particles using TG-DTA and FT-IR measurements revealed that no impurity was detected in BaTiO₃ lattice while only hydroxyl and carbonate group were detected only on the surface of these particles. Moreover, Ba/Ti atomic ratio was almost 1.00 despite of particle sizes, and these relative densities were over 97%. The dielectric constants of these particles were measured using a BaTiO₃ slurry by the modified powder dielectric measurement method. These dielectric measurements indicated that the dielectric constants of BaTiO₃ slurries over 300 nm were almost constant while below 200 nm, dielectric constants of BaTiO₃ slurries increased with decreasing particle sizes down to 70 nm. Moreover, the dielectric constants of BaTiO₃ slurries decreased with decreasing particle sizes below 70 nm. The dielectric constants of these BaTiO₃ particles were estimated by the FEM from the measured dielectric constants of BaTiO₃ slurries. As a result, the dielectric constant of BaTiO₃ particles showed a dielectric maximum over 15 000 at around 70 nm. This study revealed the existence of the size effect for $BaTiO_3$ particles, and $BaTiO_3$ particles with around 70 nm were very useful for the capacitor application.

ACKNOWLEDGMENTS
We would like to thank Mr. M. Nishido of Fuji Titanium Co., Ltd. for preparing high purity barium titanyl oxalates. We also would like to thank Mr. K. Abe of Sakai Chemical Industry Co., Ltd. for providing high purity BT-03, BT-05 and ST-03 powders. This study was partially supported by a Grant-in-Aid for Scientific Research (**12450267**) from the Ministry of Education, Science, Sports and Culture, Japan.

REFERENCES
[1]K. Kinoshita and A. Yamaji, "Grain-Size Effects on Dielectric Properties in Barium Titanate Ceramics," *Journal of Applied Physics*, **45** 371-373 (1976).
[2]G. Arlt, D. Hennings and G. De With, "Dielectric Properties of Fine-Grained Barium Titanate Ceramics," *Journal of Applied Physics*, **58** 1619-1625 (1985).
[3]K. Ishikawa, K. Yoshikawa and N. Okada, "Size Effect on the Ferroelectric Phase Transition in $PbTiO_3$ Ultrafine Particles," *Physical Review B*, **37** 5852-5855 (1988).
[4]K. Uchino, E. Sadanaga and T. Hirose, "Dependence of the Crystal Structure on Particle Size in Barium Titanate," *Journal of American Ceramic Society*, **72** 1555-1558 (1989).
[5]M. H. Frey and D. A. Payne, "Grain-Size Effect on Structure and Phase Transformations for Barium Titanate," *Physical Review B*, **54** 3158-3168 (1996).
[6]S. Wada, T. Suzuki and T. Noma, "Role of Lattice Defects in the Size Effect of Barium Titanate Fine Particles: A New Model," *Journal of Ceramic Society of Japan*, **104** 383-392 (1996).
[7]D. McCauley, R. E. Newnham and C. A. Randall, "Intrinsic Size Effects in a $BaTiO_3$ Glass Ceramic," *Journal of American Ceramic Society*, **81** 979-987 (1998).
[8]M. R. Srinivasan, M. S. Multani, P. Ayyub and R. Vuayaraghavan, "Soft Modes and Grain Size Effects in Ferroelectric Ceramics," *Ferroelectrics*, **51** 137-141 (1983).
[9]A. J. Bell, A. J. Moulson and L. E. Cross, "The Effect of Grain Size on the Permittivity of $BaTiO_3$," *Ferroelectrics*, **54** 147-150 (1984).
[10]S. Wada, M. Narahara, T. Hoshina, H. Kakemoto and T. Tsurumi, "Preparation of nm-sized $BaTiO_3$ Fine Particles Using a New 2-step Thermal Decomposition of Barium Titanyl Oxalates," *Journal of Materials Science*, (2003) in press.

[11]K. Wakino, T. Okada, N. Yoshida and K. Tomono, "A New Equation for Predicting the Dielectric Constant of a Mixture," *Journal of American Ceramic Society*, **76** 2588-2594 (1993).

[12]S. Wada, T. Hoshina, H. Yasuno, S.-M. Nam, H. Kakemoto and T. Tsurumi, "Preparation of nm-sized $BaTiO_3$ Crystallites by the 2-step Thermal Decomposition of Barium Titanyl Oxalate and Their Dielectric Properties," *Key Engineering Materials*, (2003) in press.

[13]T. Kajita and M. Nishido, "Preparation of Submicron Barium Titanate by Oxalate Process," *Extended Abstracts of the 9th US-Japan Seminar on Dielectric and Piezoelectric Ceramics*, Okinawa 425-427 (1999).

[14]S. Kumar, G.L. Messing and W.B. White, "Metal Organic Resin Derived Barium Titanate: I, Formation of Barium Titanyl Oxycarbonate Intermediate," *Journal of American Ceramic Society*, **76** 617-624 (1993).

[15]W.-S. Cho, "Structural Evolution and Characterization of BaTiO3 Nanoparticles Synthesized from Polymeric Precursor," Journal of Physical and Chemical Solids, **59** 659-666 (1998).

[16]S. Wada, T. Suzuki, M. Osada, M. Kakihana and T. Noma, "Change of Macroscopic and Microscopic Symmetry of Barium Titanate Single Crystal around Curie temperature," *Japanese Journal of Applied Physics*, **37** 5385-5393 (1998).

[17]M. Zgonik, P. Bernasconi, M. Duelli, R. Schlesser, P. Gunter, M. H. Garrett, D. Rytz, Y. Zhu and X. Wu, "Dielectric, Elastic, Piezoelectric, Electro-Optic, and Elasto-Optic Tensors of $BaTiO_3$ Crystals," *Physical Review B*, **50** 5941-5949 (1994).

# STRUCTURAL EVOLUTION, DIELECTRIC AND PIEZOELECTRIC PROPERTIES OF MODIFIED $BiFeO_3$-$PbTiO_3$ PIEZOELECTRICS

Jinrong Cheng, Richard Eitel, Nan Li and L. E. Cross
Materials Research Institute, The Pennsylvania State University,
University Park, PA 16802

## ABSTRACT

Lanthanum modified $(Bi,La)FeO_3$-$xPbTiO_3$ (BLF-PT) piezoelectric ceramics were fabricated by the standard ceramic processing. A continuous solid solution of BLF with PT has been developed. The perovskite BLF-PT had a morphotropic phase boundary (MPB) for the 0.45 PT compositions, through which the rhombohedral to tetragonal phase transition was observed. Compared with BF-PT, the modified BLF-PT exhibited improvements in dielectric and piezoelectric properties. Our work first reported the high dielectric constant K, remnant polarization and piezoelectric constant $d_{33}$ of 1200, 29 $\mu C/cm^2$ and 240 pC/N for bismuth ferrite based solid solutions near MPB. It is indicated that BLF-PT is the competitive alternative MPB piezoelectrics with superior piezoelectricity and lead reduced composition.

## INTRODUCTION

$BiFeO_3$ is considered to be a multiferroics due to the coexistence of ferroelectricity, ferromagnetism and ferroelasticity[1,2]. A lot of work has been focused on the unique ferroelectromagnet properties of $BiFeO_3$ and its solid solutions[3,4]. It is known that $BiFeO_3$ is a perovskite with a large rhombohedral angle of $89°24'$, which implies a large ferroelectric effect from cubic symmetry to rhombohedral distortion. However, the potential piezoelectric properties of $BiFeO_3$ based ceramics have not yet been realized. The major limitations are their semiconductor nature and extremely high Curie temperature (Tc) of ~850 °C making poling difficulty. Other perovskites, such as $PbTiO_3$, $BaTiO_3$, $SrTiO_3$ and $Pb(Fe_{0.5}Nb_{0.5})O_3$ have been formed in solid solution with $BiFeO_3$ to make more insulating ceramics[5-8]. Up to date, the most forward step has not been achieved to make $BiFeO_3$ based ceramics more interesting piezoelectrics.

The motivation of our work is to make insulator and polable piezoelectrics based on BF-PT solid solutions. Using PT as an end member made the process relatively easier to synthesize the pure perovskites. Lanthanum substituent was introduced into A-site $Bi^{3+}$ cations. Continuous BLF-PT solid solutions were fabricated and characterized. The La-modified BF-PT solid solutions revealed the prominent piezoelectric properties, which has never been reported yet for bismuth ferrite based ceramics.

**EXPERIMENTAL PROCEDURE**

La-modified BF-xPT crystalline solutions have been developed using the solid-state reaction method, with the La content of 20 at% for 0.25 $\leq$x$\leq$0.65. Starting materials were commercial reagent-grade of $Bi_2O_3$, $Fe_2O_3$, $La_2O_3$, $PbCO_3$, and $TiO_2$ with 99%+ purity. The oxides were mixed by ball milling for 24 hours, and then calcined at 750°C for 4 hours. After calcination, powders were pressed and sintered at 1000-1120°C for 0.8 hours in a sealed crucible. X-ray diffraction techniques (diffractomer, Sintag 2) were utilized to identify the structure. Fresh fracture surfaces of sintered pellets were observed using scanning electron microscopy (SEM, Hitachi S-3000H).

Specimens, with 10.4 mm in diameter and 0.4 mm in thickness were electroded using a post-fired silver paste for electrical measurements. The room and high temperature dielectric measurements were conducted by using a computer controlled HP4194A and HP4284 impedance analyzer respectively. Ferroelectric hysteresis loops and strain measurements were made using a modified Sawyer-Tower circuit with a linear variable differential transducer (LVDT). Specimens were poled by applying a saturated unipolar electric field at 25 °C. Piezoelectric properties were characterized by using a Berlincourt $d_{33}$ meter and HP4194A impedance analyzer with IEEE resonance methods.

**RESULTS AND DISCUSSIONS**

Dense and insulator ceramics are required to obtain good piezoelectric properties. However, the anisotropic contraction below $T_c$ of PT and the high conductivity nature of BF usually made the processing difficult. The tendency of $Fe^{3+}$ to adopt other valence states can create imbalance and cause an oxygen deficiency, which is one of reasons contributing to a fall of density in the solid solutions[7]. Our modified BF-PT was sintered to a relative density of about 98%. Figure 1(a), 1(b) and 1(c) show SEM pictures taken from fresh fracture surfaces of BLF-PT for x=0.35, 0.45 and 0.55 respectively. It can be seen that ceramics were densified without porosity. The grain size is of 1~2 μm increasing with higher PT content. Fig.1(b) shows that the fracture was transgranular rather than along the grain boundary for 0.45 PT compositions. It might be the large internal stress that prevented the fracture from beginning along the grain boundary. BLF-

PT for x=0.35 and 0.55 indicated the more intergranular fractures, as shown in Fig.1(a) and 1(c).

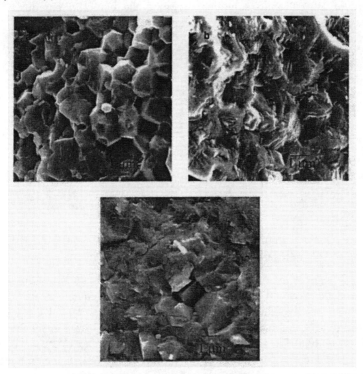

Figure 1. SEM pictures taken from the fresh fracture surface of BLF-PT solid solutions for (a) x=0.35, (b) x=0.45, (c) x=0.55 respectively.

$BiFeO_3$ is known as the only stable perovskite ferroelectrics, in which A and B-site cations are both trivalent. Previous investigations indicated that other materials, such as $BiScO_3$ and $BiGaO_3$ et al. cannot exist in the perovskite state without modifications, and more than 60 at% $PbTiO_3$ has to be used to make the perovskite state stable.

Figure 2(a) and 2(b) show the XRD patterns and lattice parameters of BLF-PT respectively through the investigated compositions. Continuous solid solutions of BLF with PT have been synthesized in single-phase perovskite states. We found that the perovskite state could be stabilized even for 0.1 PT compositions. This is a great advantage for developing the lead reduced materials. BLF-PT for x=0.35 is of the rhombohedral, whereas the tetragonal form occurs for x=0.55. There is a broadening and a split diffraction peak at 2θ of 32° and 23°, indicating that two phases coexisted in 0.45 PT compositions. This might be the source of the large internal stress reflected in SEM photos. The tetragonal distortion of c/a ratio rose up from 1.02 to 1.04 for BLF-PT from x=0.45 to 0.55, and then little changed with increasing PT content. The c/a ratio is lower than 1.06 of pure PbTiO₃ and 1.18 of BF-PT near MPB[8]. Therefore, Lanthanum modified the crystalline symmetry of BF-PT solid solutions dropping the c/a ratio obviously in the tetragonal region.

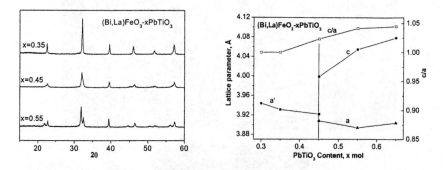

Figure 2 (a) XRD patterns of BLF-PT for x=0.35, 0.45 and 0.55, (b) Lattice parameters and c/a ratios of BLF-PT as a function of PT content.

Figure 3 presents the room temperature dielectric constant K and loss tanδ of BLF-PT as a function of PT content. The measurement frequencies are 1, 10 and 100 KHz respectively. The dielectric maximum appears at BLF-PT for x= 0.45 corresponding to K and tanδ of 1200 and 3% at 1 KHz. However, for the similar composition without La, K is only 330 of BF-PT for x=0.3 (MPB), which was examined in our current work. The loss tanδ is under 6% in the frequency of 1KHz indicating that no serious conductivity occurs in our ceramics.

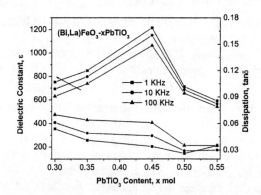

Figure 3. Dielectric constant K and loss tanδ of BLF-PT as a function of PT content at the room temperature

Ceramic Materials and Multilayer Electronic Devices

The enhancement of K for La-modified BF-PT is associated with the electronic structure of $Bi^{3+}$ and A-B bond. $La^{3+}$ has the large ionic radius of 1.46 Å, which causes the local displacement of surrounding ions tending to create an electric dipoles polarization around $Bi^{3+}$. In addition, the A-B sub-lattice reaction is weakened and the tetragonal distortion is reduced allowing less resistance to poling.

Figure 4(a) shows the dielectric constant K and loss tanδ vs. temperature relationships of BLF-PT for x=0.35, 0.45 and 0.55 respectively, using the measurement frequency of 1 MHz. The dielectric maxima were observed indicating the ferroelectric to paraelectric phase transformations. With increasing BLF, the K of peak decreased and the phase transformation became more diffuse in characteristics. A large number of ions at the A and B sites of an $ABO_3$ perovskite cause the diffused phase transition. In addition, each ion has a different polarization giving different relaxation times and diffused maxima. The composition diffusion of K disappears in the high temperature region, and K tends to be same from 500 °C. There are corresponding dielectric loss maxima to be observed at BLF-PT for x=0.45 and 0.55, however, an unknown loss peak appeared at around 50 °C for x=0.35. It can be seen that tanδ is lower than a unit at least at 500 °C. Therefore, the conductivity is not a problem in the La-modified BF-PT systems.

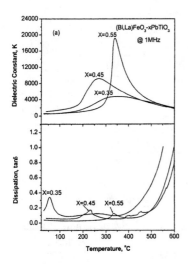 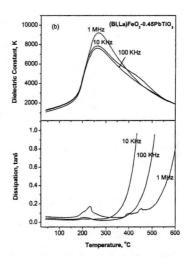

Figure 4. Dielectric constant K and loss tanδ vs. temperatures relationships of (a) BLF-PT for x=0.35, 0.45 and 0.55 respectively, (b) BLF-0.45PT using the measurement frequency of 10 KHz, 100 KHz and 1 MHz respectively.

Figure 4(b) shows K and tanδ vs. temperature relationships of BLF-PT for x=0.45 under different frequencies. The dielectric peak little shifted with frequencies indicating that BLF-PT is more diffuse rather than relaxor. It is noticed that the K of peak at 1 MHz is larger than that of other frequencies. Usually, K is in the order to decrease with increasing frequencies. The anomaly in BLF-PT may imply some defect mechanisms, which is dropping the dielectric maximum in certain frequencies.

Summarizing XRD, room and high temperature dielectric data, a phase diagram was complied as shown in Fig.5. The Curie temperature Tc was determined by high temperature dielectric data. The MPB was identified and shown in the diagram. It can be seen that Tc did not monotonously chang with PT content. Rather, the V-shaped Tc-composition relationship was found in the vicinity of MPB. Two end members of BLF-PT solid solutions have different A and B-site cations, in which V-shaped Tc-composition relationships were usually observed. The minimum Tc is 280 $^{\circ}$C near MPB with x=0.45. At the temperature of lower than Tc, the perovskite is the rhombohedral to the left of MPB, whereas to the right, is the tetragonal. Above Tc, we thought that the crystalline symmetry may not the true cubic according to the V-shaped Tc-composition curve. The pseudo phase is usually formed in the compound perovskite. The more sensitive XRD analysis are required to identify the high temperature crystalline symmetry.

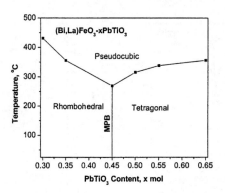

Figure 5. Complete phase diagrams for La-modified BLF-PT solid solutions.

Figure 6(a) shows large amplitude induced polarization and strain as a function of electric field of BLF-PT for x=0.45. The bipolar P-E and ε-E curves were measured using the frequency of 10 and 1 Hz respectively. The P-E loop is square and has good saturation characteristics. No significant evidence of leakage conductivity was observed. Remnant polarizations Pr and coercive fields Ec are of 30 $\mu$C/cm$^2$ and 32 kV/cm respectively. Ec of BLF-PT is 3-5 times larger than that of conventional Pb(Zr,Ti)O$_3$ (PZT) piezoelectric ceramics, showing that BLF-PT has high electrical strength, and thus can serve as a high power electromechanical materials, as the PE product is enormous. The typical butterfly ε-E curve also reveals the strong ferroelectric switching behavior of BLF-PT. The displacement jump can reach 0.35%, comparable with that of PZT.

Figure 6(b) shows Pr and Ec of BLF-PT as a function of PT content. The minimum Ec appears at 0.45 PT compositions, exhibiting that two phase coexistences gave more polable MPB characteristics. Ec increases quickly when the composition is away from MPB. Pr was enhanced in the vicinity of MPB.

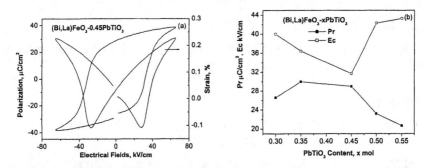

Figure 6 Ferroelectric responses of BLP-PT solid solutions, (a) P-E and ε-E curves of BLF-PT for x=0.45, (b) Pr and Ec of BLF-PT as a function of PT content

Figure 7 shows piezoelectric constant $d_{33}$ and planar coupling factor Kp of BLF-PT as a function of PT content. The high electrical field is more effective to make BLF-PT poled. It is hard to make the domain reorientation under the field near Ec even at the temperature of 120 °C. The piezoelectric maximum appears at 0.45 PT compositions. The corresponding $d_{33}$ and Kp are of 240 pC/N and 0.32 respectively. For the other compositions, $d_{33}$ and Kp dropped quickly.

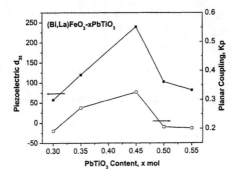

Figure 7 Piezoelectric constant $d_{33}$ and planar coupling factor Kp of BLF-PT as a function of PT content

## CONCLUSIONS

La-modified BLF-PT solid solutions have been developed. The hard and unpolable bismuth ferrite based ceramics were effectively tailored by La substituent. BLF-PT showed the great enhancement of dielectric and piezoelectric properties. The composition dependence of structure and electrical properties are in agreements to reveal the MPB of BLF-PT at 0.45 PT compositions. Apart from the comparable piezoelectric properties with PZT, BLF-PT is superior lead reduced piezoelectric ceramics having high electrical strength.

## ACKNOWLEDGEMENT

We are pleased to acknowledge support from the office of Naval Research (ONR) under contract No. N00014-99-1-1011

## REFERENCES

[1]S.Shetty, V.R. Palkar and R. Pinto, "Size effect study in magnetoelectric BiFeO$_3$ system" P$_{RAMANA}$-J Phys., **58**, 1027 (2002).

[2]M.M.Kumar and V.R.Palkar, "Ferroelectricity in a pure BiFeO$_3$ ceramics" Appl.Phys.Lett., **76**, 2764 (2000).

[3]T.Kanai, S.Ohkoshi, A.Nakajima, T.Watanabe and K.Hashimoto, "A Ferroelectric Ferromagnet Composed of (PLZT)$_x$(BiFeO$_3$)$_{1-x}$ Solid Solution," Adv. Mater., **7**, 487 (2001).

[4]Y.F.Popov, A.M.Kadomtseva, S.S.Krotov, D.V.Belov, G.P.Vorob'ev, P.N.Makhov and A.K.Zvezdin, "Features of the Magnetoelectric Properties of BiFeO$_3$ in High Magnetic Fields," Low Temperature Physics, **27**, 478 (2001).

[5]R.Gerson, P.Chou and W.J.James, "Ferroelectric Properties of PbZrO$_3$-BiFeO$_3$ Solid Solutions" J.Appl.Phys., **38**, 55 (1967).

[6]R.T.Smith, G.D.Achenbach, R.Gerson and W.J.James, "Dielectric Properties of Solid Solutions of BiFeO$_3$ with Pb(Ti,Zr)O$_3$ at High Temperature and High Frequency," J.Appl.Phys., **39**, 70 (1968).

[7]M.M.Kumar, A.Srinivas, S.V.Suryanarayana and T.Bhimasankaram, "Dielectric and Impedance Studies on BiFeO$_3$-BaTiO$_3$ Solid Solutions," Phy. Stat. Sol., (a) **165**, 317 (1998).

[8]V.V.S.S.S.Sunder, A.Halliyal and A.M.Umarji, "Investigation of Tetragonal Distortion in the PbTiO$_3$-BiFeO$_3$ System by High-temperature x-ray Diffraction," J.Mater.Res., **10**, 1301 (1995).

# MICROWAVE PROPERTIES OF ACCEPTOR-DOPED BARIUM STRONTIUM TITANATE THIN FILMS FOR TUNABLE ELECTRONIC DEVICES*

RICHARD G. GEYER[a] AND MELANIE W. COLE[b]
[a]National Institute of Standards and Technology
RF Technology Division, M.S. 813.01
Boulder, CO 80303

[b]U.S. Army Research Laboratory, Aberdeen Proving Ground, Maryland 21005

ABSTRACT

The influence of Mg-doping on the structure, microstructure, surface morphology, and dielectric properties of $Ba_{1-x}Sr_xTiO_3$ (BST) thin films is measured and analyzed. The films were fabricated on MgO substrates with the metalorganic solution deposition technique using carboxylate-alkoxide precursors and annealed at 800 °C in an oxygen atmosphere. The structure, microstructure, surface morphology, and film/substrate compositional quality were evaluated with glancing angle x-ray diffraction, field emission scanning microscopy, atomic force microscopy, and Auger electron spectroscopy studies. Dielectric properties of unpatterned films were measured at 10 GHz using a coupled and tuned split dielectric resonator system. The Mg-doped BST films exhibited improved dielectric and insulating properties compared to undoped $Ba_{0.6}Sr_{0.4}TiO_3$ thin films and are candidates for integration into tunable microwave devices.

INTRODUCTION

Thin films of $Ba_{1-x}Sr_xTiO_3$ have recently received considerable attention as promising candidates for applications in electronically tunable microwave components. Some of these components include voltage-tunable phase shifters for scanning antenna arrays, tunable filters, varactors, delay lines, voltage-controlled oscillators, and parametric amplifiers [1]. These tunable devices are based on the large, field-dependent dielectric permittivity, which permits changing the phase velocity of the device in real time for a particular application. One of the major challenges faced in utilizing BST thin films as tunable microwave devices is the minimization of thin film dielectric loss while maximizing dielectric tunability. At or below the Curie temperature, $T_c$, BST becomes spontaneously polarized and is in the ferroelectric, as compared to paraelectric, state. In the ferroelectric state, tunability is markedly

*Work supported by an agency of the U.S. government, not subject to copyright in the U.S.

enhanced, but with concomitant large increases in dielectric loss and hysteresis in permittivity. The stoichiometric ratio of Ba:Sr is generally used to control $T_c$, so that in application BST is in the paraelectric state. Hence, in practice, there is a tradeoff between material tunability and dielectric loss.

Recent efforts to improve tunability and decrease losses of BST thin films have focussed on film texturing [2], improvement of the dielectric-electrode interface [3], minimization of film stress resulting from lattice mismatches between film and substrate [1], and modification of the microstructural, surface morphological, and compositional properties of the thin film. It is well documented that small concentrations of acceptor dopants can significantly modify the dielectric properties of ferroelectric materials, such as BST [4]. In particular, $Fe^{2+}$, $Fe^{3+}$, $Co^{2+}$, $Co^{3+}$, $Mn^{2+}$, $Mn^{3+}$, $Ni^{2+}$, $Mg^{2+}$, $Al^{3+}$, $Ga^{3+}$, $In^{3+}$, $Cr^{3+}$, and $Sc^{3+}$, which can occupy the B sites of the $(A^{2+}B^{4+}O_3{}^{2-})$ perovskite structure, have been shown to lower dielectric loss. The acceptor dopants serve to lower dielectric losses by preventing electron hopping in the reduction of $Ti^{4+}$ to $Ti^{3+}$. This electron hopping is caused by the donor action of oxygen vacancies.

In this paper we examine the process-structure-property relationships of undoped and Mg-doped BST thin films prepared by the metalorganic solution deposition technique (MOSD) [5,6]. We also report microwave dielectric properties for various mol% Mg-dopings of BST thin films. A significant problem with microstrip or coplanar waveguide measurements is the dominating effect of the patterned-circuit conductor loss at microwave frequencies relative to actual dielectric loss of the thin film. A split dielectric resonator system is used for microwave thin-film dielectric measurements. In this technique, nonmetallized samples can be used so that the dominating influence of conductor loss is avoided.

## ACCEPTOR-DOPED BST THIN FILM FABRICATION AND EXPERIMENTS

Undoped and Mg-acceptor doped $Ba_{0.6}Sr_{0.4}TiO_3$ thin films were fabricated by the MOSD technique. In the process, barium acetate, strontium acetate, and titanium isopropoxide were used as precursors to form BST. Acetic acid and 2-methoxyethanol were used as solvents, and magnesium acetate was employed as the Mg-acceptor dopant precursor. The stoichiometric precursor solutions were optimized in concentration and spin coated on single crystal (100) MgO substrates. Particulates were removed from the solution by filtering through 0.2 $\mu$m syringe filters. Subsequent to coating, the films were pyrolyzed at 350 °C for 10 min in order to evaporate solvents and organic addenda and form an inorganic amorphous film. The spin coat pyrolization process was repeated until a nominal film thickness of 160-220 nm was achieved. Crystallinity was optimized with post-deposition annealing in an oxygen atmosphere at 800 °C. Crystallinity and surface morphology of the films were assessed by glancing angle x-ray diffraction (GAXRD) and atomic force microscopy (AFM). Field emission scanning microscopy (FESEM) was used to determine cross-sectional and plan-view film microstructure. Dielectric properties at 297 K were evaluated with a coupled, tuned split post dielectric resonator measurement technique.

RESULTS

Structure, Microstructure, and Surface Morphology

The as-deposited films were amorphous and postdeposition annealing was required to crystallize the films, increase the overall grain size of the film and to mitigate film strain by filling oxygen vacancies. These factors are important because the dielectric loss in ferroelectric thin films is strongly affected by stoichiometric deficiencies, which create vacancies, film strain, and the presence of a large grain boundary to grain ratio. Hence, in order to reduce microwave dielectric loss, the as-pyrolyzed films on MgO substrates were postdeposition annealed for 1 h in the temperature range from 600 to 800 °C in an oxygen atmosphere. GAXRD was used to assess film crystallinity and whether the films were single phase. Figure 1 illustrates the x-ray diffraction patterns of undoped and 1 mol% Mg-doped $Ba_{0.6}Sr_{0.4}TiO_3$ films deposited on MgO substrates annealed at temperatures of 600 to 800 °C for 1 h. The absence of diffraction peaks in the x-ray pattern for the film annealed at 600 °C indicates that the film was amorphous at this annealing temperature. As the annealing temperature increased, the x-ray peak intensity increased, and the full-width-half-maximum (FWHM) decreased, indicating enhanced crystallinity and an increase in grain size with increasing temperature up to 800 °C (Fig. 2). Plots of thin film grain size as a function of annealing temperatures are given in Fig. 3. In addition, as the annealing temperature is increased from 650 to 800 °C, there is no evidence of secondary phase formation. The x-ray diffraction pattern exhibits all major peaks corresponding to the cubic perovskite phase. The films annealed at 800 °C possessed a nontextured polycrystalline structure with no appearance of secondary phases.

It is also useful to note that the lattice parameter of the film annealed at higher temperatures contracts and approaches the bulk BST value, $a=0.39655$ nm. The presence of oxygen vacancies is known to increase the lattice parameter of the oxide films. Hence, this observed contraction of the lattice parameter as the annealing temperature approaches 800 °C is expected to decrease oxygen vacancy concentration and to improve the electrical characteristics of the film.

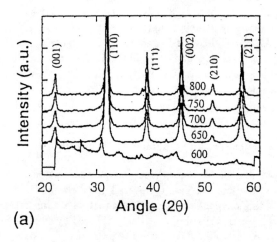

(a)

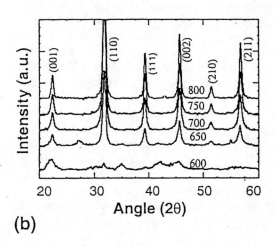

(b)

Figure 1: X-ray diffraction patterns of (a) undoped and (b) 1 mol% Mg-doped $Ba_{0.6}Sr_{0.4}TiO_3$ films deposited on MgO substrates annealed at temperatures ranging from 600 to 800 °C for 1 h.

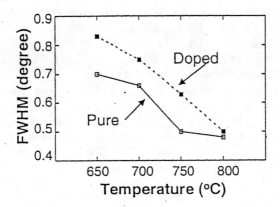

Figure 2: FWHM of the (002) x-ray peak for undoped and 1 mol% Mg-doped $Ba_{0.6}Sr_{0.4}TiO_3$ film on MgO substrate as a function of annealing temperature.

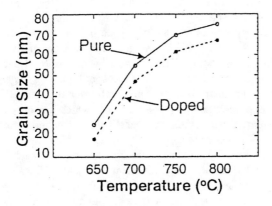

Figure 3: Grain size versus annealing temperature for undoped and 1 mol% Mg-doped $Ba_{0.6}Sr_{0.4}TiO_3$ thin films on MgO substrates.

Thin film surface morphology can be evaluated by tapping mode AFM. AFM images over a $1 \times 1~\mu m^2$ scan area are shown in Fig. 4 for both undoped and Mg-doped BST. These images illustrate a dense microstructure with no cracks or defects. They also show a larger-grained, more uniform microstructure after postdeposition annealing at 800 °C, and average surface roughness increasing with annealing temperature to an average value of $R_a = 2.25$ nm at 800 °C for both film compositions. The real permittivity of a film in the ferroelectric or paraelectric state generally is influenced by grain structure, grain size, and quality of the material throughout the volume of the film. Larger permittivities are expected with increased grain size.

Cross-sectional FESEM micrographs in Fig. 5 show that both undoped and doped films possess a dense, well-crystallized microstructure with a uniform cross-sectional thickness of 164 nm. Films were polycrystalline and composed of granular multigrains randomly distributed throughout the film thickness.

### Microwave Dielectric Property Measurements

Microwave dielectric properties at a nominal frequency of 10 GHz were evaluated with a coupled, tuned split dielectric resonator system shown schematically in Fig. 6. This technique is described and discussed elsewhere [7-14]. Specimens need not be metallized or have superimposed patterned circuitry. The use of this resonant system has several advantages. It is noncontacting, nondestructive, and can be used for dielectric measurements of laminar substrates or thin films. For uniformly thick substrates, it can also be used for rapid checking of dielectric inhomogeneity (permittivity or loss) on the mm-scale in the specimen. The nominal measurement frequency is determined by the geometry and permittivity of the low-loss, temperature stable resonators. For practical size considerations of available high-permittivity, temperature-stable dielectric resonators, this type of measurement system is suitable for microwave measurements over the 1-10 GHz range.

The dominant $TE_{01\delta}$ resonant frequency is used, which has only an azimuthal electric field component. Hence, the electric field is continuous across the dielectric interfaces, and in-plane sample electrical properties are measured. The sample insertion gap is determined by making the azimuthal electric field in the gap as uniform as possible at the nominal measurement frequency. Because the electric field is continuous across the top and bottom sample faces, no depolarization effects occur in this system, and there is no capacitive coupling between the specimen and the metal flange support.

The general laboratory procedure is to identify and perform measurements of the $TE_{01\delta}$ resonant frequency and unloaded $Q$-factor of the split dielectric resonator system, both with and without specimen insertion. The Rayleigh-Ritz variational method is used to compute resonant frequencies and unloaded $Q$-factors as a function

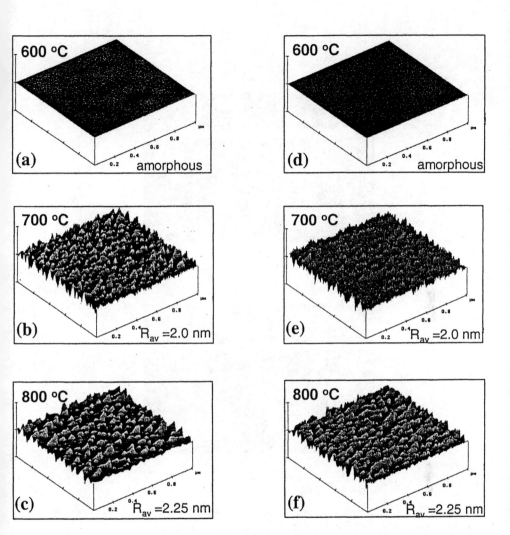

Figure 4: AFM images of film surface roughness versus annealing temperature. Undoped BST thin films on MgO substrates at (a) 600 °C, (b) 700 °C, and (c) 800 °C. Mg-doped (1 mol%) BST on MgO substrates annealed at (d) 600 °C, (e) 700 °C, and (f) 800 °C.

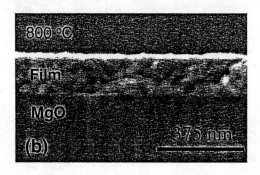

Figure 5: Cross-sectional FESEM images of the 800 °C annealed (a) undoped and (b) 1 mol% Mg-doped $Ba_{0.6}Sr_{0.4}TiO_3$ films on MgO substrates.

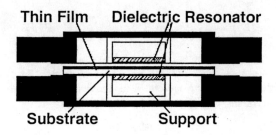

Thin Film    Dielectric Resonator

Substrate    Support

Figure 6: Schematic diagram of split dielectric resonator system.

of permittivity and geometry of the tuned split dielectric resonators and parametrically as a function of specimen real permittivity $\epsilon'_{r,s}$ and specimen thickness $t$ [9]. A lookup table is then established that enables the real part of the permittivity to be determined iteratively from

$$\epsilon'_{r,s} = 1 + (f_0 - f_s)/[tf_0 F(\epsilon'_{r,s}, t)], \qquad (1)$$

where $f_0$ and $f_s$ are the resonant frequencies of the split dielectric resonator system without specimen insertion and with specimen insertion and $F(\epsilon'_{r,s}, t)$ is a numerically determined parametric function of $\epsilon'_{r,s}$ and $t$. The specimen dielectric loss tangent, $\tan \delta_s$, is evaluated from

$$\tan \delta_s = p_{e,s}^{-1}\left(Q_0^{-1} - p_{e,DR}\tan \delta_{DR} - Q_c^{-1}\right), \qquad (2)$$

where $Q_0$ is the unloaded $Q$-factor of the resonant system containing the inserted specimen, $\tan \delta_{DR}$ is the dielectric loss tangent of the cylindrical dielectric resonators of the fixture, $Q_c^{-1}$ denotes fixture conductor losses for the resonant system containing the specimen, and $p_{e,s}$, $p_{e,DR}$ are the partial electric energy filling factors of the specimen and the split dielectric resonators of the measurement system. The sample partial electric energy filling factor is defined as the electric energy in the sample normalized by the electric energy in the entire resonant system,

$$p_{e,s} = \int\int\int_{V_s} \epsilon'_{r,s}\mathbf{E}\cdot\mathbf{E}^* dv / \int\int\int_V \epsilon'_r(v)\mathbf{E}\cdot\mathbf{E}^* dv, \qquad (3)$$

where $\mathbf{E}$ is the azimuthal electric field defined over the volume $V$ and $V_s$ is the sample volume. The partial electric energy filling factor of the split dielectric resonators is similarly defined. Fixture conductor losses are defined in terms of the metal surface resistance $R_s$ and the magnetic field $\mathbf{H}$ evaluated over the volume and surface of the resonant system,

$$Q_c^{-1} = R_s \int\int_S \mathbf{H}_\tau \cdot \mathbf{H}_\tau^* dS / \int\int\int_V \mathbf{H} \cdot \mathbf{H}^* dv. \tag{4}$$

The material perturbation theorem, used by Kobayashi, Aoki, and Kabe [15] and outlined by Harrington [16], is perhaps an easier approach for the evaluation of the partial electric energy filling factors. The material perturbation theorem in a resonant structure having negligible radiative losses yields

$$p_{e,s} = \frac{2\epsilon'_{r,s}}{f_s}\Big|\frac{\partial f_s}{\partial\epsilon'_{r,s}}\Big|, \tag{5}$$

and

$$p_{e,DR} = \frac{2\epsilon'_{r,DR}}{f_0}\Big|\frac{\partial f_0}{\partial\epsilon'_{r,DR}}\Big|. \tag{6}$$

Similarly, an easier approach for estimating conductor losses is the use of Wheeler's incremental inductance rule [17], which is valid for rotationally symmetric metal enclosures. The incremental inductance rule is discussed by Kajfez [18] and is given by,

$$Q_c = \frac{f_0}{\Delta f_0(\delta)}, \tag{7}$$

where $f_0$ is the resonant frequency of a rotationally symmetric metal enclosure, computed for the case when the metal is considered to be a perfect conductor, and $\Delta f_0(\delta)$ is the increment in resonant frequency, computed again when metal enclosing walls are moved *inward* by one skin depth, $\delta = \sqrt{1/(\pi f_0 \mu \sigma)}$, $\mu$ being the metal magnetic permeability and $\sigma$ the metal conductivity.

For unpatterned thin films, the measurement process is twofold. First, the permittivity and dielectric loss of the substrate are evaluated. Then the permittivity and dielectric loss of the thin film are determined by the resonant frequency and $Q$- factor difference between substrate and substrate with deposited thin film. Results for real relative permittivity and dielectric loss tangent for various mol% Mg-dopings of MOSD-deposited $Ba_{0.6}Sr_{0.4}TiO_3$ thin films on single crystal (100) MgO substrates are summarized in Table 1. The tunability data were obtained from metal-insulator-metal capacitor measurements at 100 kHz using Pt as top and bottom electrodes and an impedance analyzer. The insulating property data were obtained from current-voltage measurements using a semiconductor test system.

Table 1: Dielectric and insulating properties of undoped and Mg-doped BST thin films on single crystal MgO substrates.

| mol% Mg- Doping | Frequency (MHz) | $\epsilon'_{r,s}$ (zero bias) | $\tan \delta_{tf}$ (zero bias) | Tunability (%) (237 kV/cm) | $\rho$ ($\Omega$cm) (237 kV/cm) |
|---|---|---|---|---|---|
| 0 | 9487 | 742 | $2.49 \times 10^{-2}$ | 28.0 | $0.40 \times 10^{12}$ |
| 1 | 9489 | 411 | $2.58 \times 10^{-2}$ | 25.0 | $0.55 \times 10^{12}$ |
| 5 | 9495 | 362 | $2.10 \times 10^{-2}$ | 17.2 | $1.01 \times 10^{12}$ |
| 7 | 9497 | 316 | $1.65 \times 10^{-2}$ | 15.7 | $7.28 \times 10^{13}$ |
| 10 | 9509 | 223 | $1.24 \times 10^{-2}$ | 5.7 | $9.23 \times 10^{13}$ |

Theoretical uncertainty analysis has been discussed for single-layer substrate measurements [13]. For a single substrate measurement, the relative uncertainty in specimen real permittivity, $\Delta \epsilon'_{r,s} / \epsilon'_{r,s}$, depends on the uncertainties in thickness and diameter of the dielectric resonators, the diameter of the enclosing circular waveguide, the insertion gap, and the specimen thickness. Generally, the total estimated systematic or Type B [19] uncertainty in permittivity determination is dominated by the uncertainty in specimen thickness and is given by

$$\frac{\Delta \epsilon'_{r,s}}{\epsilon'_{r,s}} = T \frac{\Delta t}{t}, \qquad (8)$$

where $1 < T < 2$. Usually $T$ is close to unity except for thick, large permittivity samples. The relative dielectric loss tangent uncertainty of a single-layer specimen having a real relative permittivity less than 10 is less than 4% for loss tangents in excess of 0.001, provided $Q$-factor measurements are performed with a measurement uncertainty that is less than 1% [13].

For the thin film measurements reported here the relative thin film dielectric loss tangent uncertainty, $\Delta \tan \delta_{tf} / \tan \delta_{tf}$, is more complex and is given by the following rms sum of the relative uncertainties in partial filling factors of the thin film, substrate, and dielectric resonators, as well as the relative uncertainties in metal quality factor, unloaded $Q$-factor, and substrate and dielectric resonator loss tangents,

$$\frac{\Delta \tan \delta_{tf}}{\tan \delta_{tf}} = [\left( S_{pe,tf} \frac{\Delta p_{e,tf}}{p_{e,tf}} \right)^2 + \left( S_{Q0} \frac{\Delta Q_0}{Q_0} \right)^2$$
$$+ \left( S_{Qc} \frac{\Delta Q_c}{Q_c} \right)^2 + \left( S_{pe,DR} \frac{\Delta p_{e,DR}}{p_{e,DR}} \right)^2$$

$$+ \left( S_{pe,substrate} \frac{\Delta p_{e,substrate}}{p_{e,substrate}} \right)^2 + \left( S_{\tan \delta, substrate} \frac{\Delta \tan \delta_{substrate}}{\tan \delta_{substrate}} \right)^2$$

$$+ \left( S_{\tan \delta, DR} \frac{\Delta \tan \delta_{DR}}{\tan \delta_{DR}} \right)^2 ]^{1/2}, \tag{9}$$

where the associated sensitivity weighting functions in eq (9) are

$$S_{pe,tf} = 1, \tag{10}$$

$$S_{Q0} = 1 + \frac{p_{e,DR} \tan \delta_{DR}}{p_{e,tf} \tan \delta_{tf}} + \frac{p_{e,substrate} \tan \delta_{substrate}}{p_{e,tf} \tan \delta_{tf}} + \frac{1}{Q_c p_{e,tf} \tan \delta_{tf}}, \tag{11}$$

$$S_{pe,substrate} = S_{\tan \delta, substrate} = \frac{p_{e,substrate} \tan \delta_{substrate}}{p_{e,tf} \tan \delta_{tf}}, \tag{12}$$

$$S_{pe,DR} = S_{\tan \delta, DR} = \frac{p_{e,DR} \tan \delta_{DR}}{p_{e,tf} \tan \delta_{tf}}, \tag{13}$$

and

$$S_{Qc} = \frac{1}{Q_c p_{e,tf} \tan \delta_{tf}}. \tag{14}$$

Evaluation of thin film real relative permittivity is based on the measured frequency shift between substrate and substrate with deposited film. This frequency shift is determined by the contrast in permittivity between the film and substrate and film thickness, which affects the film electric energy filling factor. The upper bound uncertainty in frequency measurement with an automatic vector network analyzer is 1 kHz. Hence the systematic uncertainty in thin film real relative permittivity evaluation is dominantly related to thickness uncertainties in either the substrate or thin film.

Variations in frequency shift between substrate and substrate with deposited thin film are given in Fig. 7 for thin film relative permittivities that vary from 100 to 500 and for thin film thickness that range from 50 to 500 nm. These computations were performed assuming a MgO substrate having a real permittivity of 9.75 and thickness of 0.5 mm. As the film thickness becomes smaller for a given film real permittivity, the frequency shift decreases, as does the partial electric energy filling factor in the film. By measuring both the substrate and thin film thickness variations, frequency shift differences such as those shown in Fig. 7 may be used for rapid determination of the systematic uncertainty in a specimen's relative real permittivity evaluation. The films tested here were 164 nm and 218 nm thick and were very uniform, with a thickness uncertainty of 2 nm. For the measurements reported here, the total Type B relative uncertainty in ferroelectric film permittivity is principally controlled by

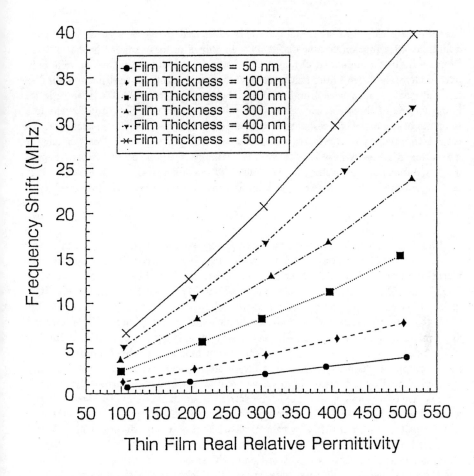

Figure 7: Frequency shift of split dielectric resonator system between substrate and substrate with deposited thin film as function of film real permittivity and thickness.

the substrate thickness uncertainty and is estimated to be as high as 20%. The dominant contribution to the uncertainty in thin film loss tangent is that arising from errors in the unloaded $Q$-factor and fixture metal quality factor, as well as in partial electric energy filling factors in both film and substrate that occur with film and substrate thickness non-uniformities. For typical uncertainties in the partial filling factors of the dielectric resonators, substrate, and thin film, and for the loss tangents of the dielectric resonators and substrate and metal surface resistance, the total estimated Type B relative uncertainty in thin film dielectric loss tangent for measurements report here is 30% for 2% accuracy in unloaded $Q$-factors. Future work will focus on increasing the parallelism of the substrates used prior to MOSD film deposition, thereby lowering the dominating substrate thickness uncertainty.

## SUMMARY

BST thin film material compositional design, combined with the optimization of MOSD film fabrication parameters and postannealing conditions, permits adjustment of tunability and dielectric loss of ferroelectric thin films at microwave frequencies. The examined annealed undoped and Mg-doped BST films were single-phase. they also possessed dense, defect-free microstructure with a thermally stable film-substrate interface and smooth continuous surface morphology. The lowering of permittivity and loss tangent with acceptor doping suggests that the contribution of the relaxation mechanism to ferroelectric thin film loss has been limited by material compositional design. Increased Mg-doping concentrations of BST thin films is accompanied by a decrease in grain size and lowered leakage current densities.

The use of a coupled, tuned split dielectric resonator system with a vector automatic network analyzer allows microwave dielectric measurements of both substrate and deposited high-permittivity thin films without any superimposed circuit patterning or metallization. This technique, measuring dielectric properties in-plane of a laminar specimen, is very sensitive to any thickness changes in film or substrate. For the measurements reported here, substrate thickness variations dominated uncertainties in both evaluated thin film permittivity and dielectric loss tangent. Measurement accuracies can be improved by decreased tolerances in substrate thickness variations.

## ACKNOWLEDGMENTS

Financial support from the U.S. Army Research Laboratory, Materials Directorate is gratefully acknowledged.

# REFERENCES

[1] J.S. Horwitz, W. Chang, A.C. Carter, J.M. Pond, S.W. Kirchoefer, D.B. Christy, J. Levy, and C. Hubert, "Structure/property relationships in ferroelectric thin films for frequency agile microwave electronics," *Integrated Ferroelectrics*, bf 22 799-809 (1998).

[2] B.H. Park, E.J. Peterson, Q.X. Jia, J. Lee, X. Zeng, W. Si, and X.X. Xi, "Effects of very thin strain layers on dielectric properties of epitaxial $Ba_{0.6}Sr_{0.4}TiO_3$ films," *Appl. Phys. Lett.*, **78** 533-535 (2001).

[3] H-D. Wu, Z. Zhang, F. Barnes, C.M. Jackson, A. Kim, and J.D. Cuchiaro, "Voltage tunable capacitors using high temperature superconductors and ferroelectrics," *IEEE Trans. Appl. Supercond.*, 4 156-160 (1994).

[4] P. Padmini, T.R. Taylor, M.J. Lefevre, A.S. Nagra, R.A. York, and J.S. Speck, "Realization of high tunability barium strontium titanate thin films by rf magnetron sputtering," *Appl. Phys. Lett.*, **75** 3186-3188 (1999).

[5] M.W. Cole, P.C. Joshi, M.H. Ervin, M.C. Wood, and R.L. Pfeffer, "The influence of Mg doping on the materials properties of $Ba_{1-x}Sr_xTiO_3$ thin films in tunable device applications," *Thin Solid Films*, **374** 34-41 (2000).

[6] M.W. Cole, P.C. Joshi, E. Ngo, C. Hubbard, M. Ervin, M. Wood, and R.G. Geyer, "Structure-property relationships in pure and acceptor-doped $Ba_{1-x}Sr_xTiO_3$ thin films for tunable microwave device applications," *J. Appl. Phys.*, **92**, 475-483 (2001).

[7] T. Nishikawa, K. Wakino, H. Tanaka, and Y. Ishikawa, "Precise method for complex permittivity of microwave substrate," CPEM '88 Digest, 154-155 (1988).

[8] G. Kent, "An evanescent-mode tester for ceramic dielectric substrates," *IEEE Trans. Microwave Theory Tech.*, bf 36 1451-1454 (1988).

[9] T. Nishikawa, K. Wakino, H. Tanaka, and Y. Ishikawa, "Dielectric resonator method for nondestructive measurement of complex permittivity of microwave dielectric substrates," 20th European Microwave Conf. Proc.-Vol. 1, 501-506 (1990).

[10] J. Krupka, R.G. Geyer, J. Baker-Jarvis, and J. Ceremuga, "Measurements of the complex permittivity of microwave circuit board substrates using split dielectric resonator and reentrant cavity," *Seventh Int. Conf. Dielectric Materials, Measure-*

ments and Applications, Conf. Pub. No. 430, 21-24 (1996).

[11]A.G. Yushchenko and V.V. Chizhov, "Precision microwave testing of dielectric substrates," *IEEE Trans. Instr. Meas.*, 46 507-510 (1997).

[12]M.D. Janezic and J. Baker-Jarvis, "Full-wave analysis of a split-cylinder resonator for nondestructive permittivity measurements," *IEEE Trans. Microwave Theory Tech.*, 47 2014-2020 (1999).

[13]J. Krupka, A.P. Gregory, O.C. Rochard, R.N. Clarke, B. Riddle, and J. Baker-Jarvis, "Uncertainty of complex permittivity measurements by split-post dielectric resonator technique," *J. Eur. Ceram. Soc.*, 21 2673-2676 (2001).

[14]R.G. Geyer and J. Krupka, "Microwave Dielectric Property Measurements," in *Dielectric Materials and Devices, Proc. Am. Cer. Soc.*, 533-560 (2002).

[15]Y. Kobayashi, T. Aoki, and Y. Kabe, "Influence of Conductor Shields on the Q-Factors of a $TE_0$ Dielectric Resonator," *IEEE MTT-S Int. Microwave Symp. Digest, St. Louis*, 281-284 (1985).

[16]R.F. Harrington, *Time-Harmonic Electromagnetic Fields*, New York: McGraw-Hill, 321-326 (1961).

[17]H.A. Wheeler, "Formulas for the skin effect," *Proc. IRE*, bf 30 412-424 (1942).

[18] D. Kajfez, "Incremental frequency rule for computing the $Q$-factor of a shielded $TE_{0mp}$ dielectric resonator," *IEEE Trans. Microwave Theory Tech.*, 32 941-943 (1984).

[19]B.N. Taylor and C.E. Kuyatt, "Guidelines for Evaluating and Expressing the Uncertainty of NIST Measurement Results," *NIST Techn. Note 1297*, (1994).

# TEMPERATURE AND STOICHIOMETRY EFFECT ON MICROSTRUCTURAL AND FERROELECTRIC PROPERTIES OF Pb(Zr$_{1-x}$Ti$_x$)O$_3$ THIN FILMS PREPARED BY CHEMICAL SOULUTION DEPOSITION

C. R. Foschini; J. F. Li; C. T. A. Suchicital;
D. Viehland
*Virginia Polytechnic Institute and State University*
*213 Holden Hall,*
*Blacksburg, VA*
*USA 24061*

B.D. Stojanovic; J. A. Varela
*Institute of Chemistry, UNESP*
*Araraquara, SP, C.P. 355*
*Brasil 14801-970*

## ABSTRACT

Lead zirconate titanate (PZT) solutions were prepared using a polymeric precursor method, Zr n-propoxide and Ti i-propoxide were used as starting materials with ethylene glycol and water as solvents. The PZT solution was spin-coated on Pt/Ti/SiO$_2$/Si substrates, baked on a hot plate, and finally heat-treated in a tube furnace between 400 and 800°C. The surface morphology and grain size of the films were characterized by atomic force microscopy (AFM), using a tapping mode with amplitude modulation. The films, thermal annealed at temperatures higher than 500ºC, exhibited a dense microstructure, without noticeable cracks or voids. Electrical properties were investigated as a function of composition and annealing temperature.

## INTRODUCTION

Lead zirconate titanate, Pb(Zr$_{1-x}$Ti$_x$)O$_3$ (PZT), ceramics are of great technological interest due to their excellent piezoelectric and ferroelectric properties[1, 2]. PZT ceramics are extensively used as electromechanical transducer materials. The electromechanical response of these ceramics is maximum when $x$ corresponds to the composition of the morphotropic phase boundary (MPB), which separates the tetragonal $T$ and rhombohedral $R$ phases.

Conventionally, the PZT phase is prepared by solid state reactive firing of the constituent oxides (PbO, ZrO$_2$ and TiO$_2$). However, due to intermediate reactions which lead to the formation of PbTiO$_3$ (PT) and PbZrO$_3$ (PZ), the PZT formed by this method is chemically heterogeneous, including compositional fluctuations, which modify the electrical properties [3, 4].

Variations in composition can result in a diffuse MPB between $T$ and $R$ phases. Chemical synthesis have resulted in PZT powders with reduced compositional fluctuations, narrowed MPB, and improved reactivity [5-7]. Amongst these chemical methods are the sol-gel technique [6], and the partial chemical methods as described by Kakegawa [5] and Yamamoto [8].

There have bean remarkable advances in the applications of PZT thin films, but the direct integration into high density metal-oxide-semiconductor (CMOS) devices is restricted by the high processing temperature. In order to be compatible with the existing high density semiconductor processing, the PZT processing temperature must be decreased below 600°C, however typical annealing temperatures for PZT are between 650 to 750°C. For annealing temperatures lower than 600°C, the perovskite phase of PZT films does not sufficiently form, and the well-defined hysteresis loops are not formed. Thus it is desirable to develop a low temperature processing for integrating PZT films into the high density CMOS devices.

In the present study, the preparation and characterization of PZT thin films with compositions of $Pb(Zr_{1-x}Ti_x)O_3$, for $0.40 \leq x \leq 0.70$, prepared by a polymeric precursor method were performed. The effects of temperature and Zr/Ti ratio on the microstructure and ferroelectric properties of the films were studied.

## EXPERIMENTAL PROCEDURE

The polymeric precursors were prepared by the Pechini process [9-11], which has been extensively used for synthesis of various polycation oxides. The method is based on polyesters obtained from citrates; a hydrocarboxylic acid, such as citric acid, is used to chelate cations in aqueous solution. Addition of a glycol, such as ethylene glycol, results in organic ester formation. Polymerization, promoted by heating of the mixture, leads to a homogeneous resin, in which metal ions are uniformly distributed throughout the organic matrix.

The amount of citric acid, determined by the citric acid to metal cation ratio was fixed at 3:1 (at.%). The amount of ethylene glycol was determined by the citric acid:ethylene glycol ratio (CA:EG). In this study the CA:EG ratio was fixed at 1:16 (at.%). The viscosity of the solution was controlled by varying the ethylene glycol content. Addition of ethylene glycol improved the wetness and uniformity of coating on the substrate.

Precursors solutions were deposited onto various substrates by spin coating operated at 6000 rpm for 40 s. Prior to coating, substrates were cleaned by immersion in a sulfochromic solution, followed by rinsing with de-ionized water and drying with hot air. Pt(111)/Ti/SiO$_2$/Si(100) were used as substrates. Particulates were removed from the solution by filtering through 0.2 μm syringe filters. After spinning onto various substrates, the films were placed on a hot plate at ~300°C in air for 10 min. After each coating, this step was repeated to ensure complete removal of volatile matter. The precursor coated films were heated to temperatures ranging from 400 to 700°C (except for glass substrates which were heated up to 550°C) in an oxygen atmosphere, maintaining the annealing temperature for 1 or 2 hours and then cooling to room temperature. The crystallinity of the prepared films was examined by X-ray diffraction (XRD: Siemens, D5000), using a Cu $K\alpha$ radiation source. The morphology was studied by Atomic Force Microscopy (AFM Digital Instruments, Nanoscope IIIa). Through AFM images on the surface of the samples, the quantification of relevant parameters such as roughness and grain size were possible. Electrical measurements were conducted on films in metal-insulator-metal (MIM) cell structure using Pt as the top and bottom electrodes. The Pt top electrodes (250 μm diameter) were deposited on the top surface of the films through a shadow mask by rf sputtering. The ferroelectric properties, such as remanent polarization ($P_r$) and coercive field ($E_c$), were measured using a Ferroelectric Test System (RT6000HVS, Radiant Technologies, Inc).

## RESULTS AND DISCUSSION

The crystallization of PZT films prepared from precursor solutions and deposited onto platinum-coated silicon substrates was monitored after thermal annealing in the temperature range from 400 to 700°C for 1 hour, by X-ray diffraction. During heating, the organic precursors decompose and at 500°C a polycrystalline PZT phase was formed. The structure of the crystallized phase was rhombohedral or tetragonal, depending on the stoichiometry of initial solution. It can be seen in Figure 1 that the perovskite phase formation temperature is around 500°C, denoted by the peak at 31.5°. As the annealing temperature was increased, the perovskite peaks were enhanced due to further crystallization and grain growth. A pyrochlore phase (peak at 30°) was not detected by XRD. Peak identification was done in accordance with the JCPDS data file.

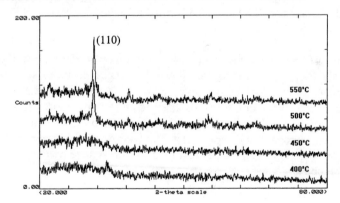

Figure 1:   XRD patterns of PZT (x = 0.47) films annealed at various temperatures ranging from 400 to 550°C.

The surface morphology of the films was characterized by AFM. Figure 2 illustrates the morphology of the PZT films annealed at 600 and 650°C for 1 hour. The films sintered at 500°C exhibited a microstructure with cracks and voids. On the other hand, the films sintered at 550°C were denser, with only microcracks at the surface. At higher magnification, some pockets of fine grains were found in samples sintered at 550°C, which can be attributed to pyrochlore phase formation. It has previously been reported that the perovskite phase of PZT films nucleates between the films and the substrate, and that grows toward the surface of the film[12]. In the present films processed at 550°C, good ferroelectric properties were obtained, demonstrating that pyrochlore phase pockets are confined to the surface of the films. The grain size of the films was also measured by AFM. Depending on annealing temperature, the grain size of the films was found to range from 20 to 200nm, as illustrated in Fig. 3.

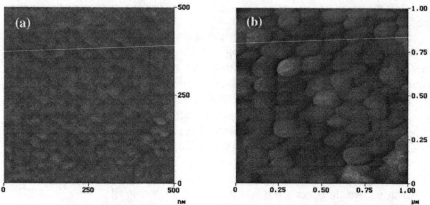

Figure 2: AFM images of PZT (x = 0.47) films annealed for 1 hour at (a) 600°C and (b) 650°C.

For PZT (x = 0.47) films processed on Pt/Silicon at 550°C, a well defined P-E hysteresis loop was formed, as shown in Figure 4. In these films, the remanent polarization ($P_r$) and coercive field ($E_c$) values ranged from 10 to 25$\mu$C/cm$^2$ and 35 to 50kV/cm, for films sintered at 550 and 600°C, respectively. These values compare well with those previously reported for PZT films prepared at low annealing temperature by sputtering. The well saturated hysteresis loops of the films annealed at 550°C indicates that the films crystallize predominantly into the perovskite phase.

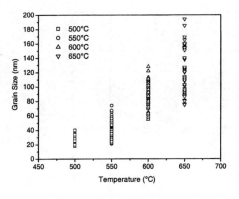 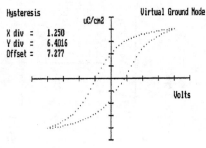

Figure 3: Grain size as a function of annealing temperature for PZT(53/47).

Figure 4: PZT(53/47) hysteresis loop of films annealed at 550°C.

Table I summarizes the remanent polarization ($P_r$) and coercive field ($E_c$) for PZT films with Zr/Ti ratios of 60/40, 53/47, 40/60 and 30/70 annealed at 500, 550 and 600°C for 1 hour in an oxygen atmosphere.

Table I: Ferroelectric properties of PZT thin films with compositions (Zr/Ti): 60/40; 53/47; 40/60 and 30/70 thermal annealed at 500, 550 and 600°C - 1 hour.

| Ferroelectric | Composition | | | |
|---|---|---|---|---|
| Properties | 60/40 | 53/47 | 40/60 | 30/70 |
| **500°C** | | | | |
| $P_r$ ($\mu C/cm^2$) | 3 | 2 | 7 | 13 |
| $E_c$ (kV/cm) | 10 | 10 | 60 | 80 |
| **550°C** | | | | |
| $P_r$ ($\mu C/cm^2$) | 3 | 10 | 15 | 20 |
| $E_c$ (kV/cm) | 15 | 35 | 80 | 100 |
| **600°C** | | | | |
| $P_r$ ($\mu C/cm^2$) | 18 | 25 | | |
| $E_c$ (kV/cm) | 40 | 50 | | |

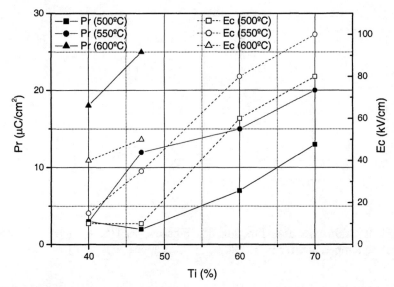

Figure 5: Remanent polarization (Pr) and coercive field (Ec) for $Pb(Zr_{1-x}Ti_x)O_3$ films for x = 0.40, 0.47, 0.60 and 0.70, annealed at 500, 550 and 600°C for 1 hour.

In Fig. 5, the ferroelectric properties of PZT films deposited onto platinum-coated silicon substrates and annealed at 550°C, show that both the $P_r$ and $E_c$ increase with titanium concentration. This fact could be related to the crystalline structure of the films, or to grain size, and is under investigation.

The ferroelectric properties for the PZT films prepared in this study compared favorably with those obtained by different methods in the literature[13-15]. Thus it is concluded that this method is an alternative to preparing PZT films at low processing temperatures.

**CONCLUSION**

Through the polymeric precursor method, we have obtained PZT films crystallized into a perovskite phase at temperature as low as 500°C. Films of lead zirconate titanate $Pb(Zr_{1-x}Ti_x)O_3$, for $0.40 \leq x \leq 0.70$, thermal annealed at 550°C presented ferroelectric hysteresis loops, confirming perovskite phase formation. The remanent polarization and coercive field for the samples annealed at 550°C for 1 hour are in the range of 3 to 20 $\mu C/cm^2$ and 15 to 100 kV/cm, respectively.

**ACKNOWLEDGEMENTS**

The authors are grateful to ONR, CAPES, CNPq and FAPESP for financial support of this work.

# REFERENCES

[1]B. Jaffe, W. R. Cook, and H. Jaffe, *"Piezoelectric Ceramics"*, pp. 135-83, Academic Press, New York (1971).

[2]H. Kanai, O. Furukawa, H. Abe, and Y. Yamashita, "Dielectric Properties of $Pb(X)ZrTiO_3$ (X= Ca, Sr, Ba) Ceramics", *J. Am. Ceram. Soc.*, **77**, 2620-24 (1994).

[3]S. S. Chandatreya, R. M. Fulrath, and J. A. Pask, "Reaction Mechanisms in the Formation of PZT Solid Solutions", *J. Am. Ceram. Soc.*, **64**, 422-25 (1981).

[4]K. Kakegawa, J. Mohri, T. Takahashi, H. Yamamura, and S. Shirasaki, "A Compositional Fluctuation and Properties of $Pb(Zr, Ti)O_3$", *Solid State Commun.*, **24**, 769-72 (1977).

[5]K. Kakegawa, K. Arai, Y. Sasaki, and T. Tomizawa, "Homogeneity and Properties of Lead Zirconate Prepared by a Combination of Thermal Spray Decomposition Method with Solid-state Reaction", *J. Am. Ceram. Soc.*, **71**, C49-52 (1988).

[6]G. Tomandl, A. Stiegelschmitt, and R. Boher, "Lowering the Sintering Temperature of PZT by Sol-gel Processing", p. 56 in *Science of Ceramic Chemical Processing. Part 1, Sol-Gel Science*. Edited by L. L. Hench and D. R. Ulrich, J. Wiley and Sons, New York (1986).

[7]M. A. Zaghete, C. O. Paiva-Santos, J. A. Varela, E. Longo, and Y. P. Mascarenhas, "Phase Characterization of Lead Zirconate Titanate Obtained from Organic Solution of Citrates", *J. Am. Ceram. Soc.*, **75**, 2089-93 (1992).

[8]T. Yamamoto, "Optimum Preparation Methods for Piezoelectric Ceramics and Their Evaluation", *Am. Ceram. Soc. Bull.*, **71**, 978-85 (1992).

[9]M. P. Pechini, US Patent N° 3.330.697, 1976.

[10]B.D. Stojanovic, M.A. Zaghete, C.R. Foschini, A.A. Cavalheiro, C.O. Paiva-Santos, M. Cilense, E. Longo, J. A. Varela, "Synthesis and characterization of 9.5/65/35 PLZT prepared from the polymeric precursors," *Mater. Chem. Phys.* **67** (1-3), 282-287 (2001).

[11]C.R. Foschini, P. Olivi, E. Longo, J.A. Varela, M.A. Zaghete, "Synthesis of PZT films by decomposition of organic precursors", *Ceramica*, **42**(275), 158-161 (1996).

[12]A. H. Carim, B. A. Tuttle, D. H. Doughty, and S. L. Martinez, "Microstructure of Solution-Processed Lead Zirconate Titanate (PZT) Thin-Films", *J. Am. Ceram. Soc.*, **74**, 1455-61 (1991).

[13]C. Yang, J. Liu, S. Zhang and Z. Chen, "Characterization of $Pb(Zr,Ti)O_3$ thin film prepared by pulsed laser deposition", *Mater. Sci. Eng. B*, in press.

[14]W.S. Moon, S.I. Woo, S. Bin Park, "Preparation and characterization of lead zirconate titanate thin films by liquid source misted chemical deposition", *Thin Solid Films*, **359** (1), 77-81 (2000).

[15]S.M. Cho, D.Y. Jeon, "Effect of annealing conditions on the leakage current characteristics of ferroelectric PZT thin films grown by sol-gel process" *Thin Solid Films*, **338** (1-2), 149-154 (1999).

# PIEZOELECTRIC PROPERTIES OF Nb AND V SUBSTITUTED $Bi_4Ti_3O_{12}$ FERROELECTRIC CERAMICS

H. Nagata, Y. Fujita, H. Enosawa and T. Takenaka
Tokyo University of Science,
Faculty of Science and Technology, Department of Electrical Engineering,
2641 Yamazaki, Noda, Chiba-ken 278-8510, Japan

## ABSTRACT

The piezoelectric properties of $Bi_4Ti_{3-x}Nb_xO_{12}$ [BITN-$x$] and $Bi_4Ti_{3-x}V_xO_{12}$ [BITV-$x$] ceramics are investigated. Furthermore, the grain orientation effects of BITN and BITV ceramics on their piezoelectric properties are studied using the hot-forging (HF) method. The optimal sintering temperature of the BITV ceramic becomes lower with increasing amount of doped-V ions. On the ordinarily fired (OF) sample with a random orientation, the electromechanical coupling factors, $k_{33}$, of BITN-0.08 and BITV-0.02 ceramics were 0.20 and 0.25, respectively. On the HF sample, the $k_{33}$ values of BITN-0.08 and BITV-0.04 ceramics were enhanced to 0.39 and 0.38, respectively.

## INTRODUCTION

Bismuth layer-structured ferroelectrics (BLSFs) [1-5] are attractive from the viewpoint of their application as electronic materials such as dielectrics, piezoelectrics and pyroelectrics, because BLSFs are characterized by their low dielectric constant, $\varepsilon_s$, high Curie temperature, $T_c$, and large anisotropy in the electromechanical coupling factor $k_t/k_p$ or $k_{33}/k_{31}$ [6-10]. Therefore, BLSF ceramics are seen as superior candidates for lead-free piezoelectric materials with high $T_c$ and large anisotropy, or for pyroelectric sensor materials with a large figure of merit.

$Bi_4Ti_3O_{12}$ (BIT) is a typical well-known BLSF [10-15]. Concerning its anisotropy, Cummins and Cross reported that the spontaneous polarizations of a BIT single crystal along the a- and c-axes are 50 and 4 $\mu C/cm^2$, respectively [12]. Therefore, it is thought that the BIT single crystal has good piezoelectricity. However, it is difficult to measure the piezoelectric properties of a BIT single crystal because it is platelike and very thin. On the other hand, the piezoelectric properties of BIT ceramics have been measured. However, large value have not been reported because of problems such as low resistivity and a large coercive field [6-7, 13-15]. To solve these problems, $Nb^{5+}$ and $V^{5+}$ ions were doped into a BIT ceramic to obtain higher resistivity [13-15]. In this study, $Bi_4Ti_{3-x}Nb_xO_{12}$ [BITN-$x$] and $Bi_4Ti_{3-x}V_xO_{12}$ [BITV-$x$] ceramics are studied regarding their piezoelectric properties. Furthermore, the grain orientation effects of BITN and BITV ceramics on their piezoelectric properties are studied using ceramics prepared by the hot-forging (HF) method.

**EXPERIMENTAL**

Ceramic samples were prepared by a conventional sintering technique (ordinarily fired, OF). Reagent-grade oxide powders of $Bi_2O_3$, $TiO_2$ $V_2O_5$ and $Nb_2O_5$ with 99+% purity were used as the starting materials. These materials were mixed by ball milling and calcined at 600 °C for 1 h and 850 °C for 2 h. After calcining, the ground and ball-milled powders were pressed into disks 20 mm in diameter and about 10 mm in thickness. These disks were sintered at 930-1170 °C for 2 h in air. Grain-oriented samples were prepared by the hot-forging method (HF) [7-9]. The grain orientation factor, $F$, was calculated using the Lotgering method [16].

The crystal structure was confirmed by X-ray diffraction analysis using CuK$\alpha$ radiation at a scanning speed of 1 deg/min. Samples were polished and thermally etched for microstructural examination by scanning electron microscopy (SEM, HITACH S-2400). The weight loss during the sintering process was analyzed by TG-DTA spectrometer (Rigaku, Thermo Plus 2). The TG measurement was performed at from RT to 1150 °C by using the BIT, BITN-0.08 and BITV-0.04 powder after the calcinations.

Electrodes made of fired-on Ag-Pd paste were formed for electrical measurements, such as dielectric properties. The temperature dependence of dielectric constant, $\varepsilon_s$, and dielectric loss tangent, tan$\delta$, were measured at 1 MHz using an automatic dielectric measurement system with a multifrequency LCR meter (YHP 4275A) in the temperature range from RT to 750 °C. The D-E hysteresis loop was observed at RT using a standard Sawyer-Tower circuit at 50 Hz. The temperature dependence of resistivity, $\rho$, was measured using a high-resistance meter (YHP 4329A and 4339B). Specimens for piezoelectric measurements were poled in stirred silicone oil at an applied field of $E_p$=7-12 kV/mm, a temperature of $T_p$=200-250°C, and a time of $t_p$= 7 min. Piezoelectric properties were measured by a resonance-antiresonance method on the basis of IEEE standards, using an impedance analyzer (YHP 4192A and 4194A). A longitudinal vibration of the 33 mode was measured using a rectangular specimen of $4 \times 2 \times 2$ $mm^3$. The electromechanical coupling factor, $k_{33}$, was calculated from the resonance and antiresonance frequencies.

**RESULTS AND DISCUSSION**

X-ray diffraction patterns for BITN and BITV ceramics (OF) show single

Table I Optimal sintering temperature and relative density for BITN and BITV ceramics.

| $x$ | BITN-$x$ | | BITV-$x$ | |
|---|---|---|---|---|
| | Sintering Temp. (°C) | Relative density (%) | Sintering Temp. (°C) | Relative density (%) |
| 0 | 1100 | 96.8 | 1100 | 96.8 |
| 0.01 | | | 1010 | 96.1 |
| 0.02 | 1100 | 97.1 | 980 | 96.6 |
| 0.03 | | | 950 | 98.5 |
| 0.04 | 1110 | 97.7 | 940 | 95.9 |
| 0.05 | | | 940 | 96.7 |
| 0.08 | 1130 | 96.6 | 930 | 96.8 |
| 0.12 | 1150 | 96.7 | | |

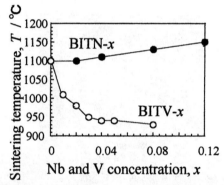

Figure 1 Compositional dependence of optimal sintering temperature.

phase of bismuth layer-structured compounds ($m=3$) with orthorhombic symmetry. No peaks of $Nb_2O_5$ and $V_2O_5$ were observed. The relative density is the ratio of observed density to theoretical density. Both BITN and BITV ceramics have a high relative density of more than 95 %. Table I and Figure 1 show the compositional dependence of optimum sintering temperature. Optimum sintering temperature was determined as obtaining the highest relative density. The optimum sintering temperature of BIT, BITN-0.08 and BITV-0.04 is at 1100, 1130 and 940 °C for 2 h, respectively. At these sintering conditions, BIT, BITN-0.08 and BITV0.04 ceramics have the highest relative density more than 95 %. For the BITN ceramic, the optimum sintering temperature becomes higher with increasing the amount of doped-Nb ions. On the other hand, that of the BITV ceramic becomes lower with increasing the amount of doped-V ions. It is supposed that V ions influence the sintering behavior by forming a liquid phase. At the lower sintering temperatures, it is

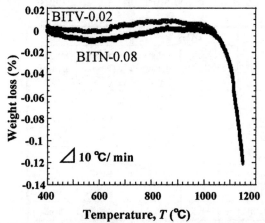

Figure 2 Weight loss as a function of the temperature on BITN-0.08 and BITV0.04 ceramics from the measurement of the TG analysis

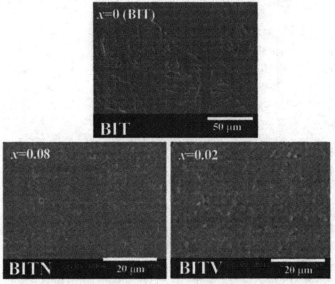

Figure 3  SEM micrographs of BITN-0 (BIT), BITN-0.08 and BITV-0.02 (OF) ceramics.

thought that an evaporation of Bi ions was suppressed in BITV ceramics.

Figure 2 shows the weight loss as a function of the temperature on BITN-0.08 and BITV0.04 ceramics from the measurement of the TG analysis. Each profile shows the weight loss at higher than nearly 1000 °C. Therefore, when samples were sintered at higher than 1000 °C, it is assumed that some components evaporated to air during the sintering process. It is thought that

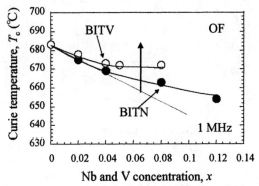

Figure 4 Curie temperature $T_c$ as a function of Nb and V concentration.

the component is Bi ions. From this result, BIT and BITN ceramics have the vaporization of Bi ions because of high sintering temperature at 1100-1130 °C. On the other hand, the evaporation of Bi ions was suppressed due to the lower sintering temperature of BITV ceramics.

Figure 3 shows SEM micrographs of BITN-0 (BIT) and BITN-0.08 ceramics and BITV-0.02 (OF). Grains of BIT are nearly rectangular and inhomogeneous. On the other hand, grains of BITN-0.08 and BITV-0.02 are spherical and relatively homogeneous. This difference of grain shape is caused by dopants. It is thought that the doped doped-Nb and V ions pinned the grain growth. This characteristic suggested that part of doped-Nb and V ions did not go into B-site of the perovskite cell on bismuth layer-structure and exist on the grain boundary and the triple point.

Figure 4 shows the Curie temperature, $T_c$, as a function of Nb and V concentration. The $T_c$ of the BIT ($x=0$) ceramic is 683 °C and gradually becomes lower with increasing Nb and V concentration. Therefore, it is thought that Nb and V ions occupy the B-site of the perovskite cell in the bismuth layer-structure. However, $T_c$ of BITV ceramics saturated with increasing a V concentration comparing to the BITN ceramics. Therefore, it is thought that V ions are difficult to substitute Ti ions and surplus V ions are exist on the grain boudary and triple point when the V concentration is increase. This consideration is due to an ionic radius of Ti, Nb and V ion. The ionic radius of $Ti^{4+}$ (IV coodination), $Nb^{5+}$ (IV coodination) and $V^{5+}$ (IV coodination) ion reported by R. D. Shannon [17] are 0.605, 0.64 and 0.54 Å, respectively. It is thought that the ionic radius of the V ion is too small to substitute to B-site of the perovskite cell in the bismuth layer-structure.

Figure 5 shows the resistivity, $\rho$, as a function of Nb and V concentration at RT. The $\rho$ of BIT ($x=0$) is about $10^{10}$-$10^{11}$ Ω·cm, and, those of BITN and BITV-0.02 ceramics are about $10^{13}$-$10^{14}$ Ω·cm. It is clear that the $\rho$ is

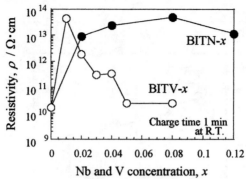

Figure 5 Resistivity, $\rho$, as a function of Nb and V concentration at RT.

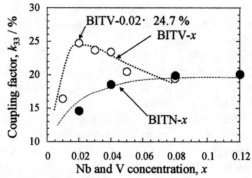

Figure 6 Compositional dependence of the electromechanical coupling factor, $k_{33}$ on OF-BITN and -BITV ceramics.

improved by donor doping. The optimum charge neutrality was observed for the composition of BITV-0.01 and BITN-0.08. It is considered that this compositional difference is due to sintering temperature, that is, the extent of evaporation of Bi ions.

Figure 6 shows the compositional dependence of the electromechanical coupling factor, $k_{33}$ on dopant concentration. For BITN ceramics, $k_{33}$ is 0.20 and is saturated for the composition of $x$=0.08 at a value of 0.20, while, BITV-0.02 exhibited a $k_{33}$ of 0.25, which very large for bismuth layer-structure ferroelectrics with a random orientation. Now, there is a question why is there a difference in $k_{33}$ between BITN and BITV ceramics. First, it is necessary to investigate up to what extent both ceramics were poled. Figure 7 shows the frequency dependence of impedance, $Z$, and phase, $\theta$, for BITN-0.08 and BITV-0.02 ceramics. These compositions of BITN and BITV ceramics had the largest $k_{33}$ value shown in Fig. 6. The maximum $\theta$ values of BITN-0.08 and BITV-0.02 are 81.0° and 88.3°, respectively. The maximum phase value is one of the standard to what extent samples were poled.  BITN

Ceramic Materials and Multilayer Electronic Devices

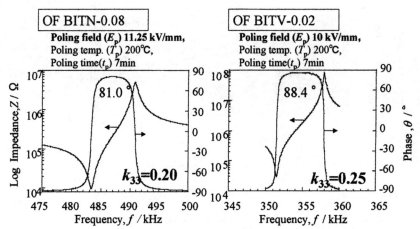

Figure 7 Frequency dependence of impedance, $Z$, and phase, $\theta$, of BITN-0.08 and BITV-0.02 ceramics.

ceramics is more difficult to pole sufficiently than BITV ceramics. From the measurement of D-E hysteresis loops, the coercive field, $E_c$, of the BITN-0.08 ceramic is larger (41 kV/cm) than that (27 kV/cm) of the BITV-0.02 ceramic. These results suggest that the domain movement in the BITN ceramic is more difficult than that of the BITV ceramic. It is supposed that these differences are due to the sintering temperature. In other words, since Bi ions evaporated from the BITN ceramic during the sintering process, many vacancies were induced and a domain pinning occurred easier in the BITN ceramics than in the BITV ceramics.

Figure 8 shows X-ray diffraction patterns of BITN-0.08 and BITV-0.04 ceramics for the OF and the perpendicular plane (polished) HF ceramics. Intensities of the 00$l$ plane of the HF samples are very high, so it is clear that grains were oriented along the c-axis. Orientation factors, $F$, of BITN-0.08 and BITV-0.04 were 91 % and 75 %, respectively.

Figure 9 shows SEM micrographs of parallel plane (//) for the forging axis of the HF BITN-0.08 and BITV-0.04 ceramic sintered at 1150 °C and 950 °C. The HF ceramics exhibited a unique microstructure in which plate-like grains were aligned along the perpendicular direction for the forging axis. A grain size of BITV ceramics is smaller than that of BITN ceramics because of the low sintering temperature.

Figure 10 shows the frequency dependence of the impedance, $Z$, and phase, $\theta$, on HF-BITN-0.08 and HF-BITV-0.04 ceramics. Good profiles were obtained and $k_{33}$ values BITN-0.08 and BITV- 0.04 ceramics were enhanced to 0.39 and 0.38, respectively. These values are about twice as large as than those of non-oriented one, and are larger than reported value [3] of HF BIT ceramics ($k_{33}$=0.27). In this investigation, a saturated $k_{33}$ value of the BIT

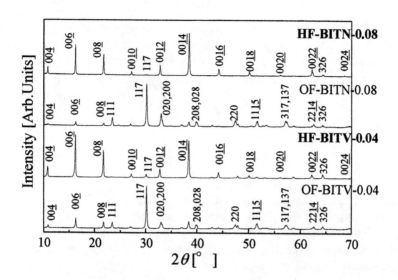

Figure 8 X-ray diffraction patterns of BITN-0.08 and BITV-0.04 ceramics for the OF and the perpendicular plane (polished) HF ceramics.

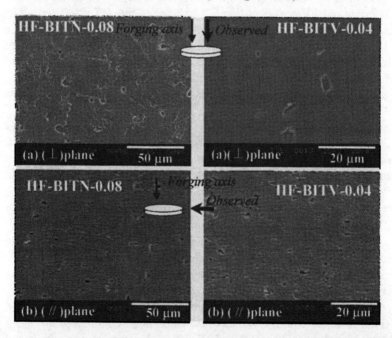

Figure 9 SEM micrographs of polished and thermally etched surfaces of the HF BITN-0.08 and BITV-0.04 ceramic sintered at 1150 ℃ and 950 ℃, respectively, ((a) perpendicular plane (⊥) and (b) parallel plane (//) for the forging axis).

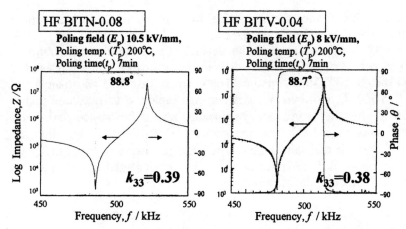

Figure 10 Frequency dependence of the impedance, Z, and phase, $\theta$, on HF-BITN-0.08 and HF-BITV- 0.04 ceramics.

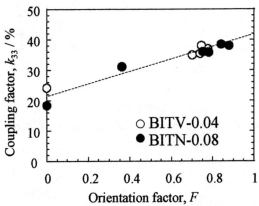

Figure 11 Coupling factor, $k_{33}$ versus orientation factor, $F$.

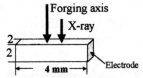

Figure 12 Shape of the $k_{33}$ specimen for XRD.

ceramic was not observed because of an electrical breakdown during the poling process.

Figure 11 shows the $k_{33}$ versus orientation factor, $F$. Accurate $F$ was obtained using the $k_{33}$ specimen, that is, XRD was performed directly on the $k_{33}$ specimen shown in fig. 12. From this measurement, the relationship between $k_{33}$ and $F$ is clear. $k_{33}$ increases linearly with increasing orientation factor. From this figure, the $k_{33}$ value for the specimen with a perfect orientation ($F$=1) would be almost 0.42.

Figure 12 shows the temperature dependence of the $k_{33}$ and a ratio of impedance peak/deep, P/D, obtained from the resonance and antiresonance wave on the HF BITN-0.08 ceramic. The $k_{33}$ more than 0.35 was maintained from RT to 650 °C. However, the P/D decrease rapidly at temperatures higher than 350 °C. In other words, sharp resonance and antiresonance peaks with high P/D more than 1000 was present up to 350 °C. It is clear that HF BITN-0.08 ceramic maintains high piezoelectric properties from RT to 350°C. The donor doped-BIT ceramics seem to be good candidate for lead-free high-temperature piezoelectric materials.

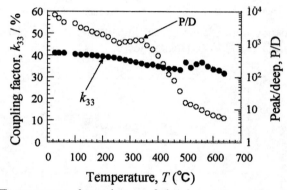

Figure 12 Temperature dependence of the $k_{33}$ and a ratio of impedance peak/deep, P/D on the HF BITN-0.08 ceramic.

## CONCLUSIONS

The piezoelectric properties of $Bi_4Ti_{3-x}Nb_xO_{12}$ [BITN-$x$] and $Bi_4Ti_{3-x}V_xO_{12}$ [BITV-$x$] ceramics are studied. Furthermore, grain orientation effects of BITN and BITV ceramics on their piezoelectric properties are studied using the hot-forging (HF) method. For the ordinarily fired (OF) samples, the electromechanical coupling factors, $k_{33}$, of BITN-0.08 and BITV-0.02 ceramics were enhanced to 0.20 and 0.25, which are very large for bismuth layer-structured ferroelectrics with a random orientation. For HF samples, the $k_{33}$ values of BITN-0.08 and BITV-0.04 ceramics were enhanced to 0.39 and 0.38, respectively. The BITN and BITV ceramics seem to be good candidate as lead-free high-temperature piezoelectric materials.

## ACKNOWLEDGMENT

This work was partially supported by a Grant-in-Aid for Scientific Research (B) (No. 15360352) from the Japan Society for the Promotion of Science.

Ceramic Materials and Multilayer Electronic Devices

**REFERENCES**

[1] B. Aurivillius, "Mixed Bismuth Oxides with Layer Lattices", *Ark. Kemi.*, **1** (1949), p. 499.

[2] G. A. Smolenskii, V. A. Isupov and A. I. Agranovskaya, "Ferroelectrics of the Oxygen-Octahedral Type with Layered Structure", *Sov. Phys.-Solid State*, **3** [3] (1961), p. 651.

[3] E. C. Subbarao, "Crystal Chemistry of Mixed Bismuth Oxide with Layer-Type Structure", *J. Am. Ceram. Soc.*, **45**, [4] (1962), p. 166.

[4] R. A. Armstrong and R. E. Newnham, "Bismuth Titanate Solid Solutions", *Mat. Res. Bul.l*, **7** (1972), p. 1025.

[5] L. E. Cross and R. C Pohanka, "Ferroelectricty in Bismuth Oxides Type Layer Structure Compounds", *Mat. Res. Bull.*, **6** (1971), p.939.

[6] S. Ikegami and I. Ueda, "Piezoelectricity in Ceramic of Ferroelectric Bismuth Compound with Layer Structure", *Jpn. J. Appl. Phys.*, **13** [10] (1974), p. 1572.

[7] T. Takenaka and K. Sakata, "Dielectric and Piezoelectric Properties of Some Bismuth Layer-Structure Ferroelectric Ceramics", *Jpn. J. IEEE (C)*, **J65-C** (1982), p. 512. (in Japanese)

[8] T. Takeuchi, T. Tani and Y. Saito, "Piezoelectric Properties of Bismuth Layer-Structured Ferroelectric Ceramics with a Preferred Orientation Processed by the Reactive Templated Grain Growth", *Jpn. J. Appl. Phys.*, **38** [9B] (1999), p. 5553.

[9] H. Nagata, T. Takahashi and T. Takenaka, "Piezoelectric Anisotropies of Bismuth Layer-Structured Ferroelectrics", *Transactions of the Materials Research Society of Japan*, **25** [1] (2000) p. 273.

[10] J. F. Dorrian, R. E. Newnham, D. K. Smith and M. I. Kay, "Crystal Structure of $Bi_4Ti_3O_{12}$", *Ferroelectrics*, **3** (1971), p. 17.

[11] S. E. Cummins and L. E. Cross, "Electrical and Optical Properties of Ferroelectric $Bi_4Ti_3O_{12}$ Single Crystal", *J. Appl. Phys.*, **39** [5] (1968), p. 2268.

[12] T. Takenaka and K. Sakata, "Grain Orientation and Electrical Properties of Hot-forged $Bi_4Ti_3O_{12}$ Ceramics", *Jpn. J. Appl. Phys.*, **19** [1] (1980), p. 31.

[13] M. Villegas, A. C. Caballero, C. Moure, P. Duran and J. F. Fernandez, "Factors Affecting the Electrical Conductivity of Donor-Doped $Bi_4Ti_3O_{12}$ Piezoelectric Ceramics", *J. Am. Ceram. Soc.*, **82** [9] (1999), p. 2411.

[14] H. S. Shulman, M. Testorf, D. Damjanovic and Nava Setter, "Microstructure, Electrical Conductivity, and Piezoelectric Properties of Bismuth Titanate", *J. Am. Ceram. Soc.*, **79** [12] (1996), p. 3124.

[15] Y. Noguchi and M. Miyayama, *Appl. Phys. Lett.*, Vol. **78** [13] (2001) p. 1903.

[16] F. K. Lotgering, *J. Inorg. Nucl. Chem.*, **9** (1959), p. 113.

[17] R. D. Shannon, "Revised Effective Ionic Radii and Systematic Studies of Interatomic Distances in Halides and Chalcogenides", *Acta Cryst.* **A 32** (1976) p. 751.

# ORIENTATION DEPENDENCE OF RESISTIVITY IN ANISOTROPIC CERAMIC COMPOSITES

David S. Mebane and Rosario A. Gerhardt[*]
Georgia Institute of Technology
School of Materials Science and Engineering
771 Ferst Dr. NW
Atlanta, GA 30332-0245

ABSTRACT

Anisotropic ceramic composites, composed of an alumina matrix containing various ratios of silicon carbide whisker inclusions, were measured using impedance spectroscopy and pole figure analysis. The impedance spectra were found to contain two semicircles: one at high frequencies, corresponding to bulk impedance phenomena; and one at low frequencies, corresponding to interfacial phenomena. The bulk resistivity of samples measured parallel to the hot-pressing direction showed a dramatic decrease in resistivity at a volume fraction of 8-10% $SiC_w$. The degree of sample anisotropy, as measured by taking bulk resistivity values parallel and perpendicular to the hot-pressing direction, was found to increase as $SiC_w$ volume fraction decreased towards the percolation threshold. The electrical property anisotropy was confirmed by texture analysis. Pole figure data for composites containing 10 and 20% volume fraction $SiC_w$ showed fairly consistent whisker orientation distributions for both measured orientations.

## INTRODUCTION

Whisker inclusions added to a ceramic matrix greatly improve the material's fracture toughness. For this reason, researchers continue to heavily investigate the properties of ceramic-matrix composites whose inclusions (generally the minority phase) possess whisker or fiber morphology. Early work established that the orientation of these anisotropic inclusions influences the resultant mechanical properties of the composite material[1-2]. More recent work showed that oriented inclusions often impart anisotropic electrical properties to the composite material, especially in systems wherein the inclusion phase possesses a higher conductivity than that of the matrix phase[3-4]. Ongoing efforts at the Georgia Institute of Technology focus on developing non-destructive characterization techniques by establishing relationships between the orientation and electrical properties of anisotropic systems[3,5-10]. The present work describes progress made in this area through direct observations on a series of silicon carbide whisker ($SiC_w$) –alumina ($Al_2O_3$) composites. In order to further investigate the complex relationships between whisker orientation and electrical anisotropy, both impedance spectroscopy and pole figure analysis were employed.

## EXPERIMENTAL

(1) Sample Preparation

Advanced Composite Materials Corporation of Greer, SC prepared alumina pellets with 0, 2, 4, 6, 8, 9, 10, 20 and 30% by volume $SiC_w$ (Silar® SC-9). The average whisker diameter is ~0.5 μm with an aspect ratio of ~10. Each specimen received the same hot-pressing treatment of 4400 psi at 1700°C for 20 minutes. The hot-pressing treatment is expected to create a whisker orientation resembling that shown in Figure 1[3]. A Buehler Isomet 1000 fitted with a diamond

**Figure 1**

Electrical measurements made normal to plane of slide. 'Z' and 'X' directions are parallel to measurement directions for each cut shown. Whiskers are not drawn to scale.

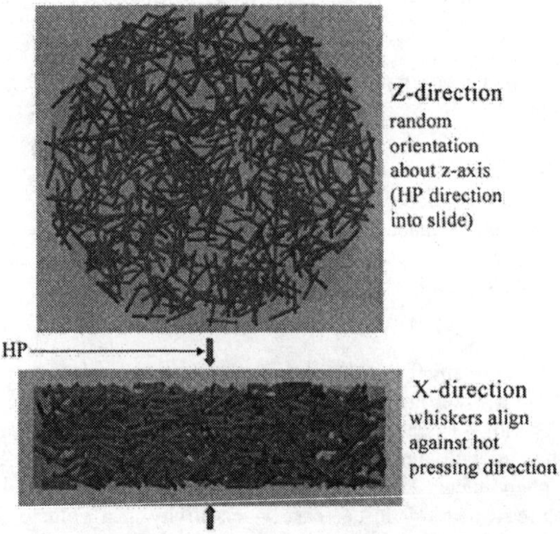

Z-direction
random orientation about z-axis (HP direction into slide)

HP

X-direction
whiskers align against hot pressing direction

wafering blade was used to section each sample of 10% SiC$_w$ content and above into ~1mm thick specimens oriented in 'z' and 'x' directions as shown in the figure. The electric field used for the measurements was applied parallel to the hot-pressing direction (labeled z-direction) and perpendicular to the hot-pressing direction (labeled x-direction).

(2) Electrical Measurements

Three impedance analyzers combined to provide the electrical analysis of the specimens. An HP 4192A produced impedance spectra for all samples of 10% SiC$_w$ content and above in the frequency range $10 - 10^7$ Hz, supplemented by an Agilent E4991A in the frequency range $10^6 - 10^9$ Hz. In addition, a Solartron SI 1260 with a 1296 dielectric attachment measured all samples of 8% SiC$_w$ content and below in the frequency range $10^{-2} - 10^6$ Hz.

(3) X-ray diffractometry

A Philips PW1800 diffractometer produced initial phase-identification scans of each sample with SiC$_w$ content equal to or greater than 10%. Indexing revealed that 4H-SiC constitutes the majority of the SiC phase (hexagonal structure). Diffractometry performed on a glass slide sprinkled with SiC whiskers confirmed the <001> direction as the whisker main axis.

A Philips X'Pert PW3040 MRD completed a goniometer scan, creating pole figure data for five distinguishable SiC peaks for 10% and 20% SiC$_w$ samples: (100), (004), (102), (110) and (114). The analysis program popLA turned the raw data into full texture through the method of harmonic analysis (to 20 coefficients)[11]. The program then produced re-calculated pole figures.

RESULTS AND DISCUSSION

A representative impedance plot in the complex plane, showing equivalent circuit and fitted curve, appears in Figure 2. The low-frequency semi-circle fits the model of a pure capacitor and resistor in parallel very well, displaying almost perfect semi-circular shape. The slightly depressed semicircle of the high frequencies requires the use of the constant phase element (CPE) construction in parallel with a resistor to obtain a good fit. (Using a CPE for both semicircles does not affect the quality of the fit since a CPE becomes a pure capacitor as its exponential term approaches 1.) Previous work by one of the authors suggests that the two loops shown represent an interfacial process (such as charge-transfer) at low frequencies and a bulk (charge-transport) process at high frequencies[3]. The current work confirms this conclusion. Evidence includes two primary factors: first, the perfection of the low-frequency semicircles indicates a mechanism very similar to a pure capacitor and resistor in parallel, which probably requires a smooth parallel plate geometry[12]. Second, circuit modeling reveals low-frequency capacitance figures in the range of 3.5-5.5 nF, values too high to represent anything other than an interfacial phenomenon for this particular system.

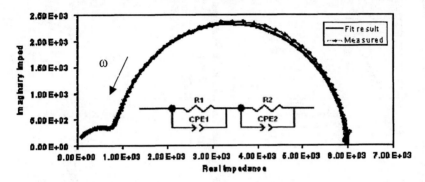

**Figure 2.** Sample Impedance Spectrum with equivalent circuit and fitted curve.

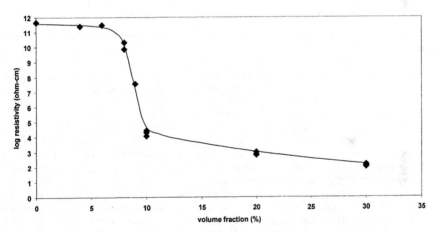

**Figure 3.** Bulk resistivity of $SiC_w$-$Al_2O_3$ composite pellets measured in the z-direction and plotted as a function of SiC whisker volume fraction. Sudden drop in resistivity indicates onset of percolation.

High-frequency intercepts, calculated for a wide variety of samples at different compositions are plotted against volume fraction for compositions in the range of 0-30% $SiC_w$ in Fig. 3. The graph shows that the percolation threshold for this system occurs in the region of 8-10% $SiC_w$. All measurements shown in the figure constitute data from measurements taken from as-received samples in the z-direction.

For those samples above the percolation threshold, specimens were measured both in the x-as well as the z-direction. As the data in Fig. 4 shows, the two-semicircle impedance spectrum appears for all samples, not just for those with whiskers aligned mostly against the measurement direction. It seems clear that, at least for the $Al_2O_3$-$SiC_w$ system studied here, the two semicircles do not represent responses of the matrix and inclusions separately, as reported for the $SiC_w$-$Si_3N_4$ system (in which the resistivity of the matrix is very near to that of the inclusions)[4].

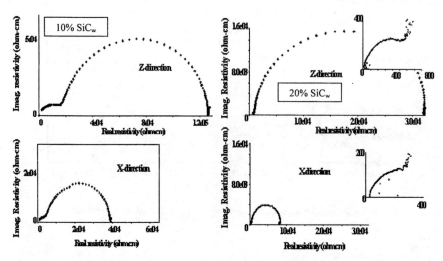

**Figure 4.** Impedance spectra in the z- and x-directions for samples containing 10% and 20% $SiC_w$.

Our results also differ considerably from those obtained by Zhang et al.[13], who obtained inductive loops for $Al_2O_3$-$SiC_w$ of similar compositions. Perhaps the larger aspect ratio of their whiskers (~20 vs 10 in this study) or other issues concerning sample homogeneity or measurement setup played a role in this discrepancy. Recent work by Mason et al.[14-16] on simulated cement containing small volume fractions of steel and carbon fiber inclusions showed that the bulk impedance arc splits into two upon addition of fibers at volume fractions they believe are below the percolation threshold. Although no similar effect appeared in the spectra for the samples below the percolation threshold in this study (<8% $SiC_w$), the extremely high resistivity of the $Al_2O_3$ matrix with respect to the $SiC_w$ may cause an arc overlap. However, one expects that fiber connectivity (the number of complete conducting pathways through the sample in the direction of measurement) will dominate the bulk resistance above the percolation threshold[9], and that the impedance spectra will display the two-arc character as in Fig. 4. The appearance of the high-frequency semicircle at frequencies above $10^7$ Hz for x-direction samples in the present study may partially account for previous investigators' inability to detect separate high-frequency responses for certain orientations.

The results of texture analysis for two representative samples (10 and 20% $SiC_w$) appear in Figures 5(a) and (b) respectively. The figures show the findings in two formats: as pole figures of the <001> (whisker-axis) direction, and the corresponding misorientation curves for both z- and x-directions. The misorientation curves represent the volume fraction of whiskers that hold a particular orientation with respect to the sample normal, i.e., the number on the graph at 0°

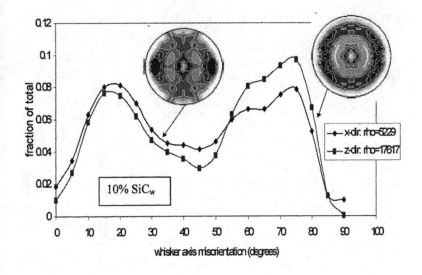

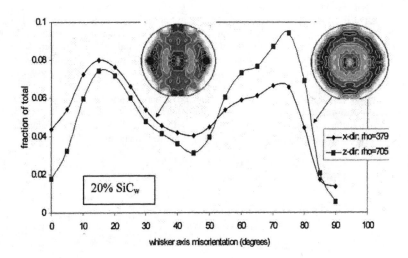

**Figure 5.** <001> Pole figures and misorientation curves for the x-dir and z-dir 10% and 20% SiC$_w$-alumina composite samples. Resistivity of each specimen is included in the figures.

Ceramic Materials and Multilayer Electronic Devices

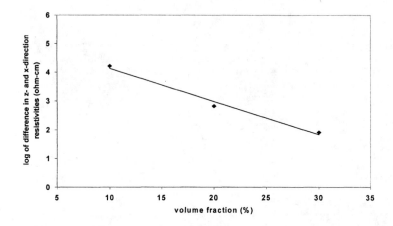

**Figure 6.** Resistivity difference between z- and x- directions plotted against volume fraction of SiC$_w$.

corresponds to a whisker pointing straight up toward the sample surface (parallel to either the z- or x-direction). These curves clearly illustrate the preferred orientation found in these samples.

Figure 6 shows the log of the difference in bulk resistivity between x- and z-directions in the two samples represented in Figure 5 plus the data for a 30% SiC$_w$ sample plotted versus volume fraction. The curve fit shows an inverse linear relationship between the composition and the log of the difference in resistivity between the two measured directions. The consistency shown in the shape of the misorientation curves for the 10% SiC$_w$ (Figure 5(a)) and 20% SiC$_w$ (Figure 5(b)) specimens along with the quantitative correspondence derived by integrating each graph from 0 to 45° (Table 1) means that the linear relationship described by Figure 6 probably holds significance for this system.

The slope of the graph in Figure 6 will depend on dispersion quality, whisker aspect ratio, constituent component conductivity, the shapes of the misorientation curves and other factors. Future work will focus on uncovering the meaning of this slope as well as modeling the dependence of overall conductivity on the shape of the misorientation curves.

**Table 1**
Total orientations within a 45° span for 10 and 20% SiC$_w$ samples

| Sample | Percentage of Orientations Within 0-45° |
|--------|----------------------------------------|
| 10% (x) | .532 |
| 10% (z) | .461 |
| 20% (x) | .574 |
| 20% (z) | .473 |

Ceramic Materials and Multilayer Electronic Devices

CONCLUSIONS

Impedance spectroscopy analysis shows that the high-frequency semicircle of the impedance spectra represents bulk impedance while the low frequency semicircle represents an interfacial-type impedance response, such as charge transfer, in the measured $Al_2O_3/SiC_w$ composite samples. Bulk resistivities of samples measured in the z-direction (parallel to the hot-pressing direction) showed that the percolation threshold in the $Al_2O_3/SiC_w$ composite system lies between 8-10% $SiC_w$. The investigation also uncovered a definite, quantifiable relationship between the bulk resistivity of $Al_2O_3/SiC_w$ composites and the orientation of the whiskers, expressed as a linear relationship between the difference in samples' resistivities measured parallel and transverse to the hot-pressing direction and volume fraction. Texture analysis allows for the validity of the model. Future work will utilize x-ray diffraction texture analysis techniques along with impedance spectroscopy and modeling to derive a more rigorous relationship between the orientation of whiskers and the anisotropic resistivity.

ACKNOWLEDGEMENTS

The authors thank the NSF for its support of this research under grant DMR-0076153. Special thanks to Tom Quantrille, Jim Rhodes, Bill Rogers and Hillar Rootare at Advanced Composite Materials Corporation for providing the samples used in this study. Thanks also to Hamid Garmestani and Dongsheng Li for help with the texture analysis. Finally, Runqing Ou for assistance with impedance spectroscopy.

REFERENCES

1. P. F. Becher and G. C. Wei, "Toughening Behavior in SiC-Whisker Reinforced Alumina," *J. Am. Ceram. Soc.*, **67** [12] C-267 – C-269 (1984).

2. F. Lee, M. S. Sandlin and K. J. Bowman, "Toughness Anisotropy in Textured Ceramic Composite," *J. Am. Ceram. Soc.*, **75** [6] 1522-28 (1993).

3. R. A. Gerhardt and R. Ruh, "Volume Fraction and Whisker Orientation Dependence of the Electrical Properties of SiC-Whisker-Reinfirced Mullite Composites," *J. Am. Ceram. Soc.*, **84** [10] 2328-34 (2001).

4. C.-A. Wang, Y. Huang, Z. Xie, Y. Li, and Z. Zhang, "Complex Impedance Analysis on the Orientation Effect of Whiskers in Oriented Silicon Carbide Whisker/Silicon Nitride Composites," *J. Am. Ceram. Soc.*, **83** [11] 2689-92 (2000).

5. R. A. Gerhardt, "Microstructural Characterization of Composites Via Electrical Measurements" *Ceram. Eng. Sci. Pro.*, **15**, 1174 (1994).

6. R. A. Gerhardt, "Electrically Based Non-Destructive Microstructural Characterization of All Classes of Materials," *Mat. Res. Symp. Proc.*, **591**, 93-104 (2000).

7. J. Runyan, R. A. Gerhardt and R. Ruh, "Electrical Properties of Boron Nitride Matrix Composites: I, Analysis of McLachlan Equation and Modeling of the Conductivity of Boron Nitride-Boron Carbide and Boron Nitride-Silicon Carbide Composites," *J. Am. Ceram. Soc.*, **84** [7] 1490-96 (2001).

8. J. Runyan, R. A. Gerhardt and R. Ruh, "Electrical Properties of Boron Nitride Matrix Composites: II, Dielectric Relaxations in Boron Nitride-Silicon Carbide Composites," *J. Am. Ceram. Soc.*, **84** [7] 1497-503 (2001).

9. R. A. Gerhardt, J. Runyan, C. Sana, D. S. McLachlan and R. Ruh, "Electrical Properties of Boron Nitride Matrix Composites: III, Observations Near the Percolation Threshold in BN-B4C Composites," *J. Am. Ceram. Soc.*, **84** [10] 2335-42 (2001).

10. R. Ou, R. A. Gerhardt and R.J. Samuels, "Structure-Electrical Property Study of Anisotropic Polyaniline Films," *J. Polymer Sc. Part B: Polymer Physics vol. 41*, 823-841(2003).

11. H.-J. Bunge, *Texture Analysis in Materials Science: Mathematical Methods*, London, Boston: Butterworths, 1982.

12. W. Scheider, "Theory of the Frequency Dispersion of Electrode Polarization. Topology of Networks With Fractional Power Frequency Dependence," *J. Phys. Chem.*, 79 [2] 127-36 (1975).

13. J. Zhang, H. Huang, L. Cao, F. Xia and G. Li, "Semiconductive Property and Impedance Spectra of Alumina-Silicon Carbide Whisker Composites," *J.Am.Ceram.Soc.* **75**[8],2286-88(1992).

14. T. O. Mason, M. A. Campo, A. D. Hixson and L. Y. Woo, "Impedance Spectroscopy of Fiber-Reinforced Cement Composites," *Cem. Concr. Comp.*, 24 [5] 457-65 (2002).

15. A. D. Hixson, L. Y. Woo, M. A. Campo, T. O. Mason and E. J. Garboczi, "Intrinsic Conductivity of Short Conductive Fibers in Composites by Impedance Spectroscopy," *J. Electrocer.*, 7, 189-95 (2001).

16. J. M. Torrents, T. O. Mason and E. J. Garboczi, "Impedance Spectra of Fiber Reinforced Cement-Based Composites: A Modeling Approach," *Cem. Concr. Res.*, **30** [4] 585-92 (2000).

# ELECTRICAL PROPERTIES OF $Al_2O_3$-$CeO_2$ COMPOSITES

R. Ou and R. A. Gerhardt
School of Materials Science and Engineering
Georgia Institute of Technology
Atlanta, GA 30332-0245

D. Semler-Rosenthal and R. A. McCauley
Department of Ceramic and Materials Engineering
Rutgers – The State University of New Jersey
Piscataway, NJ 08854-8065

ABSTRACT
The electrical properties of $Al_2O_3$:$CeO_2$ composite are interesting because of the drastically different electrical characteristics of the two components. $Al_2O_3$ is an insulator while $CeO_2$ is an ionic conductor. In this study, the electrical properties of ceramic compacts containing various ratios of $Al_2O_3$ and $CeO_2$ were studied by the impedance spectroscopic method in the frequency range between $10^{-5}$ Hz to $10^9$ Hz. It was found that the high frequency room temperature dielectric constant increases and the resistivity decreases as a function of increasing $CeO_2$ volume fraction. X-ray diffraction reveals two separate crystalline phases in the composite, corresponding to pure $Al_2O_3$ and pure $CeO_2$. For high $Al_2O_3$ and low $CeO_2$ compositions ($CeO_2\% \leq 20\%$), a new phase is also found. Presence of the new compound modifies the electrical behavior of the composites.

INTRODUCTION
$Al_2O_3$-$CeO_2$ is a composite, which finds its use in environmental applications, where it serves as a catalyst support for treating exhaust gases.[1] $CeO_2$ is also a possible sintering agent for $Al_2O_3$ since it was found that addition of $CeO_2$ to $Al_2O_3$ enhances the mechanical properties of $Al_2O_3$.[2] Since $Al_2O_3$ is an insulator[3] and $CeO_2$[4] is an ionic conductor, the $Al_2O_3$-$CeO_2$ system can be expected to exhibit a wide spectrum of electrical properties.

The purpose of the present study is to address the electrical properties of the $Al_2O_3$-$CeO_2$ system by the AC impedance method. By combining three different impedance analyzers, we are able to collect impedance data over a broad frequency range (from $10^{-5}$ Hz to $10^9$ Hz). In addition to providing frequency dependent electrical responses of the composites, impedance data can be used to obtain important structural information when coupled with other structural characterization tools.

EXPERIMENTAL

Sample Fabrication[2]

A 1:1 ratio of mixed $Al_2O_3$-$CeO_2$ powder and distilled water were combined in a beaker and wet mixed with a magnetic stirrer for one hour. This mixture was then placed into a drying oven overnight at 100°C. Seven percent distilled water was then added to the mixture along with 20 mm diameter alumina milling media and the mixture was ball-milled for ½ hour. The mixture was then passed through a 60 mesh sieve and pressed at 10,000 psi into bars of dimensions 102.1mm × 25.7mm × 10.2mm.

The bars were fired to 1600°C in eight hours, soaked for two hours, and cooled to room temperature in eight hours. Test specimens were sliced from the bars and polished into rectangles of dimensions 21mm × 8mm × 2mm. For impedance measurements, the test specimens were coated with silver paint and dried overnight.

X-ray Diffraction

The X-ray diffraction patterns were run on a Philips PW 1800 X-ray diffractometer with a wavelength of 1.5406 Å. The 2θ angle range measured was from 10° to 80°. The step size was 0.04° and the collection time was 1 second/step.

Impedance Measurements

Impedance measurements were performed using three different instruments: Solartron 1260 Impedance/Gain Phase Analyzer with Solartron 1296 Dielectric Interface, HP 4192A LF Impedance Analyzer, and Agilent 4991A RF Impedance/Material Analyzer. A summary of the measurement conditions is listed in Table I.

Table I. Impedance equipment and conditions used in the experiments.

| Instrument | Frequency range (Hz) | AC level(V) | DC bias(V) |
|---|---|---|---|
| Solartron 1296/1260 | $10^{-5} \sim 10^7$ | 0.1 | 0 |
| HP 4192A | $5 \sim 10^7$ | 0.5 | 0 |
| Agilent E4991A | $10^6 \sim 3 \times 10^9$ | 0.1 | 0 |

RESULTS AND DISCUSSION

X-ray Diffraction

Figure 1 shows the X-ray diffraction patterns of the $Al_2O_3$ –$CeO_2$ composites together with those of pure $Al_2O_3$ and pure $CeO_2$. Pure $Al_2O_3$ has a rhombohedral structure while pure $CeO_2$ has a cubic structure. Except for specimens with 90% $Al_2O_3$ - 10% $CeO_2$ and 80% $Al_2O_3$ - 20% $CeO_2$, the diffraction patterns of the composites are a mere mixture of the two individual components, with no new peaks and no evidence of peak shifting. It is clear that for these compositions, the composites exist in two distinct phases. The lack of strong interaction between $Al_2O_3$ and $CeO_2$ is in contrast with the AlN-SiC system we studied earlier where an extended solid solution of SiC in AlN was found to exist.[5]

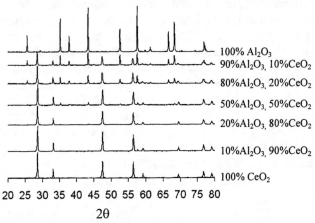

Figure 1. X-ray diffraction patterns of $Al_2O_3$-$CeO_2$ composites.

For specimens with 90% $Al_2O_3$ - 10% $CeO_2$ and 80% $Al_2O_3$ - 20% $CeO_2$, some new peaks, albeit small, are also found in addition to the pure $Al_2O_3$ and pure $CeO_2$ peaks. Figure 2 is an expanded view of the diffraction patterns of the two composites together with those of pure $Al_2O_3$ and pure $CeO_2$. The peaks indicated by the arrows neither belong to $Al_2O_3$ nor to $CeO_2$. However, these peaks correspond quite well with those reported for the compound $LaAl_{11}O_{18}$.[6] It is believed that the compound $CeAl_{11}O_{18}$ has very similar crystal structure to

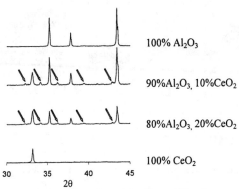

Figure 2. Detailed inspection of the X-ray diffraction patterns of high $Al_2O_3$-low $CeO_2$ compositions. Arrows indicate the presence of a new phase.

LaAl$_{11}$O$_{18}$ since the elements Ce and La belong to the same family and they are adjacent in the periodic table. The crystal radii of Ce$^{3+}$ and La$^{3+}$ are 1.15Å and 1.17Å,[7] respectively. It is very likely that the unidentified peaks are due to the compound CeAl$_{11}$O$_{18}$ since there is no reason to believe La exists in the system in any significant amount.

Electrical Properties

The frequency dependent dielectric constants of the Al$_2$O$_3$-CeO$_2$ composites are shown in Figure 3. In all cases, the dielectric constant is seen to increase at lower frequencies. The increase, which is more significant for specimens containing CeO$_2$, can be attributed to the existence of ionic conducting species and space charges accumulated at the interfaces in the case of pure Al$_2$O$_3$. The inset of Figure 3 shows the high frequency end of the dielectric spectra. Data plotted in this figure came from two instruments. Data below 10$^6$ Hz were obtained with Solartron 1260/1296 while data above 10$^6$ were obtained using the Agilent E4991A. Overall, the match of datapoints between the two instruments is good except for samples with higher dielectric constant, and hence higher loss, where the Agilent instrument gives slightly higher values.

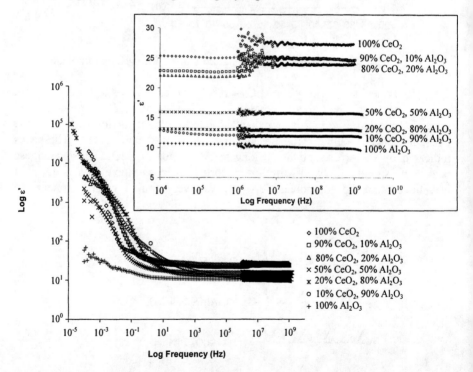

Figure 3. Dielectric constant vs. frequency for various Al$_2$O$_3$-CeO$_2$ compositions.

　Ceramic Materials and Multilayer Electronic Devices

Figure 4 shows the high frequency dielectric constant vs. the mole fraction of $CeO_2$. As expected, the dielectric constant of the composite increases with increasing $CeO_2$ content.

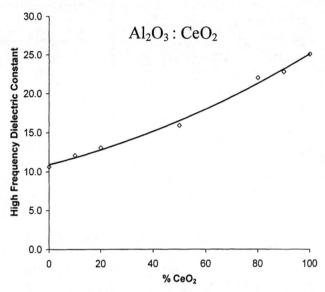

Figure 4. High frequency dielectric constant vs. %$CeO_2$.

Since $CeO_2$ is an ionic conductor, it would be interesting to examine the electrical properties of the composite with the impedance function. Figure 5 shows the complex plane resistivity plot of the specimen with 10% $Al_2O_3$ - 90% $CeO_2$. Complex resistivity rather than impedance is used in this figure to remove the effect of sample geometry. The open symbols are experimental data while the solid curve is a fitted result for an equivalent circuit model containing two parallel R-CPE circuits in series as shown to the right of Figure 5. Close to the origin of Figure 5 is a semicircle, followed by a large tail, which is in fact the beginning of another large semicircle. As data of increasing frequency goes from right to left in the complex resistivity plot, the large semicircle represents the low frequency data. This low frequency semicircle is generally caused by an interfacial polarization. The small high frequency semicircle, on the other hand, is due to the bulk composite material. The bulk and interfacial relaxations are described by the two parallel R-CPE circuits, respectively. In the model, the CPE is a constant phase element which is used in place of a capacitor to account for a depressed semicircle.[8] From equivalent circuit fitting, the bulk resistivity, which corresponds graphically to the intercept of the extrapolated semicircle to the real axis, can be calculated.

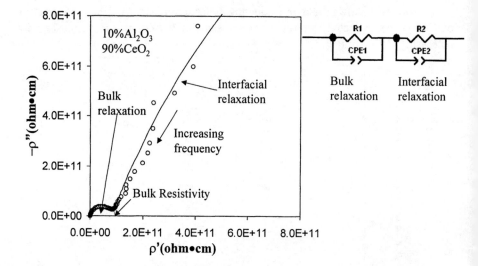

Figure 5. Complex plane impedance plot of 10%Al$_2$O$_3$-90%CeO$_2$ specimen.

Figure 6 shows the calculated bulk resistivity as a function of CeO$_2$ content. A general trend of decreasing bulk resistivity with increasing CeO$_2$ content is observed. This is reasonable since CeO$_2$ is the more conducting material. However, the decrease in bulk resistivity is steeper for low CeO$_2$ content and a minimum in bulk resistivity is obtained at 20 CeO$_2$%. This may be attributed to the existence of a new compound, CeAl$_{11}$O$_{18}$, as suggested by X-ray diffraction.

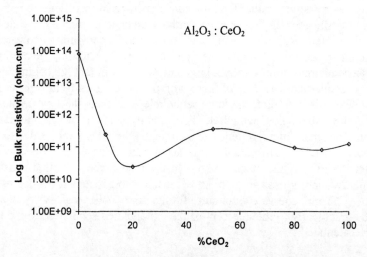

Figure 6. Bulk resistivity vs. CeO$_2$ fraction.

## CONCLUSIONS

A series of $Al_2O_3$ - $CeO_2$ composites have been examined by X-ray diffraction and AC impedance spectroscopy. Two separate crystalline phases were identified in the composite, corresponding to pure $Al_2O_3$ and pure $CeO_2$. A new phase is also found for high $Al_2O_3$ and low $CeO_2$ compositions (CeO2% $\leq$ 20%) in addition to the two pure phases. With increasing CeO2%, the high frequency dielectric constant of the composite increases while the bulk resistivity decreases. For high $Al_2O_3$ and low $CeO_2$ compositions, where a new compound is found, the bulk resistivity decreases more significantly.

## ACKNOWLEDGEMENT

The authors would like to acknowledge funding support from the National Science Foundation under DMR-0076153.

## REFERENCES

[1] B. Djuricic, S. Pickering, D. McGarry, P. Tambuyser, and P. Thomas, "Preparation and Properties of Alumina-Ceria Nano-Nano Composites," *Journal of Materials Science*, **34**, 1911-19 (1999).

[2] D. Semler-Rosenthal, MS Thesis, "Characterization of Ceria-Alumina Mixtures," Rutgers – The State University of New Jersey (1986).

[3] A. J. Moulson, and J. M. Herbert, "Alumina"; pp. 212-221 in *Electroceramics – Materials properties applications*. Chapman & Hall, London, 1990.

[4] H. L. Tuller, "Highly Conductive Ceramics"; pp. 379-433 in *Ceramic Materials for Electronics-Processing, Properties, and Applications*, Edited by R. C. Buchanan. Marcel Dekker, New York, 1991.

[5] R. Ou, R. A. Gerhardt, and R. Ruh, "Electrical Properties of SiC-AlN Composites," *Ceramic Engineering and Science Proceedings*, 24 [3-4], in press, (2003).

[6] R. C. Ropp, and G. G. Libowitz, " The Nature of the Alumina-Rich Phase in the System $La_2O_3$-$Al_2O_3$," *Journal of the American Ceramic Society*, **61** [11-12] 473-75 (1978).

[7] R. D. Shannon, and C. T. Prewitt, "Effective Ionic Radii in Oxides and Fluorides," *Acta. Cryst.* **B25**, 925-46 (1969).

[8] J. R. Macdonald, *Impedance Spectroscopy*, John Wiley and Sons, New York, 1987.

# FINITE ELEMENT ANALYSIS OF CURRENT DENSITY PATTERNS IN CONDUCTOR-INSULATOR COMPOSITES

Aparna Trimurty Jue and Rosario A. Gerhardt
School of Materials Science and Engineering
Georgia Institute of Technology
Atlanta, GA 30332-0245

## ABSTRACT
The objective of this research is to evaluate if the current density ($j$) distribution of conductor-insulator composites is affected by the arrangement of the respective materials within a composite. The results obtained are compared with the theoretically expected values of the Maxwell-Wagner two-layer condenser model. In this study, series and parallel composite models are simulated via finite element analysis and their current density is mapped. In addition, the total effective composite resistivity is calculated for later comparison studies. The results indicate that Maxwell-Wagner theory does not hold when the resistivity difference of the composite layers is significantly large. This demonstrates that the number and the arrangement of layers within a composite is indeed a factor in determining the effective electrical properties of a composite.

## INTRODUCTION
The Maxwell-Wagner effect illustrates that an applied electric field will induce electrical charges at the boundary between a particle and the surrounding medium when electrical properties such as dielectric constants and electrical resistivities are dissimilar. The Maxwell-Wagner two-layer condenser model[1] consists of successive metal-insulator layers of similar thickness and volume fraction as depicted schematically in Figure 1. The model postulates that as long as the total volume fraction of the two materials is kept constant, as shown in Figs. 1(a)-(c), the electrical response ought to remain identical. This is true for when a DC field is suddenly applied to the condenser so that the initial field distribution corresponds to the electrostatic requirement of constant flux density. However, due to the different electrical responses of the two constituent phases, an interfacial polarization is expected to occur at the interfaces between these two materials. Moreover, this polarization occurs due to the motion of charge carriers in electrically heterogeneous materials, where charge displacement may occur more easily through one phase than the other. This different response results in charge build up at the interfaces between the two materials. Therefore, even though nothing has really changed, subdividing the material into more layers while preserving volume fraction and total thickness of each material, may under some conditions alter the effective properties of the composite.

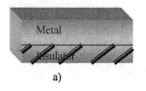 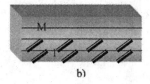 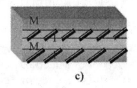

a)                          b)                          c)

**Figure 1. Maxwell-Wagner condensers with equivalent electrical**

Early work by Sillars[2] demonstrated that field distortions occur when the shape and orientation of the particles changes with respect to the direction of the applied electric field. This is especially obvious by comparing series and parallel arrangements of layers. More recently, work by Hilfer[3] suggested that for a given volume fraction of porosity, the dielectric properties can change substantially as the size and distribution of pores is varied. Many other experimental results[4-6] also point to the possibility that size, shape and distribution of the second phase can have substantial effects on the resultant effective electrical properties of composites.

The purpose of the present study is to provide a platform for comparison with future experimental results of series and parallel composites. Finite element simulations of the current density distributions of layered composites are used to evaluate the effect of the resistivity ratio of the two components and the number of layers present.

EXPERIMENTAL

The composite models were simulated using QuickField 4.3 FEA software. A summary of the model combinations is seen in Table I. A primary concern during model simulation was the extent to which real world experimental conditions could be accounted for. This was resolved by comparing the current density patterns of specimens subjected to three different surface conditions: (1) no surrounding air with no electrodes, (2) surrounding air with no electrodes and (3) surrounding air with contacting electrodes. Figure 2 displays the Maxwell-Wagner FEA Quickfield 2-Layer series model. The model depicted includes air

**Table I.** Experimental simulation models run with Quickfield.

| Material Type | Resistivity/ ρ (ohm-cm) | Combination materials | Configuration | Phase volume fractions (%) |
|---|---|---|---|---|
| Conductor | $1 \times 10^{+6}$ | Insulator | Series, Parallel | 50-50;25-75;40-60 |
| Insulator | $1 \times 10^{-6}$ | Conductor | Series, Parallel | 50-50;25-75;40-60 |
| High conducting semiconductor | $1 \times 10^{+3}$ | Insulator; Low conducting semiconductor | Series, Parallel | 50-50;25-75;40-60 |
| Low conducting semiconductor | $1 \times 10^{-3}$ | High conducting semiconductor | Series, Parallel | 50-50;25-75;40-60 |

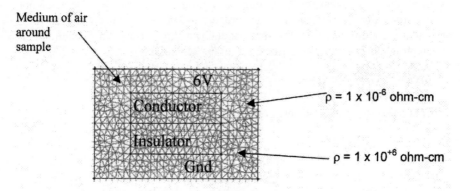

Medium of air around sample

6V

Conductor

Insulator

Gnd

$\rho = 1 \times 10^{-6}$ ohm-cm

$\rho = 1 \times 10^{+6}$ ohm-cm

Figure 2. Sample Quickfield model file of the two-layer condenser.

as the surrounding medium. As shown, a voltage of 6V was used as the applied voltage. Fig.2 also shows an example of the mesh used for the simulations. All of the initial simulations were conducted with the voltage applied to the lower resistivity material. The results for the three surface conditions described above are presented in Figure 3. It was found that when the model does not include surrounding air or electrodes, the calculated resistivity is almost four orders of magnitude below the minimum expected value. As a result, this model was immediately discarded as a non-physical result. In the second scenario, addition of an air layer but not separate electrode contacting layers results in a reasonable calculated resistivity; however, the current density map generated appears erroneous, as the patterns are contrary to what is expected. There appears to be current activity in the solid part of the conducting material, which is contrary to classical conductor physics, where charge accumulates in the edges of a conductor while the solid part exhibits zero electrical field. This was the elimination factor used for this model. The final model has an air layer surrounding the composite as

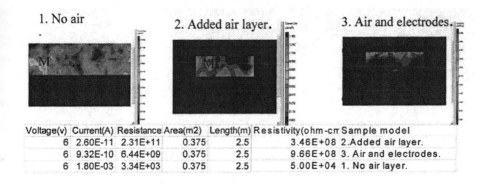

| Voltage(v) | Current(A) | Resistance | Area(m2) | Length(m) | Resistivity(ohm-cm) | Sample model |
|---|---|---|---|---|---|---|
| 6 | 2.60E-11 | 2.31E+11 | 0.375 | 2.5 | 3.46E+08 | 2. Added air layer. |
| 6 | 9.32E-10 | 6.44E+09 | 0.375 | 2.5 | 9.66E+08 | 3. Air and electrodes. |
| 6 | 1.80E-03 | 3.34E+03 | 0.375 | 2.5 | 5.00E+04 | 1. No air layer. |

Figure 3. Effect of FEA experimental conditions on 2-layer condenser model.

well as a separate layer for the voltage and ground electrodes. This yields a good resistivity value, as well as an appropriate current density map. Therefore, the boundary conditions used for this model (i.e. air surrounding specimen and contacting electrodes) were utilized for all the remaining simulations.

RESULTS AND DISCUSSION

(1) Metal/Insulator 4-layer series model

Current density is overwhelmingly higher in the metal phases as can be seen in Figure 4. This is an expected result, as the metal phase has a much lower resistivity than the insulating phase. However, changing the sequence of the layers (i.e. substituting the metal layers for the insulator and vice versa) alters both the current density, as seen in Figure 4(b), and the overall properties. It can be seen in Fig. 4, that the resistivity of the insulator/metal(I/M) model is higher in magnitude than that of the metal/insulator(M/I) model.

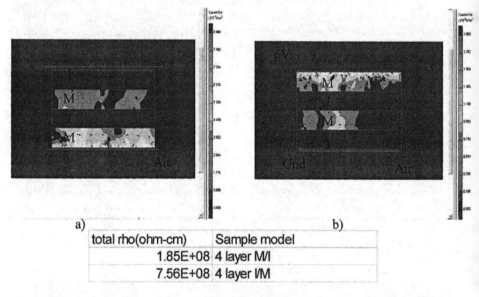

| total rho(ohm-cm) | Sample model |
|---|---|
| 1.85E+08 | 4 layer M/I |
| 7.56E+08 | 4 layer I/M |

Figure 4. Metal/Insulator and Insulator/Metal models with calculated resistivity.

(2) Insulator/High conducting semiconductor 2, 4, and 6-layer models

In this case, more current density activity is noted in the semiconductor layer as it has a lower resistivity. This is displayed in Figs. 5(a)-(c). Another observation that can be made is that total composite sample resistivity increases with the number of layers as we increase the layers from 2, to 4 and then 6 while keeping the total thickness constant. The graph in Figure 6 depicts this trend and also shows that the arrangement of layers (i.e. whether the more insulating or the

Ceramic Materials and Multilayer Electronic Devices

more conducting layer is first) alters the properties of the composite just as it was observed for the insulator-conductor composite presented in Fig. 4. All of the results presented so far lead to the conclusion that the initial assumption that only volume fraction matters and that the number of layers in a composite would not affect the properties, appears not to be obeyed.

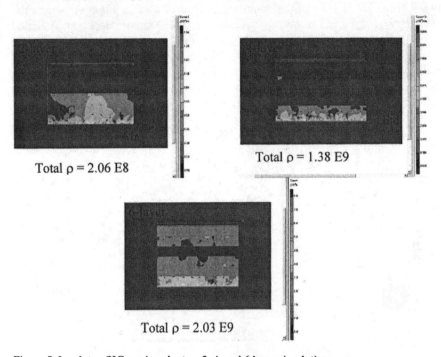

Figure 5. Insulator /HC semiconductor: 2, 4, and 6 layer simulations.

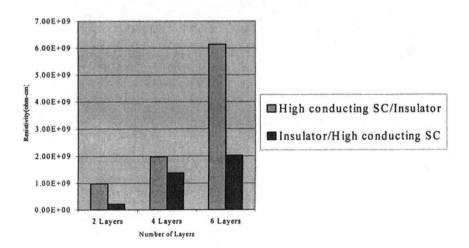

Figure 6. Summary chart for HC Semiconductor and Insulator composites.

Ceramic Materials and Multilayer Electronic Devices                           285

(3) Low conducting semiconductor/High conducting semiconductor 2, 4, and 6-layer models

This case differs from those presented above as it appears that once a minimum number of sample layers is reached, Maxwell-Wagner theory appears to hold. This effect is seen in the summary chart presented in Figure 7 where the data for the 4-layer and 6-layer composites are quite similar. However, it should be mentioned that an anomalous result was obtained for the first bar on the graph, which corresponds to the 2-layer HC semiconductor versus the LC semiconductor. The reasons for the resistivity value obtained, which is much larger than for the other models, are not known at present and are perhaps attributable to experimental sources of error within the FEA software.

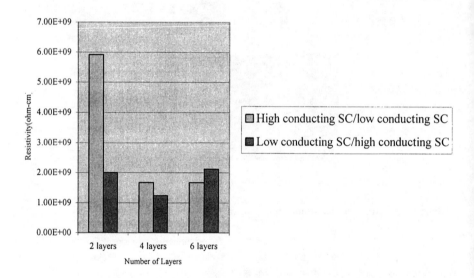

Figure 7. Summary chart for HC Semiconductor/ LC Semiconductor models.

(4) Metal/Insulator parallel model

Various cases of the parallel model have also been run. This model has the layers arranged parallel to the applied field, i.e. the voltage is identical for each element of the sample. Data from these models match expectations, with the current overwhelmingly taking the 'easiest' route from voltage source to ground in all material combination cases. The path of least resistance for the metal/insulator case containing 4 and 6 layers is depicted in Fig. 8.

Ceramic Materials and Multilayer Electronic Devices

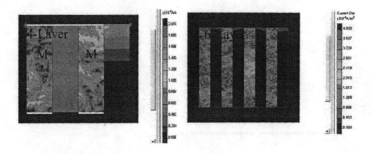

**Figure 8. Metal/Insulator parallel model showing expected _j_ paths.**

CONCLUSIONS

From the simulations, it is apparent that the simplified Maxwell-Wagner 2-layer condenser model theory does not hold for composites with high resistivity contrast. Results indicate that for a given total thickness, the number of layers present do affect the effective resistivity of the composites. This was very clearly seen with the metal/insulator and the high conducting semiconductor /insulator series composites. Additional experiments are needed to establish differences seen in composites with less contrasting components.

ACKNOWLEDGEMENT

The authors would like to acknowledge funding support from the National Science Foundation under DMR-0076153.

REFERENCES

1. A.R. von Hippel, Dielectrics and Waves, pp. 228-234, John Wiley & Sons, New York, 1953.
2. R. W. Sillars, *J. Inst.Elec.Engs. (London)* 80, 378(1937).
3. R. Hilfer, "Geometric and dielectric characterization of porous media," *Phys.Rev. B* 44[1], 60-75 (1991).
4. Y. Kim, R.A. Gerhardt and A. Erbil, "Dynamical Properties of Epitaxial Ferroelectric Heterostructures,"*Phys.Rev.B.*55, 4477-4485 (1997-II).,
5. R.A. Gerhardt and R. Ruh, "Volume Fraction and Whisker Orientation Dependence of the Electrical Properties of SiC Whisker Reinforced Mullite Composites," *J. Am.Ceram.Soc. 84[10]*,2328-2334(2001).
6. R.A. Gerhardt, J. Runyan, C. Sana, D.S. McLachlan and R. Ruh, "Electrical Properties of BN Matrix Composites – Part III: Observations Near Percolation Threshold in BN-B$_4$C Composites", *J.Am.Ceram.Soc. 84[10]*, 2335-2342(2001).

# THE EFFECT OF LEAD STOICHIOMETRY ON THE DIELECTRIC PERFORMANCE OF NIOBIUM MODIFIED PZT 95/5 CERAMICS

Pin Yang, James A. Voigt, Steve J. Lockwood, Mark A. Rodriguez, George R. Burns, and Chad S. Watson
Sandia National Laboratories
Albuquerque, NM 87185

ABSTRACT
    The electrical properties of lead zirconate titanate ceramics near the 95/5 composition are extremely sensitive to the chemical composition and processing conditions. To precisely control the lead stoichiometry in a solid solution has been a challenge because of lead volatility during high temperature sintering. In this study, we investigated the effect of the amount of lead in the solid solution on crystal structure, dielectric behavior, and phase transformation characteristics for chemically prepared niobium modified PZT 95/5 ceramics. Implications are important for process control and assurance of material performance.

INTRODUCTION
    The control of lead oxide volatility during high temperature sintering of lead zirconate titanate (PZT) solid solution is important in the preparation of reproducible electroceramics. Lead oxide starts to evaporate from the PZT powder at 1130°C through a diffusion-controlled mechanism and forms a lead depleted layer on the surface.[1] Micro-Raman and energy dispersive spectrometry results show that these light-color, lead deficient regions in the sintered PZT ceramics are typically poorly sintered, zirconia rich regions. The loss of lead oxide results in variation of the densification,[2] microstructure,[2,3] fracture mode,[4] and changes the optical[3,5] and electromechanical properties[4,6,7] of PZT ceramics. A similar behavior has also been reported for relaxor ferroelectrics.[8] To compensate for lead loss in these ceramics excess lead oxide is usually added during batch preparation. Sintering is also carried out in the presence of atmospheric powders with multiple protection crucibles[5,9] to prevent lead loss and keep the lead activity[10] of the PZT ceramic and the surrounding atmosphere nearly the same. This paper investigated the effect of lead content in solid

solution on the electrical properties and the pressure induced transformation behaviors of a chemically prepared niobium modified PZT 95/5 ceramic. Unlike earlier works[1-7] concentrated near the morphotropic phase boundary (PZT 53/47), this work is focused near the orthorhombic antiferroelectric (AFE) and rhombohedral ferroelectric (FE) phase boundary. Investigation in this region of the phase diagram changed the focus from the electromechanical response to the phase transformation characteristics, as the application changed from piezoelectric transducers[11] to phase switching actuators[12,13] or ferroelectric power supplies.[14] For the field-enforced AFE-to-FE phase transformation used in digital actuator applications, increasing the PbO content in the solid solution lowers the antiferroelectric-to-ferroelectric phase transformation temperature and increases the transformation field.[15] However, the effect of lead content in PZT ceramics on the pressure induced FE-to-AFE phase transformation has not been reported, and is the subject of this study. Special emphasis was placed on the charge storage and transformation characteristics, which are important for power supply applications.

EXPERIMENTAL PROCEDURE

The niobium modified PZT 95/5 powders were prepared by precipitating a lead acetate and Zr, Ti, Nb n-butoxide-glacial acetic acid solution with an oxalic acid-n-propanol solution.[16] The specific composition used for this study was $Pb_{0.9910}(Zr_{0.955}Ti_{0.045})_{0.9820}Nb_{0.018}O_3$. An additional 0.5 to 4.5 mole% lead was added to the formulation to compensate for lead loss during the process. These chemically prepared powders were first pyrolyzed at 400°C and then calcined at 900°C for 16 hours. An appropriate amount of pore former (lucite; spherical, polymerized methyl methacrylate) was added and mixed with the dry calcined PZT powder, then a 2 wt% binder solution (HA4, acrylic binder (Allied Colloid)) was sprayed into the tumbling powder. Approximately 70 grams of the granulated powder was then fed into a tool steel die and uniaxially pressed at 96 MPa. Ceramic compacts were slowly heated up to 750°C and held for 4 hours to burn out all the organic additives. To prevent lead loss during the high temperature sintering, a double crucible technique with 95/5 PZT powder was used as an atmospheric control. Sintering was performed at 1350°C for 6 hours. Typical weight loss was controlled to less than 0.2%. The Archimedes method was used to measure the densities of the specimens. These sintered billets were then ground, sliced and electroded with a fired on silver paste (DuPont 7095).

The phases of the calcined powders were examined using X-ray diffractometry (XRD, Siemens, D500) with a 2θ angle range from 20° to 100°. A step scan with a step size of 0.04° was used with a counting time of 20 s/step. Structural refinement was performed with TOPAS software (Bruker, Madison, WI). The composition of these powders was determined by an induction coupled plasma (ICP, atomic emission spectroscopy) technique, using a reference powder batch to monitor the variations from batch to batch. The composition of the sintered samples was measured by an electron microprobe analyzer (EMPA,

JEOL 8600). Special backgrounds for titanium and niobium were calibrated due to the interference of zirconium and lead in the PZT ceramics. Microstructure of the fractured surface was studied using a scanning electron microscope (SEM, Hitachi S-4500) with a backscattered electron (BSE) detector to identify possible existence of a second phase. The temperature dependence of the dielectric constant was measured at temperatures ranging from –20° to 115°C with a heating and cooling rate of 3°C/min at 10 kHz, using an impedance analyzer (HP4192A, Hewlet-Packard, Palo Alto, CA). Dielectric hysteresis measurements were made with a modified Sawyer-Tower circuit at room temperature. The pressure induced FE-to-AFE phase transformation was measured at room temperature. Hydrostatic pressure was increased at a rate of 10.3 MPa/s and the amount of charge release was monitored by a capacitor in series with the PZT ceramic.

RESULTS

Composition and Density

Previous work on niobium modified PZT 95/5 showed that small variations in titanium content and density changed the dielectric response and pressure induced transformation behavior.[17] These results indicate that an increase in titanium content in the solid solution increases the transformation pressure and reduces the polarization release during the pressure induced FE-to-AFE phase transformation. Similarly, an increase of bulk density boosts the remanent polarization, decreases the coercive field, and increases the transformation pressure. To control these effects, a group of powder batches with minimum variation in titanium content and sintered over a narrow density range were selected for this investigation. The composition (mole) and density of these batches after calcination and sintering are tabulated in Table 1 and Table 2, respectively. Except for slight deviations in TSP68 and TSP75A, both ICP and EMPA results show a consistent trend in the composition from powder to sintered ceramic.

Table I. Composition of the calcined powders determined by ICP.

| Lot number | Pb content | Ti content | Nb content |
|---|---|---|---|
| TSP 69 | 1.0204 | 0.0427 | 0.0182 |
| TSP 70-2 | 1.0047 | 0.0426 | 0.0182 |
| TSP 68 | 0.9961 | 0.0425 | 0.0182 |
| TSP 75-A | 0.9697 | 0.0425 | 0.0184 |
| TSP 75-B | 0.9638 | 0.0426 | 0.0181 |
| TSP74 | 0.9531 | 0.0430 | 0.0181 |

X-ray Diffraction and Structure Refinement

X-ray diffraction patterns of these calcined powders indicated that in addition to the PZT 95/5 perovskite structure there was a second phase, monoclinic zirconia, present. The presence, if any, of free lead oxide was under the detection limits of XRD analysis. Fig.1 shows the amount of residual zirconia in the

Table II. Composition of sintered samples determined by EMPA.

| Lot number | Pb content | Ti content | Nb content | O content | Density $(kg/m^3)$ |
|---|---|---|---|---|---|
| TSP 69 | 1.0294 | 0.04320 | 0.0186 | 3.070 | 7463 |
| TSP 70-2 | 1.0076 | 0.04206 | 0.0193 | 2.997 | 7401 |
| TSP 68 | 1.0089 | 0.04390 | 0.0192 | 3.021 | 7468 |
| TSP 75-A | 1.0026 | 0.04382 | 0.0199 | 2.988 | 7410 |
| TSP 75-B | 1.0010 | 0.04419 | 0.0200 | 2.993 | 7310 |
| TSP 74 | | | | | 7403 |

calcined powders as a function of deviation in lead concentration from the stoichiometric value (0.9910) (x, $Pb_{0.9910+x}(Zr_{0.955}Ti_{0.045})_{0.9820}Nb_{0.018}O_{3+x}$), based on ICP analysis for lead. The XRD results indicate that as the total amount of lead content increases the zirconia phase decreases. The XRD observation was confirmed by BSE images of fractured surfaces from sintered ceramic (see Fig. 2), where the amount of zirconia particles (dark gray, by atomic contrast) decreased qualitatively with increasing lead content. Notice that the zirconia phase was not observed in the highest lead content specimen. These observations suggest that increasing the lead content in the starting powder will increase the Zr content in the PZT solid solution. To confirm this argument, structural refinement calculations were performed based on these calcined powders. For comparison purposes with neutron diffraction data, [18] a hexagonal unit cell (equivalent to the rhombohedral structure) was used in the structural calculations. Fig. 3 illustrates the calculated volume of the hexagonal unit cell (using XRD data) as a function of lead stoichiometry. Results show that, in general, as the lead content increases the volume of the unit cell increases. A similar behavior can be calculated in the PZT rhombohedral ferroelectric phase region where the volume of the unit cell (based on calculated volume of an hexagonal unit cell) increases with increasing zirconia content. These results suggest that Zr must be incorporated into the lattice structure thereby increasing the unit cell volume. Therefore, the reduction of the zirconia second phase in the calcined powders can be attributed to the enhancement of Zr content by the excess lead present in the PZT solid solution.

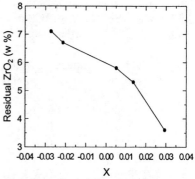

Fig.1 The effect of Pb stoichiometry on the residual $ZrO_2$ content in the calcined powders.

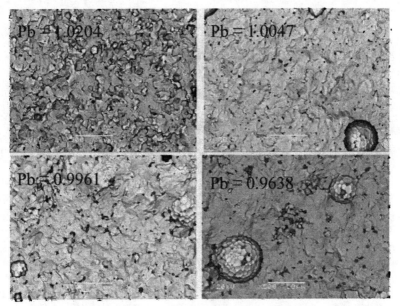

Fig. 2 The BSE images of fractured surface of PZT 95/5 ceramics with different lead contents.

## Dielectric Characterization

*Low field response - Lead content on dielectric behavior*: The effect of lead stoichiometry on the dielectric constant as a function of temperature is given in Fig. 4. Data are reported at 10 kHz during the cooling cycle. The phase transformation from high temperature ($FE_{RH}$) to low temperature ($FE_{RL}$) rhombohedral phase occurs around 40 to 45°C (as indicated by the slight increase in dielectric constant near the transformation temperature) for these compositions. Results indicate that the dielectric constant increases and transformation temperature decreases as the lead content in the solid solution increases. The observed increase in dielectric constant with a slight increasing of lead content in

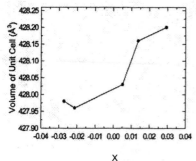

X

Fig. 3  The effect of Pb stoichiometry on the unit cell volume.

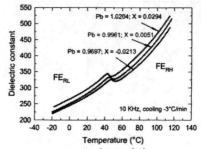

Fig. 4 The effect of Pb stoichiometry on dielectric constant as a function of temperature.

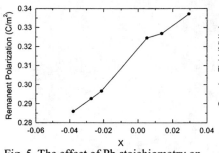

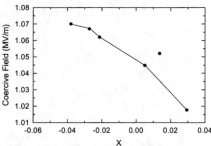

Fig. 5 The effect of Pb stoichiometry on the remanent polarization.

Fig. 6 The effect of Pb stoichiometry on the coercive field.

the ceramics is consistent with data reported for relaxor ferroelectrics,[8] and ferroelectric thin layers prepared by sol-gel[19] or pulsed laser deposition[20] methods. However, the shift in the transformation temperature with respect to the amount of lead content has not been reported.

*High field response -Lead content on dielectric hysteresis*: Polarization reversal of sintered ceramics was measured at 0.05 Hz at room temperature. The amount of remanent polarization and the magnitude of coercive field for samples with different lead stoichiometry are shown in Fig. 5 and Fig. 6, respectively. Results show that the amount of remanent polarization increases while the coercive field decreases with increasing lead content. Samples made with the highest lead content (Pb = 1.0204, X =0.0294) possess the highest remanent polarization, and therefore, have the potential to store more charge, which is highly desirable for power supply applications. For the powder batch with 4.5% excess lead, a 13.7% increase in the remanent polarization is observed in comparison with the baseline material (TSP68, where only 0.5% excess lead was added to the batch formulation). Similar behavior has been reported for thin layer deposition of lanthanum modified PZT ceramics.[19,20] In addition, the decrease of coercive field with increasing lead content has been reported for other bulk PZT

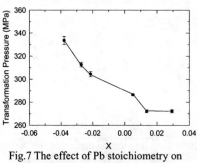

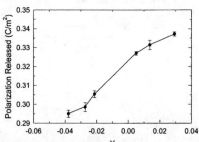

Fig.7 The effect of Pb stoichiometry on the pressure induced FE-to-AFE phase transformation.

Fig. 8 The effect of Pb stoichiometry on the charge release during pressure induced FE-to-AFE phase transformation.

ceramics.[5]

*Lead content on phase transformation:* At the orthorhombic antiferroelectric and rhombohedral ferroelectric phase boundary (PZT 95/5), the free energy difference between these two phases is very small. Under applied hydrostatic pressure the FE phase can be induced to the AFE phase and release bonded charge stored on the surface of the electrodes. Depending on the relative phase stability, the pressure required to induce such transformation can vary. For example, if the free energy difference between these two phases is large, a higher pressure is required to induce the FE-to-AFE phase transformation. Fig. 7 and Fig. 8 illustrate the transformation pressure and the amount of polarization released as a function of lead stoichiometry. The transformation pressure was determined at a pressure where $0.15$ C/m$^2$ of stored polarization is released, which is about half of the total charge released under the applied pressure. Results show that as the lead content increases the transformation pressure decreases and the total amount of polarization release increases. The increased release of polarization is consistent with the increase of remanent polarization with increasing lead content. For the powder batch with 4.5% excess lead, a 10.5% increase in the total charge release was observed when compared to the baseline material (TSP68) where only an additional 0.5% excess lead was added into batch formulation. The decrease of the transformation pressure with increasing lead content suggests that the free energy difference between the FE and AFE phases is reduced.

DISCUSSION

Transformation characteristics indicate that the increase of lead content in PZT ceramics decreases the $FE_{RH}$-to-$FE_{RL}$ phase transformation temperature (see Fig. 4) and the pressure required for the FE-to-AFE transformation (see Fig. 8). By re-examining the PZT phase diagram, the only plausible mechanism that can meet both observations is that the increase of lead content increases the Zr concentration in the solid solution, which moves the overall composition closer to the FE/AFE phase boundary. From the PZT phase diagram, it can be seen that as the overall Zr content in the solid solution increases toward the FE/AFE phase boundary, the $FE_{RH}$-to-$FE_{RL}$ phase transformation temperature decreases and the free energy between the FE and AFE phases decreases. Consequently, the pressure for the FE-to-AFE phase transformation decreases. This mechanism implies that Zr content is enhanced by increasing of the lead content, which is in accordance with the X-ray analysis and the BSE images. Further support for the proposed mechanism can be demonstrated by examining the change in other electrical properties as a function of chemical composition. Dai and Vielhand studied the effect of compositional change on the dielectric behavior of PZT ceramics.[21] Their results show that an increase in Zr content in the PZT solid solution increased the saturated polarization values. In addition, data obtained by Levett[6] indicates that an increase in Zr content for a composition near the morphotropic phase boundary (PZT 53/47) increases the remanent polarization and decreases the coercive field. These observations are similar to our results where the increase in lead content increases the remanent polarization (see Fig. 5) and decreases the coercive field (see Fig. 6). These results are consistent with our proposed mechanism that increasing lead content increases the Zr concentration in the PZT solid solution, which in turn changes the dielectric and phase transformation behavior.

## SUMMARY

The effect of lead content in solid solution on the electrical performance and phase transformation behavior was studied for a niobium modified PZT 95/5 ceramics. Results show that increasing the lead content in these ceramics enhances the Zr content in solid solution, which in turn reduces the $FE_{RH}$-to-$FE_{RL}$ phase transformation temperature, decreases the coercive field, lowers the pressure required to induce the FE-to-AFE phase transformation, and increases the capacity of charge storage (> 10%) for ceramic components.

## ACKNOWLEDGEMENT

The authors would like to acknowledge Emily Rodman, Roger H. Moore, Michael Hutchinson, Paul Hlava, and Timothy Scofield for their support on powder synthesis, ceramic fabrication, electron microprobe analysis, and depoling evaluation. Sandia is a multiprogram laboratory operated by Sandia Corporation, a Lockheed Martin Company, for the United States Department of Energy under Contract No. DE-AC04-94AL85000.

## REFERENCES

[1] D.A. Northrop, "Vaporization of Lead Zirconate-Lead Titanate Materials," *J. Am. Ceram. Soc.*, **50** [9] 441-45 (1967).

[2] A.I. Kingon and J.B. Clark, "Sintering of PZT Ceramics," *J. Am. Ceram. Soc.*, **66** [4] 256-60 (1983).

[3] B. Song, D. Kim, S. Shirasaki, and H Yamamura, "Effect of Excess PbO on Densification of PLZT Ceramics," *J. Am. Ceram. Soc.*, **72** [5] 833-36 (1989).

[4] A. Garg and D.C. Agrawal, "Effect of Net PbO Content on Mechanical and Electromechanical Properties of Lead Zirconate Titanate Ceramics," *Mat. Sci. and Eng.*, **B56** 46-50 (1999), and the references within.

[5] G.S. Snow, "Fabrication of Transparent Electrooptic PLZT Ceramics by Atmosphere Sintering," *J. Am. Ceram. Soc.*, **56** [2] 91-96 (1973).

[6] P.D. Levett, "Factors Affecting Lead Zirconate-Lead Titanate Ceramics," *Ceram. Bull.*, **42** [6] 348-52 (1963).

[7] A.H. Webster, T.B. Weston, and N.F.H. Bright, "Effect of PbO Deficiency on the Piezoelectric Properties of Lead Zirconate-Titanate Ceramics," *J. Am. Ceram. Soc.* **50** [9] 490-91 (1967).

[8] H. Fan and H. Kim, "Effect of Lead Content on the Structure and Electrical Properties of Pb(($Zn_{1/3}Nb_{2/3}$)$_{0.5}$($Zr_{0.47}Ti_{0.53}$)$_{0.5}$)$O_3$ Ceramics," *J. Am. Ceram. Soc.*, **84** [3] 636-38, (2001).

[9] A.I. Kingon and J.B. Clark, "Sintering of PZT Ceramics: I, Atmosphere Control," *J. Am. Ceram. Soc.*, **66** [4] 253-56 (1983).

[10] R.L. Holman and R.M. Fulrath, "Intrinsic Nonstoichiometry in Single-Phase Pb($Zr_{0.5}Ti_{0.5}$)$O_3$," *J. Am. Ceram. Soc.*, **55** [4] 192-95 (1972).

[11] B. Jaffe, W.R. Cook, Jr., and H. Jaffe, *Piezoelectric Ceramics*, Academic Press, New York, 1971.

[12] K. Uchino and S. Nomura, "Electrostriction in PZT Family Antiferroelectrics," *Ferroelectrics*, **50** 517-522 (1983).

[13] P. Yang and D.A. Payne, "Thermal Stability of Field-Forced and Field-Assisted antiferroelectric-Ferroelectric Phase Transformations in Pb(Zr,Sn,Ti)$O_3$," *J. Appl. Phys.*, **71**, 1361-67 (1991).

[14] J.J. Dick and J.E. Vorthman, "Effect of Electrical State on Mechanical and Electrical Response of a Ferroelectric Ceramic PZT 95/5 to Impact loading," *J. Appl. Phys.*, **49** [4] 2494-98 (1978).

[15] Y.W. Nam and K.H Yoon, "Effect of PbO Content on Dieleectric and Electric Field Induced Strain Properites in Y-Modified Lead Zirconate Titanate Stannate," *Mat. Res. Bull.*, **33** [2] 331-39 (1998).

[16] J.A. Voigt, D.L. Sipola, B.A. Tuttle, and M. Anderson, "Nonaqueous Solution Synthesis Process for Preparing Oxide Powders of Lead Zirconate Titanate and Related Materials," U. S. Pat. No. 5 908 802, June 1, 1999.

[17] P. Yang and J.A. Voigt, Unpublished data.

[18] D.L. Corker, A.M. Glazer, R.W. Whatmore, A. Stallard, and F. Fauth, "A Neutron Diffraction Investigation into the Rhombohedral Phases of the Perovskite Series PbZr$_{1-X}$Ti$_X$O$_3$," *J. Phys.: Condens. Matter.*, **10** 6251-6269 (1998).

[19] T. Tani and D.A. Payne, "Lead Oxide Coating on Sol-Gel Derived Lead Lanthanum Zirconium Titanate Thin Layers for Enhanced Crystallization into the Pervoskite Structure," *J. Am. Ceram. Soc.*, **77** [5] 1242-48, (1994).

[20] Z. Wang, K. Kikuchi, and R. Maeda, "Effect of Pb Content in Target on Electrical Properties of Laser Ablation Derived Lead Zirconate Titanate Thin Films," *Jpn. J. App. Phys.*, **39** 5413-17 (2000).

[21] X. Dai, Z. Xu, and D. Vielhand, "Effect of Oxygen Octahedron Rotations on the Phase Stability. Transformation Characteristics, and Polarization Behavior in the Lead Zirconate Titante, Crystalline Solution Series," *J. Am. Ceram. Soc.*, **78** [10] 2818-27 (1995).

# DIELECTRIC TUNABILITY OF MICROWAVE SINTERED BST:MgO COMPOSITES

S. Agrawal, H. Manuspiya, R. Guo, D. Agrawal, A. S. Bhalla
Materials Research Institute, The Pennsylvania State University, University Park, PA 16802, USA

ABSTRACT:
Composites of ferroelectric BST and non-ferroelectric MgO are sintered for obtaining low dielectric constant and controlled microstructure of the two phases. Microwave sintering route was used for controlling the reactivity and the grain boundaries in the final sintered material. $Ba_{1-x}Sr_xTiO_3$:MgO composites were sintered in the microwave at a frequency of 2.45 GHz. The low dielectric constant & tangent loss and high tunability could be achieved in the resulted composites. With microwave sintering, the high relative density and controlled microstructure (and particle size) of BST:MgO composites could be achieved. In microwave sintered BST:MgO, minimum reactivity and high K-factor values are obtained.

KEYWORDS:
BST, BST:MgO, composites, field dependence, tunability

INTRODUCTION:
$Ba_{1-x}Sr_xTiO_3$ (BST) ceramics have high dielectric constants and low losses under DC bias field. To make it useful for microwave applications, it is necessary to reduce the dielectric constant [1]. Earlier studies suggest that $Ba_{0.6}Sr_{0.4}TiO_3$ (BST60:MgO) composites have high dielectric tunability, low dielectric constant and low loss tangent in the vicinity of room temperatures and are useful for microwave applications [2,3]. Compositions of $Ba_{0.4}Sr_{0.6}TiO_3$ (BST40:MgO) may be useful for the low temperature applications.

BST:MgO composites were prepared by using the microwave sintering instead of conventional method of sintering. The microwave processing provides rapid, uniform and internal volumetric heating of a material, which results in controlled microstructure, clean and finer grain boundaries and hence the better dielectric and mechanical properties of a material [4]. Also, clean boundaries in a dense composite may provide the high field breakdown strength material.

In this paper, we report the first results on the processing and dielectric characteristics of microwave sintered $Ba_{1-x}Sr_xTiO_3$:MgO ($x$ = 0.4, 0.6) composites. The purpose of the studies is to finally establish the sintering : grain size relationship to achieve highly tunable materials. In our first approach in this report, specific particle sizes were not taken into consideration.

EXPERIMENTAL PROCEDURE:

The calcined powders of respective $Ba_{1-x}Sr_xTiO_3$:MgO ($x$ = 0.4, 0.6) compositions were mixed in the ratio of 40:60 weight percentages. The mixed powder was ball-milled for 24 hours. Binder was added by 2% of the weight of BST:MgO powder. The pellets (d = 6.40mm & t = 1.5mm) were prepared and preheated at 550°C in a conventional furnace to release volatile substances and binder. The pellets were then sintered at temperatures between 1200 °C and 1600 °C in a 6 KW, 2.45 GHz. Microwave furnace. Details of the microwave apparatus are provided elsewhere [5]. The optimum sintering conditions were achieved to get the relative density of 97 to 99%. Samples were polished with 12μm $Si_3N_4$ powder to remove the outer layers.

X-ray measurements were done in a Sintag system to study the diffraction pattern and further reaction between BST and MgO during sintering.

The samples were thinned down to suitable thickness and sputtered with gold electrodes for dielectric measurements. The measurements were done using an LCR meter (Hewlett Packard: 4284A). A close cycle helium cooled cryostat was used for maintaining temperatures between 15K to 300K. These instruments and systems were interfaced with a desktop computer.

Tunability measurements were done using the same configuration with the addition of high voltage blocking circuit and an additional voltage source (TREK 610, Trek Inc.).

The dielectric tunability is calculated by the following equation [6]:

$$\% \text{ Tunability} = \left( \frac{K_{field} - K_{0\,field}}{K_{0\,field}} \right) \times 100\%$$

SEM studies were carried out to reveal the microstructure features and identification of the phases in the composites.

RESULTS AND DISCUSSION:

$Ba_{1-x}Sr_xTiO_3(40)$:MgO(60) with $x$ = 0.4,0.6 composites have been prepared. The maximum density of $Ba_{0.4}Sr_{0.6}TiO_3$:MgO at 1575°C sintered for 45min. and of $Ba_{0.6}Sr_{0.4}TiO_3$:MgO at 1550°C sintered for 30min. was achieved. The relative optimum sintering temperature and time for the two compositions apparently could be due to the higher strontium content in BST40:MgO as compared to BST60:MgO.

XRD pattern shows perfect peaks for BST and MgO compounds as shown in figure 1. There is no further reaction between BST and MgO as they show proper individual peaks of two individual compounds.

SEM studies show the presence of two distinct phases. As shown in the figure 2 their chemical compositions correspond to MgO and BST without the presence of any new phase.

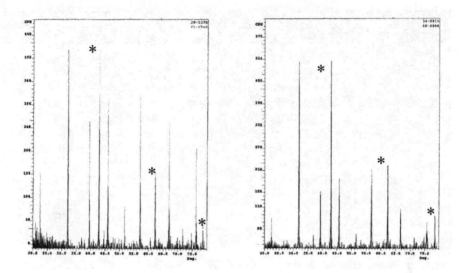

Figure 1: XRD data shows proper peaks of BaSrTiO$_3$ and MgO (marked as "*") composites

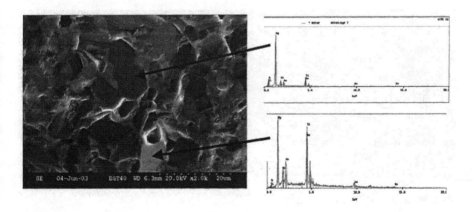

Figure 2: SEM micrograph of fractured surface of BST40:MgO composite sintered at 1575°C, 45min.

Figures 3 and 4 show the variation of dielectric constant measured at frequency of 10 & 100 KHz and as a function of temperature (-150°C to 150°C). Figure 3 shows the dielectric behavior of BST40:MgO composites sintered at various temperatures and having the corresponding achievable densities. The results show the maximum dielectric constant corresponding to 99% relative density sample sintered at temperature of 1575°C for 45min. Similarly, BST60:MgO shows the maximum dielectric constant for the sample sintered at 1550°C for 30 min. and with relative density of 98%.

The dielectric constants were finally measured on the optimum sintered samples in the temperature range of –250°C to 25°C and are shown in figures 5 & 6. In figure 5, the dielectric constant vs. T behavior of BST40:MgO suggests two clear phase transitions, at –60°C and at the maximum dielectric value of 260 at –116°C. The dielectric losses are low and in the range of ~0.0008 near 0°C. Similarly, the dielectric constant of BST60:MgO sample near room temperature is 146, which increases to maximum value of 320 at –163°C. Again, the measurements do suggest the two clear phase transitions in the sample. Also, there is a slight shift to the lower temperatures of the various Tc in both composite samples as compared to the respective BST compositions. This could be due to the built in stress in the composites.

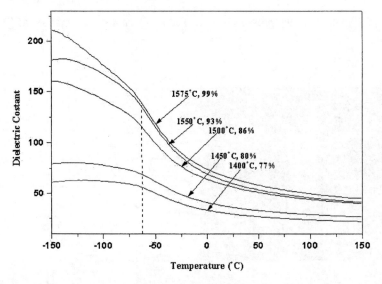

Figure 3: Temperature dependence of BST40:MgO composites at 10 KHz with different sintering temperatures and relative density

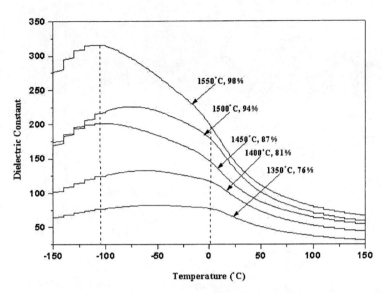

Figure 4: Temperature dependence of BST60:MgO composites at 10 KHz with different sintering temperatures and relative density

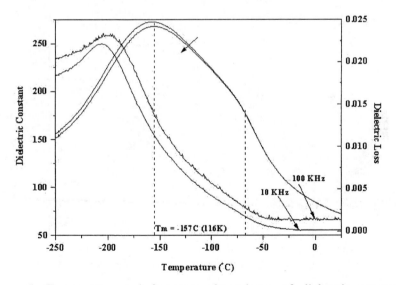

Figure 5: Temperature and frequency dependence of dielectric constant & dielectric loss of BST40:MgO composite sintered at 1575°C for 45min.

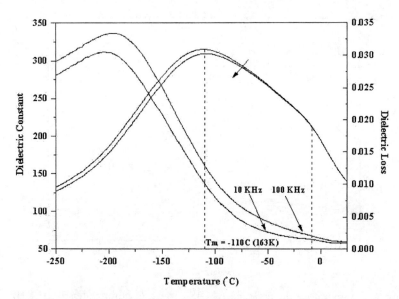

Figure 6: Temperature and frequency dependence of dielectric constant & dielectric loss of BST60:MgO composite sintered at 1550°C for 30min.

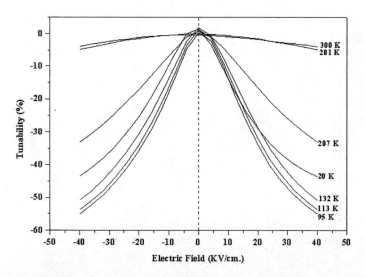

Figure 7: Tunability measured at different temperatures as a function of electric field of BST40:MgO composite

Ceramic Materials and Multilayer Electronic Devices

The tunability measurements were done applying the field up to 40 KV/cm. Tunability as a function of field is shown in figures 7 & 8 at different fields & temperatures for the two composites. BST40:MgO shows 57% tunability at 95K and BST60:MgO shows the maximum tunability of 54% at 151K. The maximum tunability values at room temperature and at 40 KV/cm. are ~ 5 and 17% respectively for the two composites.

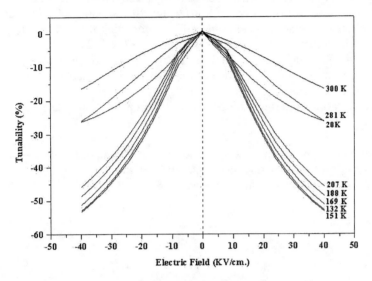

Figure 8: Tunability measured at different temperatures as a function of electric field of BST60:MgO composite

CONCLUSION:
For the BST60:MgO composite at ~ 281K tunability of 27% and tanδ<0.001 were obtained. These measurements render the values of ~270 for the K-factor (=tunability*Q). BST:MgO composites fabricated by microwave processing shows that high density samples can be achieved in shorter sintering time. Minimum reactivity between MgO and BST phases were observed. X-ray and SEM studies showed the presence of pure MgO and BST. Low dielectric constant and dielectric losses were observed in these composites. High tunability (at low frequency) was measured in these samples.

Studies on the grain size : tunability is in progress and results will be reported in the forthcoming reports.

ACKNOWLEDGEMENTS:
The work is supported by the DARPA – FAME and Meta Materials grants. S Agrawal is thankful to Yi Fang and Jiping Cheng for giving their help and support during microwave sintering experiments.

REFERNCES:

1) E. F. Elberta, R. Guo, A. S. Bhalla, "Novel BST:MgTiO$_3$ composites for frequency Agile Applications," Ferroelectrics, **268**, 169-174 (2002).
2) L. C. Sengupta, J. Synowcyznski, L. H. Chiu, "Investigation of the effect of particle size on the optical and electronic properties of Ba$_{1-x}$Sr$_x$TiO$_3$ composite ceramics," Integrated Ferroelectrics, **17**, 287-296 (1997).
3) Yoshitaka Somiya, A. S. Bhalla, L. Eric Cross, "Study of dielectric properties of (Sr$_{1-x}$Pb$_x$)TiO$_3$:MgO composites for field tunable devices," Ferroelectric Letters (To be published).
4) D. K. Agrawal, "Microwave Processing of Ceramics," Solid State and Material Science, **3**, 480-485 (1998) .
5) R. Roy, D. Agrawal, J. P. Cheng, M. Mathis, "Microwave Processing: Triumph of Applications – Driven Science in WC composites and Ferroic titanates," Ceramic Transactions, **80**, 3-26 (1997).
6) L. Wu et. al, Journal of American Society, **83**, 1713 (2000).

# Electronic Devices: Design and Properties

# Effect of Rheological Parameters of Conductor Pastes on Thick Film Fine Line Screen Printing

Shang-Ho Hung
Materials Research Laboratories, Industrial Technology Research Institute
Bldg. 77, 195-5 Chung Hsing Rd., Section 4 Chutung, Hsinchu, Taiwan 310, R.O.C.

Kuen-Fwu Fuh
Materials Research Laboratories, Industrial Technology Research Institute
Bldg. 77, 195-5 Chung Hsing Rd., Section 4 Chutung, Hsinchu, Taiwan 310, R.O.C.

Tsung-Wen Chen
Materials Research Laboratories, Industrial Technology Research Institute
Bldg. 77, 195-5 Chung Hsing Rd., Section 4 Chutung, Hsinchu, Taiwan 310, R.O.C.

Abstract
    Various paste-printing benchmarks were performed to investigate the effects of rheological behavior on thick film fine line printing. DuPont 951 AT LTCC green tape and 6142D conductor paste were chosen to be the common evaluation platform. The rheological parameters, such as viscosity, thixotropy, yield stress and ratio of viscous property/elastic property, of each paste sample were changed by increasing solid content of the 6142D paste. The screen printing conditions of each benchmark were kept the same except for the paste samples. The experimental results show that pastes with higher viscosity, yield stress and lower ratio of viscous property/elastic will get fine line patterns with well shape and size definition.

Introduction
    To meet the needs for advanced electronic components and packages with smaller size and greater functionality. It will be concerned about the forming technologies of thick film fine line circuits. Therefore, various techniques such as the stencil printing[1], screen printing, gravure offset printing[2, 3], photosensitive/photo-imageable[4, 5], photo-etchable[6, 7] and direct writing

(Laser and Micro-Pen) [8, 9] have been established to obtain thick film fine line. Each technique, however, has different advantages and applications as well as process. Which technique to choose would depend on the needs of products and cost. All these technologies have the ability to form thick film fine line which is smaller than 50 μm line width/line space (L/S) except stencil printing.

Although there are many techniques of thick film fine line but the screen printing is the most popular technology for manufacturers due to its low cost and suitable for mass production. It is widely used to produce thick film passive components like resistors, inductors, capacitors, microwave hybrid circuit modules and even new generation low temperature co-fire ceramic (LTCC) multilayer ceramic substrates. Although fine line screen printing technique could increases the high density of circuits and devices to meet minute devices and high functional modules. But the impedance precision (size variation) of devices and metal circuits become the important parameters on manufacturing when increase the signal speed and system frequency.

The design rule of the most manufacturers is about 100 μm L/S for layout design which is achievable by screen printing before year 2001 for LTCC process. It could be achieved about 75 μm L/S under the best conditions when the best screen mesh, emulsion and printing parameters are employed. Although screen printing involve the properties of screen, rheological properties of paste and substrates etc.. The key of screens on manufacturing is the diameter of threads couldn't be drawn out from smaller ones. So the conductor paste is difficult to through the mesh or the amount of paste is not enough to form a conductor line well due to small opening on screens. It had a big advancement on screen manufacturing around few years ago. The diameter of threads could be drawn out down to 16 μm (28 μm traditional). So the conductor paste can through the screen mesh easily and smoothly to define the conductor lines. It is general to form 50μm L/S thick film fine line by screen printing in LTCC process. The shape of the lines and variation after screen printing decide upon rheological properties of paste and surface properties of substrates (e.g. contact angle). The thick film fine line should keep low variation on line width and suitable film thickness to avoid shot circuit during sintering. Therefore the special rheological properties are needed for conductor pastes. Actually the fine line conductor paste (L/S ≤ 50 μm) has completely different viscosity behavior comparison with non-fine line conductor pate according to Ref. [10].

A commercially available silver-based LTCC green tape system was used in this study to eliminate the influence of surface property of substrate. Change the rheology behavior by increasing the solid content in pastes. Then the relative rheological behavior of the paste for screen printing is the most important factor in our experiment and will be described.

## Experiment
### *Materials*
It has long been understood [11] that low viscosity pastes are more likely to lose

their printed definition than high viscosity pastes. In other words, the paste with low viscosity will slump or spread easily and then affect the pattern shape, size and accuracy. Not only the viscosity but also gravitation, surface tension [12, 13] and surface property of the substrate are the reasons to cause slump or spread. The materials chosen for this study were 951AT green tape and 6142D (solid content 67.7%) silver thick film conductor from DuPont. The 6142D is made specifically to be co-fired as a buried conductor film in a LTCC green tape substrate. The pastes with relative high viscosity were prepared by adding silver powder into the 6142D paste which had a mean size of ~ 1 μm and were spherical. The solid content of the pastes is 70%, 75% and 80% respectively. After that, a high speed mixer (Keyence HM-500) will be used to mix the original 6142D paste and added silver powder. Consequently, the rheological behavior has been changed due to different solid content. Then the relationship between the rheological behavior and the definition of thick film fine line will be notable. It is worth to assess the influence of rheological behavior on fine line screen printing. A Thermogravimetric analyzer (TGA, Perkin Elmer TGA7) was used to confirm the real solid content in the paste after mixing.

*Equipments and Parameters*

It is common to assess the rheological behavior by employed the viscosity, thixotropy[13], yield stress/value[11, 14, 15] and viscous property/elastic property ratio as important parameters index which could be obtained directly from a viscometer (Haaka viscometer RS150). And these indexes will be the key for how they affect the definition of fine line printing. 500 mesh stainless steel screen with 16 μm wire diameter and 10 μm emulsion was used. The screen printer is SPM-AV made by MPM Corp.. Leveling time is 10 minutes after printing and then another 10 minutes for drying. The line space / with and surface roughness of the printed conductor lines were measured by 3-dimension and surface profiler (Veeco Dektak[3]) respectively. Sintering was carried out in an oven.

Results and Discussion
*Viscosity and Thixotropy*

Figure 1 shows the shear stress versus shear rate for pastes with different solid content. The viscosity is increased with increasing solid content as well as the thixotropy. It has long been understood that the viscosity will rise by increasing solid content but thixotropy. Hence, it is worth to discuss the phenomenon of thixotropy in this result. It was know from rheological theory [16] that the meaning of thixotropy is the work done during the flow when the paste was encountered a stress. Fig. 2 illustrates the ideal silver particles distribution in the pastes. It can be seen from Fig. 2 that the amounts of silver particles were increased per volume with increasing the solid content in the paste. The paste had to overcome the friction from (1) silver particle between solvent and (2) silver between silver particles when flow occurred. Thus, if we want to get the same deformation for both pastes with low and high solid content respectively, the shear stress ($\tau2$)

applied on the paste with high solid content should be higher than that with low solid content ($\tau 1$). Substituting $\tau$ into the equation (1) we will know that W2 (work done by the paste with high solid content) would be higher than W1 (work done by the paste with low solid content). Therefore, it is well known that thixotropy is increased with increasing solid content in the paste.

And it is also known that if $\tau 2$ is higher than $\tau 1$ then $\eta 2$ would be higher than $\eta 1$ from equation (2). Fig. 1 also shows the trend that the viscosity is increased with raising solid content for different solid content at the same shear rate.

$$W \ (Work) = F \ (Force) \times S \ (Distance) \tag{1}$$

$$\eta \ (viscosity) = \frac{\tau \ (shear \ \ stress)}{\overset{\bullet}{\gamma} \ (shear \ \ rate)} \tag{2}$$

*Yield Stress*

Figure 3 shows the values of the yield stress for different solid content pastes. The yield values are 6252Pa, 6487Pa, 7646Pa and 11750Pa for solid content 67.7%, 70%, 75% and 80% respectively. It can be clearly seen that the yield values are increased with increasing solid content. All liquids can be divided into Newtonian and non-Newtonian flow behavior according to rheological theory [17]. Furthermore, non- Newtonian liquids can be divided into pseudoplastic, dilantant and Binhang plastic liquids. The pastes used in thick film printing are belongs to pseudoplastic in non-Newtewtonian liquids. This kind of flow liquid exhibits the combination of viscous property and elastic property which could be represented as the dashpot (as loss) and spring (as storage or recovery) model [16] respectively. Again from Fig. 2, the interparticle distance become shorter when the solid content increased. This also means that the deformation length of springs become shorter. In other words, the recovery ability of the springs becomes faster which can be represented as the cohesive force of the paste. Viscosity is lowered when the conductor paste is encountered by the swiping action of the squeegee. Hence, it is easily to spread due to the influence of the surface tension. According to relating surface tensions to the equilibrium contact angle $\theta$, may be written as:

$$\gamma_{SA} = \gamma_{SL} + \gamma_{LA} \cos \theta \tag{3}$$

Where $\gamma_{SA}$ is the solid –air surface energy, $\gamma_{SL}$ is the solid liquid surface energy and $\gamma_{LA}$ is the liquid-air surface energy. The thick film fine line will spread or slump when $\gamma_{SA} > \gamma_{SL} + \gamma_{LA} \cos\theta$. The meaning of yield stress is that the minimum shear stress which is necessary to obtain flow from rheological theory. The item $\gamma_{SA}$ in Eq. (3) can be represented as foreign applied force and this force is higher than yield stress. The item $\gamma_{SL}$ in Eq. (3) will be higher if the cohesive force of the paste is increased and the spreading phenomenon will be reduced. From these results we can expect that pastes with relative higher yield stress will not spread or slump easily and the printed thick film fine line will have better shape and size definition.

*Viscous Property and Elastic Property*

The film thickness before and after firing for 50 μm, 40 μm and 30 μm L/S are showed in Fig. 4. It shows that the definition of fine line pattern is getting better (less variation) with increasing solid content. As expected from previous discussion, this is due to the higher viscosity and yield stress. Fig. 5 shows the photography of 50 μm, 40 μm and 30 μm L/S with solid content 80% after firing. The white part is the conductor line and the black part is the substrate. What's remarkable is that the conductor line with lower solid content (70%) has apparent holes on surface due to shrinkage during firing because of low solid content and thin film thickness. This phenomenon will not be observed with increasing solid content. Fig. 6 illustrates the film thickness and surface roughness for solid content 70%, 75% and 80% after screen printing. The results show that the film thickness and surface roughness rise with increasing solid content of conductor paste. The film thickness are 7.53±0.9 μm, 7.71±0.47 μm and 9.13±0.58 μm respectively. And the surface roughness are 0.57±0.21 μm, 0.64±0.19 μm and 1.03±0.3 μm respectively. It can be understand from the ratio of viscous property(G″)/elastic property(G′) in Fig. 7 to explain the roughness rise with increasing solid content. It can be seen from Fig. 7 that the ratio of G″/G′ decreases with increasing solid content. Where G″ represents the flow ability when the paste is subjected to a force while G′ (can be represented as a spring) represents the recovery ability after the force is released. Hence, the elastic modulus increases relatively when the solid content is increased. In other words, the flow ability is reduced by the recovery ability lead to less flow ability of the paste during leveling. Therefore the surface roughness is higher relatively at higher solid content. The curves in Fig. 7 are not continuous because of the elastic property is nearly zero at high shear rate and only the viscous property could be measured from the viscometer. High frequency loss typically comes from the following origins: ceramic, metal conductor, metal-ceramic interface, radiation and surface roughness. There is a concern about the contribution to the loss from the surface roughness (skin effect). Therefore, surface roughness and conductor trace geometry (edges) may have significant effect on the microwave loss at high frequencies. The loss can be reduced with decreasing surface roughness. From previous discussion, however, it is not easy to satisfy conductor trace geometry and surface roughness at the same time.

Conclusion

50 μm 、 40 μm & 30 μm L/S is achievable by increasing solid content of

commercial paste which is not suitable for fine line screen printing. We find that pastes with higher viscosity, thixotropy, yield stress and lower $G''/G'$ ratio can print finer patterns and better size definition but higher surface roughness of the conductor line. LTCC design rule can be extended to finer line width / line space easily by using improved pastes and screen printing process.

Reference

[1] A. Dziedzic, J. Nijs and J. Szlufcik, "Thick-film Fine-line Fabrication Techniques-Application to Front Metallisation of Solar Cells," Hybrid Circuits, (30) (1993) 18-22, 26.

[2] M. Lahti, K. Kukkola and S. Leppavuori, "The Utilising of Gravure Offset Printing for Miniaturising of Electronic Packages," Microelectronics International, (37) (1995) 22-24.

[3] V. Golovanov, J. L. Solis, V. Lantto and S. Leppavuori, "Different thick-film methods in printing of one-electrode semiconductor gas sensor," Sensors and Actuators B, (34) (1996) 401-406.

[4] M. A. Skurski, M. A. Smith, R. R. Draudt, D. I. Amey, S. J. Horowitz and M. J. Champ, "Photoimageable Silver Cofireable Conductor Compatible With 951 Green Tape$^{TM}$," International Symposium Microelectronics, (1998) 393-398.

[5] M. Vrana, J. D. Baets and A. V. Calster, "High Density Thick Film Multilayers with Ag-based Conductors," International Symposium Microelectronics, (1998) 789-794.

[6] P. Barnwell and J. Wood, "Fabrication of Low Cost Microwave Circuits and Structures Using an Advanced Thick Film Technology," IEMT/IMC Proceedings, (1998) 327-332.

[7] P. Barnwell and M. P. O'Neill, "Integrated Microwave Structures Using an Advanced Thick Film Technology," IEEE, (1999) 259-262.

[8] V. Kripesh, S. K. Bhatnagar, H. Osterwinter and W. Gust, "Fine-line Passive Components for Hybrid Microelectronics," Microelectronics International, (41) (1996) 9-11.

[9] D. Dimos, B. H. King and P. Yang, "Direct-Write Fabrication of Integrated, Multilayer Passive Components," International Symposium on Advanced Packaging Materials, (1999) 186-190.

[10] M. Hashimoto, A. Hamano, Y. Nakada and T. Kubo, "Thick Film System for High Integrated Circuit Substrates," ISHM Proceedings, (1992) 200-203.

[11] Q. Reynolds, H. G. MacMahon and J. Freitag, "Essential Paste Properties for Fine Line Thick Film," Hybrid Circuits, (35) (1994) 22-24.

[12] J. R. Larry, "Influence of Surface Energies on Line Resolution in Screen Printing," Solid state Technology, (1972) 48-50, 58.

[13] T.-X. Liang, W. Z. Sun, L.-D. Wang, Y. H. Wang and H.-D. Li, "Effect of Surface Energies on Screen Printing Resolution," IEEE Transactions on Components, Packaging and Manufacturing Technology-Part B, 19(2) (1996) 423-426.

[14]A. V. Fraioli, "Yield Values in Thick-Film Rheology," Solid State Technology, (1974) 48-50.
[15]L. F. Miller, "Screenability and Rheology," Solid State Technology, (1974) 54-60.
[16]G. Schramm, A Practical Approach to Rheology and Rheometry, 2nd Ed., HAAKE, Germany, (2000) 15-35.
[17]J. E. Sergent and C. A. Harper, Hybrid Microelectronics Handbook, 2nd Ed., McGraw-Hill, New York, 3-103~3-149.

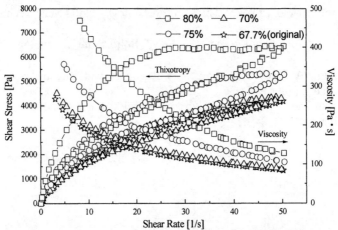

Figure 1 Viscosity and thixotropy for solid content 67.7%, 70%, 75% and 80%.

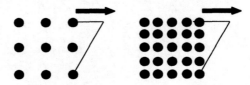

Figure 2 Ag particles with different solid content per volume (a) high solid content (b) low solid content.

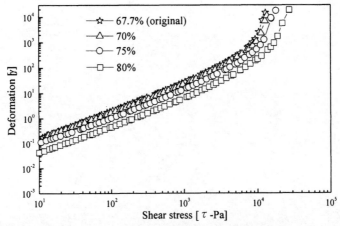

Figure 3 Yield stress values for solid content 67.7%, 70%, 75% and 80%.

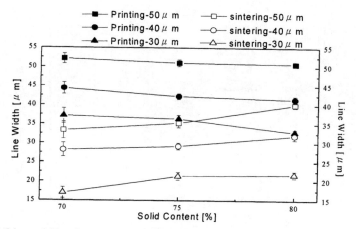

Figure 4 Line width after screen printing and firing.

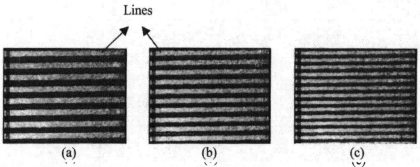

Figure 5 Thick film fine lines after firing for solid content 80% (a)50 μm (b)40 μm (c) 30 μm.

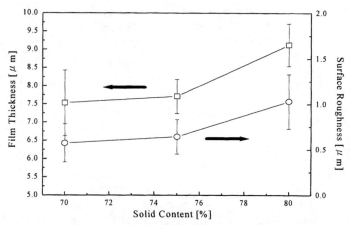

Figure 6 Film thickness and surface roughness after screen printing.

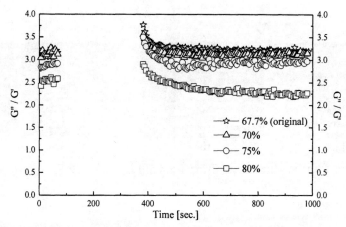

Figure 7 The ratio of viscous/elastic property for solid content 67.7%, 70%, 75% and 80%.

# THE APPLICATION OF NEURAL NETWORK ON DESIGN OF EXPERIMENT FOR FINE LINE SCREEN PRINTING PROCESS

Chiu, Kuo-Chuang
Material Research Laboratories, Industrial Technology Research Institute
I000, MRL/ITRI Bldg.77, 195 Sec.4, Chung Hsing Rd.
Chutung, Hsinchu, Taiwan 310, R.O.C


Lin, Jiang-Tsair
Material Research Laboratories, Industrial Technology Research Institute
S000, MRL/ITRI Bldg.77, 195 Sec.4, Chung Hsing Rd.
Chutung, Hsinchu, Taiwan 310, R.O.C

ABSTRACT

LTCC fine line screen printing to 50μm line width tolerance of ±5μm is crucial to applied facilitates wireless communication product miniaturization and modularization for the increasing yield rate and reducing manufacturing cost. This study presents an integrated method in which neural networks, backpropagation algorithm, and design of experiment are used to optimize the fine line screen printing process parameter control. The goals to develop line width finer than 50μm, better line resolution and roughness can be successfully achieved through this kind of combination from DOE and neural network simulation. Therefore, the experimental work and cost can be substantially reduced to meet the requirement of fast time-to-market and the modern green engineering.

INTRODUCTION

Screen-printing is widely used as a dominant method for LTCC technology.

However it is difficult to prepare the conductor line finer than 100 μm because a lot of processing parameters are hard to control well. Line width less than 50 μm is desirable for compact circuit applications such as RF integrated modules and CSP packages. Design of experiment (1,4) had been proven to be a successful tool reducing the number of testing and find out the optimal experimental conditions. Many models of the printing process had been developed. However, fine line printing is still difficult for most of the industry.

A new tool that combines neural network and design of experiment model is used to develop the process control factors on screen-printing. If the parameters can be obtained from the 1st stage experiment of DOE, it is then plausible to apply the neural network simulation to get the optimal experimental conditions. In this study, the line width smaller than 50μm is focused as the primary target to test the feasibility of such kind of new model. If this model functions pretty well, then, the experimental work and processing cost can be substantially reduced and the stringent fast time-to-market requirement will be also fulfilled.

DOE AND NEURAL NETWORK MODEL

Experimental procedure of this study was based on DOE and back-propagation neural network model (2,3). DOE is a two-stage experimental technique. The purpose of the first-stage experiment is to identify and control the significant factors for screen-printing, while the goal of the second stage is to find out the working window for those significant factors. From the basics of the neural network simulation, the first stage experiments data were used to train and build the network. According to neural network training, it would be easily to find second step solution approximately. After this procedure, parameters were fed into ANOVA analysis to find optimal conditions for screen-printing of 50μm line.

The data were then analyzed by statistical method, i.e., the analysis of variance (ANOVA) to obtain the degree of contribution and interactions from each factor. From ANOVA analysis, significant factors can be identified and controlled in the subsequent process.

Back-propagation neural network is one of the widely used neural network models. It is a non-linear feed-forward network. There are input layer, hidden layer, and output layer. Fig. 1 shows architecture comprised of one-layer input, two-layer hidden, and three-layer output neural cells. The fundamental back-propagation neural network theory takes advantage of the gradient steepest descent method to consolidate and minimize error functions. An additional hidden layer represents some kinds of relationship between input units. It will be changed to a smoothly differentiable transfer function and allows network to apply the gradient steepest descent method. An adjusted and weighted network equation can be then introduced.

The back-propagation neural network belongs to a kind of parallel architecture layers; it has very strong mirror edibility. Therefore, optimal designs can take the advantage of such characteristics to obtain structuralized optimized designs and multi-target optimizations. It is doable to apply finite element technique for architecture analysis on various samples. These samples could be used by back-propagation neural network to train samples and then establish the working neural network model. This kind of analytical architecture from such models will take the place of finite element.

Therefore, when one try to use the neural network mirror ability to optimize designs, it is better to avoid settling down each target-function weighted Wi to reach an effective design. To build up a neural network, it should be done first to find the target function. Secondly, network-input quantity and each target functioning, as network output-quantity has to be adjusted or modified. Finally, it is critical to apply exact parameters to train this network and define each connection-weighted value.

The fish-bone causal analysis of materials recipe and process flow on the fine line printing is given in Fig. 2. Parameters affecting fine line printing include paste reheology, screen, squeegee, printing machine, tape, and printing process. Experimental parameters can be classified from Fig. 2 and listed below as variables and constants according to preliminary results.

Variables:

(1)   Paste viscosity

(2)   Screen mesh

(3)   Emulsion thickness

(4)   Screen open area

(5)   Print squeegee speed

(6)   Squeegee pressure

(7)   Snap-off distance

Constants:

(1)    Screen printer
(2)    Squeegee hardness
(3)    Squeegee material
(4)    Screen tension
(5)    Squeegee size and shape of edge

EEPERIMTAL PROCEDURE

The First-Stage Experiment

This is a two-level experiment from the basics of DOE. First, one had to decide two levels for a specific variable. The selection guideline is the maximum and minimum parameters allowable by the experimental apparatus. The variables and their content levels are listed in Table 1. The mutual interactions among variables are also taken into consideration. Using the Ishikawa Chart (point-line graph) as developed by Taguchi; a suitable chart is shown in Table 1. The chart is then translated into a $L_{16}2^{15}$ orthogonal array listed in Table 2, while $L_{16}2^{15}$ means examination of 15 experimental parameters in 16 test runs. The notation 1 and 2 in the orthogonal array represent the level 1 and level 2 of the control factors.

The experimental parameters were taken from the orthogonal array as seen from Table 1. To avoid artifacts and environmental effects, experiments were carried out in a random order. Following the direction of D.O.E. method and regulations for constants, 16 test runs were carried out in four steps: paste viscosity, screen mesh, and squeegee speed, and snap-off distance. Test pattern is shown in Figure 3. Line width, line thickness, and line roughness of the screen-printed features was performed accordingly. By using ANOVA, the significant factors were therefore identified from those 16 tests run data.

The Second-Stage Experiment

First, the back-propagation neural network model was used for the second-stage experiment. Using 16 runs input and output data to train neural network and which then can be used to build the fine line process neural network model. It could find second stage approximately simulation.

The variables of the second-stage experiment are extracted from the significant factors of the first-stage experiment. This is a three-level experiment.

The variables and chosen levels are given in Table 3. Paste viscosity (A), print squeegee speed (F), and squeegee pressure (G) were defined as the variables; and a suitable point-line graph is then drawn in Table 3. A $L_{27}3^{13}$ orthogonal array is given and shown in Table 4. It is a 27-test run experiment. Following the same procedure as the first-stage experiments, neural network model was used to simulate the 27-test run experiments. The simulation data were again analyzed by ANOVA, which would identify the optimal formulation effectively. Finally, a test run using this formula is carried out to check the reproducibility of the resultant optimal conditions.

RESULTS AND DISCUSSION

Data of the first-stage experiment are shown in Fig. 4. Line widths ranged from 42.87 to 100µm. The overall deviation was about 21.24%. The maximum line thickness measured was 20.7µm in test run #16. Line thickness was minimal at 9.08µm in test run #3. On the other hand the maximum line roughness was 0.8427µm in test run #1, the minimum value of 0.1168µm was found in test run #8. These data were statistically analyzed by ANOVA and the results can be found in Table 5. The significant factors in affecting the line width were paste viscosity (A2, 58.81%), screen open area (D2, 11.3%), squeegee pressure (G2, 7.27%), snap-off distance (H1, 2.97%), and the interaction of A2H2, B1D2, A2D1, A2G1, and F1G2 as shown in Table 4(a). Those significant factors in affecting the line thickness were paste viscosity (A2, 54.19%), print squeegee speed (F1, 20.13%), screen open area (D2, 4.02%), and interaction of A2D2 as shown in Table 4(b). The significant factors in affecting the line roughness were paste viscosity (A2, 16.32%), screen mesh (B2, 16.32%), print squeegee speed (F1, 10.88%), screen open area (D2, 10.88%), snap-off distance (H1, 6.53%), and interaction of A2D1, A2B2, A2H1, B1D2 as shown in Table 4(c). The selected level and the degree of contribution of all variables were listed in Table 5. The results of analysis were summarized as follows:

(1) Screen mesh (B): It only affects line roughness. Therefore, B2 is chosen as a fixed (or called constant) factor in the second-stage experiment.

(2) Emulsion thickness (C): It is not a significant factor. C2 is then selected as a constant in the consideration of its effect on the line

thickness.

(3)     Screen open area (D): It will affect the line width, thickness, and roughness. So D2 is chosen as a fixed factor in the second-stage experiment.

(4)     Snap-off distance (H): It affects line width, and roughness. So H1 is chosen as a fixed factor in the second-stage experiment.

The variables in the second-stage experiment are set as follows:

Paste viscosity: A2

Print squeegee speed: F1

Squeegee pressure: G2

The simulated results of the second-stage experimental data are plotted in Fig. 5. The goal of controlling line width targeted at $50\pm5\mu m$ had been successfully achieved.

Line widths are ranged from 48.17 to $49.15\mu m$ in 27 test runs and overall amount of deviation was reduced to 0.25%. Average line thickness is $19.03\pm0.09\mu m$ and line roughness is $0.51\pm0.01\mu m$. From the ANOVA data analysis of line width, line thickness, and line roughness there was no significant factor can be found in the present study. Which indicates that a working window has been successfully identified for those chosen variables.

Optimal conditions of the experimental parameters are completely determined from the second-stage experiment modeled by the neural network. Paste viscosity is found to be A3, print squeegee speed will be F1, and squeegee pressure is G1. From the results of the first and second stage experiments, the optimal conditions were found and listed in Table 6. The reproducibility test run using this formula was carried out in another large-batch experiment. The results, as given in Fig. 6. Show line width is narrowly ranged from 48.2 to $53.4\mu m$ with the standard deviation of only $1.5\mu m$. The goal of controlling line width at $50\pm5\mu m$ is then obtained successfully. Photographs of fine line screen printed on LTCC were demonstrated and shown in Fig.7.

CONCLUSIONS

The main purpose of the present study is to control the line width using Design of Experiment (DOE) method with the simulation of the second-stage experiments by the neural network model. From the two-stage experiment, following conditions can be concluded:

(1)     Paste viscosity: This is a significant factor controlling the line width, thickness, and roughness. The optimal level is found to be A3.

(2)     Screen mesh: This factor only affects shrinkage and B2 is chosen.

(3)     Emulsion thickness: It is not a significant factor. The optimal level is found to be C2.

(4)     Screen open area: The open area affects line width, thickness, and roughness. The optimal level is found to be D2.

(5)     Print squeegee speed: This variable has more significant effect on line thickness than on roughness. The optimal level is F1.

(6)     Squeegee pressure: The variable G2 is obviously a critical factor in affecting line width. The optimal level was G2.

(7)     Snap-off distance: This factor will affect line width and roughness. The optimal level is H1.

(8)     The design of experiment in combination with the neural network simulation in the screen-printing of fine line is proven as a useful tool to increase the rate and efficiency of the experimental work, which then in term reduce the manufacturing cost substantially.

ACKNOWLEDGMENT

The authors would like to thank the Ministry of Economic Affairs (MOEA) of Taiwan, R.O.C., for the financial support on this research under contract No. D315KF1250.

REFERNCES

[1]K.C. Chiu and Y.S. Chen ,"Better Shrinkage Control of Alumina Ceramic Substrates by Design of Experiment Technique," Multilayer Electronic Ceramic Devices, American Ceramic Society, pp.143-156, (1997).

[2]P.D. Wasserman, "Neural Computing Theory and Practice," ANZA Research Inc., 1989.

[3]B. Windrow et al., "Layered Neural Nets for Pattern Recognition," IEEE Trans. on Acoustics, Speech. And Signal Processing, 36(7) pp.1109-1117, 1988.

[4]Chang Jung-Pu, "Design of Experiment", Eurekacp, 1984.

Table 1. Selected factors and levels for the first-stage experiment and point-line graph of various factors.

| | Factor | Level 1 | Level 2 | Interaction |
|---|---|---|---|---|
| A | Paste viscosity | A1 | A2 | |
| B | Screen mesh | B1 | B2 | |
| C | Emulsion thickness | C1 | C2 | |
| D | Screen open area | D1 | D2 | |
| F | Print squeegee speed | F1 | F2 | |
| G | Squeegee pressure | G1 | G2 | |
| H | Snap-off distance | H1 | H2 | |

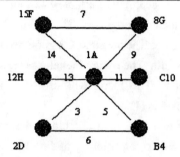

Table 2. Orthogonal array of the first-stage experiment

| | 1 | 2 | 3 | 4 | 5 | 6 | 7 | 8 | 9 | 10 | 11 | 12 | 13 | 14 | 15 |
|---|---|---|---|---|---|---|---|---|---|---|---|---|---|---|---|
| | A | D | AD | B | AB | BD | FG | G | AG | C | AC | H | AH | AF | F |
| 1 | 1 | 1 | 1 | 1 | 1 | 1 | 1 | 1 | 1 | 1 | 1 | 1 | 1 | 1 | 1 |
| 2 | 1 | 1 | 1 | 1 | 1 | 1 | 1 | 2 | 2 | 2 | 2 | 2 | 2 | 2 | 2 |
| 3 | 1 | 1 | 1 | 2 | 2 | 2 | 2 | 1 | 1 | 1 | 1 | 2 | 2 | 2 | 2 |
| 4 | 1 | 1 | 1 | 2 | 2 | 2 | 2 | 2 | 2 | 2 | 2 | 1 | 1 | 1 | 1 |
| 5 | 1 | 2 | 2 | 1 | 1 | 2 | 2 | 1 | 1 | 2 | 2 | 1 | 1 | 2 | 2 |
| 6 | 1 | 2 | 2 | 1 | 1 | 2 | 2 | 2 | 2 | 1 | 1 | 2 | 2 | 1 | 1 |
| 7 | 1 | 2 | 2 | 2 | 2 | 1 | 1 | 1 | 1 | 2 | 2 | 2 | 2 | 1 | 1 |
| 8 | 1 | 2 | 2 | 2 | 2 | 1 | 1 | 2 | 2 | 1 | 1 | 1 | 1 | 2 | 2 |
| 9 | 2 | 1 | 2 | 1 | 2 | 1 | 2 | 1 | 1 | 1 | 2 | 1 | 2 | 1 | 2 |
| 10 | 2 | 1 | 2 | 1 | 2 | 1 | 2 | 2 | 2 | 2 | 1 | 2 | 1 | 2 | 1 |
| 11 | 2 | 1 | 2 | 2 | 1 | 2 | 1 | 1 | 1 | 1 | 2 | 2 | 1 | 2 | 1 |
| 12 | 2 | 1 | 2 | 2 | 1 | 2 | 1 | 2 | 2 | 2 | 1 | 1 | 2 | 1 | 2 |
| 13 | 2 | 2 | 1 | 1 | 2 | 2 | 1 | 1 | 1 | 2 | 1 | 1 | 2 | 2 | 1 |
| 14 | 2 | 2 | 1 | 1 | 2 | 2 | 1 | 2 | 2 | 1 | 2 | 2 | 1 | 1 | 2 |
| 15 | 2 | 2 | 1 | 2 | 1 | 1 | 2 | 1 | 1 | 2 | 1 | 2 | 1 | 1 | 2 |
| 16 | 2 | 2 | 1 | 2 | 1 | 1 | 2 | 2 | 2 | 1 | 2 | 1 | 2 | 2 | 1 |

Table 3 Selected factors and levels for the second-stage experiment and point-line graph of various factors.

| | Factor | Level 1 | Level 2 | Level 3 | Interaction |
|---|---|---|---|---|---|
| A | Paste viscosity | A1 | A2 | A3 | |
| F | Print squeegee speed | F1 | F2 | F3 | |
| G | Squeegee pressure | G1 | G2 | G3 | |

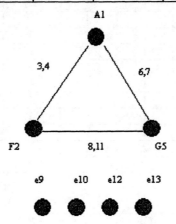

Table 4. ANOVA analysis for the first-stage experiment. (a) line width, (b) line thickness, (c) line roughness.

(a) line width

| FACTOR | Si | DF | V | F | @% | |
|---|---|---|---|---|---|---|
| A | 4000.562 | 1 | 4000.562 | | 58.8154 | ** |
| D | 770.0625 | 1 | 770.0625 | | 11.3146 | ** |
| G | 495.0625 | 1 | 495.0625 | | 7.27105 | ** |
| AH | 451.5625 | 1 | 451.5625 | | 6.63143 | ** |
| BD | 297.5625 | 1 | 297.5625 | | 4.36704 | * |
| H | 203.0625 | 1 | 203.0625 | | 2.97753 | * |
| AD | 162.5625 | 1 | 162.5625 | | 2.38202 | * |
| AG | 126.5625 | 1 | 126.5625 | | 1.85268 | * |
| FG | 105.0625 | 1 | 105.0625 | | 1.53655 | * |
| F | 85.5625 | 1 | 85.5625 | | 1.24982 | |
| AC | 39.0625 | 1 | 39.0625 | | 0.56609 | |
| B | 33.0625 | 1 | 33.0625 | | 0.39700 | |
| AB | 27.5625 | 1 | 27.5625 | | 0.03675 | |
| AF | 3.0625 | 1 | 3.0625 | | 0.03675 | |
| e | 0.5625 | 1 | 0.5625 | | 0.12406 | |
| St= | 6800.937 | | | @t= | 99.8759 | |

(b) line thickness

| FACTOR | Si | DF | V | F | @% | |
|--------|------|-----|-------|-----|---------|-----|
| A | 81 | 1 | 81 | 324 | 54.1946 | ** |
| F | 30.25 | 1 | 30.25 | 121 | 20.1342 | ** |
| AD | 12.25 | 1 | 12.25 | 49 | 8.05369 | * |
| D | 6.25 | 1 | 6.25 | 25 | 4.02684 | * |
| AB | 4 | 1 | 4 | 16 | 2.51677 | |
| G | 4 | 1 | 4 | 16 | 2.51677 | |
| C | 2.25 | 1 | 2.25 | 9 | 1.34228 | |
| BD | 2.25 | 1 | 2.25 | 9 | 1.34228 | |
| FG | 2.25 | 1 | 2.25 | 9 | 1.34228 | |
| AH | 1 | 1 | 1 | 4 | 0.50335 | |
| AG | 1 | 1 | 1 | 4 | 0.50335 | |
| B | 1 | 1 | 1 | 4 | 0.50335 | |
| H | 1 | 1 | 1 | 4 | 0.50335 | |
| e | 0.5 | 2 | 0.25 | | 2.51677 | |
| St= | 149 | | | @t= | 97.4832 | |

(c) line roughness

| FACTOR | Si | DF | V | F | @% | |
|--------|----------|-----|----------|-----|---------|-----|
| A | 0.075625 | 1 | 0.075625 | 121 | 16.3265 | ** |
| AD | 0.075625 | 1 | 0.075625 | 121 | 16.3265 | ** |
| B | 0.075625 | 1 | 0.075625 | 121 | 16.3265 | * |
| F | 0.050625 | 1 | 0.050625 | 81 | 10.8843 | * |
| AB | 0.050625 | 1 | 0.050625 | 81 | 10.8843 | * |
| D | 0.050625 | 1 | 0.050625 | 81 | 10.8843 | * |
| H | 0.030625 | 1 | 0.030625 | 49 | 6.53061 | * |
| AH | 0.015625 | 1 | 0.015625 | 25 | 3.26530 | * |
| BD | 0.015625 | 1 | 0.015625 | 25 | 3.26530 | |
| C | 0.005625 | 1 | 0.005625 | 9 | 1.08843 | |
| AG | 0.005625 | 1 | 0.005625 | 9 | 1.08843 | |
| AF | 0.005625 | 1 | 0.005625 | 9 | 1.08843 | |
| FG | 0.000625 | 1 | 0.000625 | 1 | 6E-16 | |
| e | 0.00125 | 2 | 0.000625 | | | |
| St= | 0.459375 | | | @t= | 97.9591 | |

Table 5. Multiple analysis of cross table.

| | A | B | D | F | G | H | AB | AD | AG | AH | BD | FG |
|---|---|---|---|---|---|---|---|---|---|---|---|---|
| **Line width** | ** | | * | | * | * | * | * | * | * | * | * |
| **Contribution** | 58.8 | | 11.3 | | 7.2 | 2.9 | 2.3 | 1.85 | 6.6 | | 4.3 | 1.5 |
| | A2 | | D2 | | G2 | H1 | | A2D1 | A2G1 | A2H2 | B1D2 | F1G2 |
| **Line thickness** | ** | | * | ** | | | | * | | | | |
| **Contribution** | 54.1 | | 4.0 | 20.1 | | | | 8.0 | | | | |
| | A2 | | D2 | F1 | | | | A2D2 | | | | |
| **Line roughness** | ** | ** | * | * | | * | ** | * | | * | * | |
| **Contribution** | 16.3 | 16.3 | 10.8 | 10.8 | | 6.5 | 10.8 | 16.3 | | 3.2 | 3.2 | |
| | A2 | B2 | D2 | F2 | | H1 | A2B2 | A2D1 | | A2H1 | B1D2 | |
| **Selected factor** | A2 | B2 | D2 | F1 | G2 | H1 | | | | | | |

Table 6. Optimized conditions for 50μm line screen printing process.

| | Factor | |
|---|---|---|
| A | Paste viscosity | A3 |
| B | Screen mesh | B2 |
| C | Emulsion thickness | C2 |
| D | Screen op en area | D2 |
| F | Print squeegee speed | F1 |
| G | Squeegee pressure | G2 |
| H | Snap-off distance | H1 |

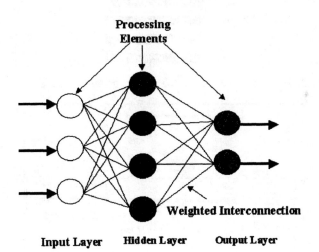

Fig. 1. Back-propagation neural network.

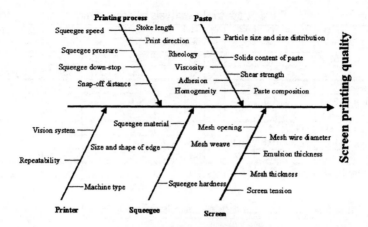

Fig. 2. Fish-bone causal analysis

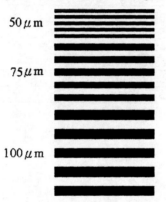

Fig.3. Test patterns for fine line screen-printing process.

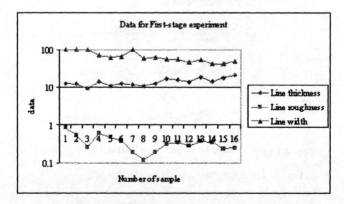

Fig.4. Data of Fine line printing for first-stage experiment.

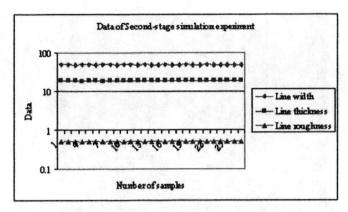

Fig.5. Data of Fine line printing for second-stage simulation experiment

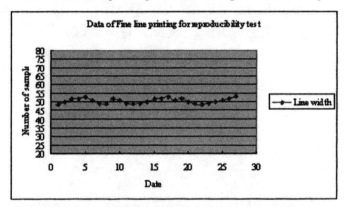

Fig.6. Data of fine line printing for reproducibility test.

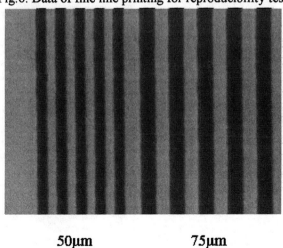

50µm                    75µm

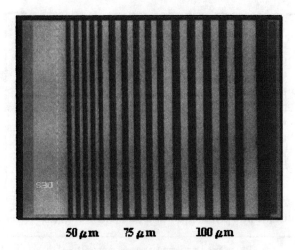

50 μm     75 μm     100 μm

Fig.7. 50μm fine line screen-printing on LTCC.

# UPPER FREQUENCY LIMITS OF PIEZOCERAMIC RESONATORS

Arthur Ballato
US Army Communications-Electronics Command
Fort Monmouth, NJ 07703-5201

ABSTRACT
New piezoceramic materials currently under development promise low intrinsic acoustic losses, along with high coupling factors. These will make appealing candidates for frequency control and selection applications in the burgeoning telecommunications market. Piezoceramic resonators, however, are often judged by a number of differing metrics, depending upon the intended application. Acoustic quality factor (Q) and electromechanical coupling factor (k) are two most often used. None of the usual performance figures is fully adequate for characterizing resonators for telecommunication frequencies. This paper describes various metrics traditionally applied to resonators, and introduces another criterion that is much more suitable for ranking materials intended for resonator and filter uses. The new material criterion can be expressed as an upper frequency limit, beyond which resonance behavior is inadequate.

INTRODUCTION
Ferroelectric materials are used in a variety of electromechanical devices, such as resonators, filters, transducers, and delay lines, [1-6] as well as sensors and actuators [7-11]. The material properties of primary importance vary with the application. In wideband filters, for example, coupling coefficient considerations are paramount, whereas in narrowband designs, minimizing loss is most important. Resonators have been gauged by a variety of material or circuit measures over the years. To an extent, the differing measures pertain to the intended uses, but none of the usual performance figures is entirely adequate for characterizing high frequency resonator materials for cellular radio, radar, and similar applications.

This paper considers some of the performance metrics traditionally applied to resonators and resonator materials. It then introduces a new metric for judging material suitability for high frequency resonator use, and tabulates its value for a number of materials. The new metric is a combination of all of the physical quantities associated with acoustic wave propagation in piezoelectric substances: mass density, dielectric permittivity, piezoelectric modulus, elastic stiffness and viscosity. Use of this characteristic number to rank resonator materials yields some unobvious and somewhat counterintuitive conclusions that reflect on the directions the technology of these devices might take, and where the emphases for future progress might be placed.

PIEZOELECTRIC RESONATORS

The earliest bulk wave piezoelectric resonators were bars [1]. To achieve the higher frequencies required by current applications, resonators now employ the thickness modes of plates [1,2,4,12-16], and variants such as ring-supported [17-20], and thin-film [21-50] configurations. For the past half-century and more, the push to higher frequencies was driven by practical applications and miniaturization [51,52]; this trend continues today. During this time, a recurring question has been "What is the highest useful acoustic resonator frequency?" We shall find that there is substantial reason to believe that the material-limited upper frequency for many piezoelectrics is considerably higher than usually thought, and that in many cases the upper limit on frequency achieved is more a result of manufacturing limitations than of material deficiency.

–Acoustic Velocity

Acoustic velocity, given by $v = \sqrt{(c/\rho)}$, is one of the important attributes characterizing an acoustic medium, as the resonance frequency of a plate of a given thickness is directly proportional to the velocity. The velocity depends primarily on the elastic stiffness $c^E$ and mass density $\rho$ of the medium, and to a lesser extent on the piezoelectric properties of the medium through the piezoelectric contribution to the effective elastic stiffness $c = c^E + e^2/\varepsilon^S$.

– Piezoelectric Coupling

The piezoelectric coupling factor k [4,12,13,20,53-55], is a dimensionless measure of electromechanical energy conversion efficiency in a piezoelectric resonator. It is determined by the piezoelectric, elastic, and dielectric constants as $k = |e|/\sqrt{(\varepsilon^S c)}$, and is bounded by $(0 \le k < 1)$. The coupling factor is important in characterizing an acoustic medium, since it determines whether a resonator may be driven by an impressed voltage, and is a primary determinant of certain distinguishing frequencies of interest. Two distinct types are used for excitation of piezoelectric plates, depending on whether the excitation takes place via a thickness- or laterally-directed field.

– Quality Factor

Mechanical quality factor, Q, is a measure of the ratio of energy storage to loss in a system. In a resonator, it can depend upon material impurities and defects, surface finish, and ambient gases, etc. Other things being constant, higher Q translates into higher stability and accuracy in oscillators; phase noise close to the carrier is proportional to $Q^{-4}$ [56]. It is found experimentally that for high

Ceramic Materials and Multilayer Electronic Devices

frequency plate resonators, Q is a function of both geometry and absolute frequency. Figure 1 [57,58] shows measured Q versus plate frequency; the plate frequency is determined by the thickness dimension. For a constant plate diameter, as the thickness is successively reduced, the measured Q at first rises and then declines. The initial rise has been traced to the lessening of losses arising from acoustic energy being carried away by the mounting structure. Beyond a diameter/thickness ratio of 20 to 50, the mounting losses are unimportant; the greatest contributor to loss comes from the intrinsic acoustic viscosity (internal friction) of the material. We are concerned solely with this loss mechanism, as it prevails at high frequencies.

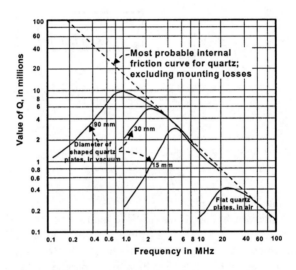

Fig. 1. Acoustic Q for quartz plates of various diameters, as function of the frequencies obtained when the plate thickness is successively reduced.

– Acoustic Loss

The material-limited (high frequency) losses in acoustic materials such as quartz are often discussed in terms of the product (Q · frequency) being a constant. A related, and, for many purposes, a better measure is the motional time constant $\tau_1$ [59-65], given by $\tau_1 = \eta/c$. This quantity is independent of frequency, depending only upon the acoustic viscosity and elastic stiffness of the medium [59,66,67]. These latter quantities are sensibly constant over a very wide range of frequencies, yielding a constant $\tau_1$. The reciprocal of $\tau_1$ is a relaxation frequency;

in quartz, it falls in the infrared, and is correlated with the IR absorption spectrum [68-70].

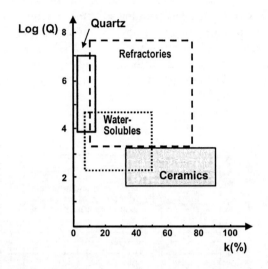

Fig. 2. Quality factor (Q) versus coupling factor (k) for generic categories of piezoelectrics.

– Equivalent Network

The Butterworth-Van Dyke (BVD) equivalent network of a piezoelectric resonator [1,50,63,65,71-73] is a simple, four-element circuit used to characterize the mechanical vibrations of the resonator in electrical terms. The network consists of a series $R_1$, $L_1$, $C_1$ combination in parallel with a second capacitor, $C_o$. The nominal frequency of the resonator at harmonic N is given by $f^{(N)} = N\ v/2t$, where t is the frequency-determining dimension of the resonator; for plates, as are considered here, t is the thickness.

This frequency is often called the series resonance frequency, $f_s$, and is used for normalizing the network functions. If present, dc conductivity is modeled by the addition of a resistance $R_o$ in parallel with $C_o$ [72]. In deriving the new material metric, we assume negligible dc conductivity. However, the conclusions we arrive at regarding loss and the directions for future work are germane to the general case of arbitrary dc conductivity.

The BVD circuit element values [12,13,15,53,54,63,72] depend upon the physical parameters of the medium and the geometry of the structure. We consider the case of a thin plate of thickness t, with coextensive electrodes of area A on the major surfaces. The capacitance ratio, $r = C_o/C_1$ and the piezoelectric coupling factor k are related by $r \cdot k^2 = \pi^2/8$, while $R_1 C_1 = \tau_1$.

Ceramic Materials and Multilayer Electronic Devices

# FIGURE OF MERIT CRITERION

The immittance functions, e.g., reactance, of the BVD circuit may be obtained by standard network analysis. Despite the simplicity of the BVD circuit, there are quite a few distinguishing frequencies defined by the zeros and extrema of the various network functions [71]. For example, setting the reactance function to zero yields the quadratic equation

$$[(1 - x)^2 + x/Q^2] + (1 - x)/r = 0; \quad x = (f/f_s)^2 \tag{1}$$

the roots of which define the resonance and antiresonance frequencies, $f_R$ and $f_A > f_R$. Between $f_R$ and $f_A$ the reactance is positive, indicating that the crystal looks like an inductor; outside this range the reactance is negative and the crystal looks like a capacitor. For most oscillator applications, the crystal is operated in the region of positive reactance. It is found from (1) that the frequency separation ($f_A - f_R)/f_s$, also known as the "pole-zero separation," depends jointly on Q and r.

Various measures used to describe the region and extent of resonance are detailed in references [4,71]. For our purposes here it is enough to recognize that resonance as usually construed ceases to exist when the condition ($f_R = f_A$) is satisfied. At this point the crystal just ceases to achieve a positive reactance, and its utility for frequency control and selection purposes is limited. The point at which ($f_R = f_A$) is found by setting the discriminant of (1) equal to zero. This leads, in turn, to another quadratic on the square of the figure of merit, $M \equiv Q/r$, as function of r:

$$r^2 M^4 - 2r (2r + 1) M^2 + 1 = 0. \tag{2}$$

The roots of equation (2) can be factored to yield $M = 1 + \sqrt{(1 + 1/r)}$.

Only the positive root applies, from which the criterion $M \approx 2$ is obtained for typical values of r. For values of M of 2 or less, resonance ceases to exist [2,4,74-77]. Since Q decreases with absolute frequency and r increases with harmonic, M is diminished both by increasing the harmonic as well as the frequency of operation. The limiting condition $M = 2$ thus imposes a constraint jointly upon frequency (or equivalently, the thickness) and harmonic. This is a very simple criterion, and we shall see that it leads to interesting conclusions. On the other hand, particular situations may require other criteria for M or Q, etc.; yet $M = 2$ is a suitable condition for many purposes. Moreover, it is proportional to the criterion utilized by designers of bandpass filters, as will be seen subsequently.

# FREQUENCY LIMITS

We now invoke the $M \equiv Q/r = 2$ criterion to infer the frequency limits imposed on thickness mode resonators by the phenomenological material constants of piezoelectric acoustic media. The quality factor Q is found from the motional time constant and the operating frequency $f^{(N)}$ at the $N^{th}$ harmonic as $Q = 1/(2\pi\,f^{(N)}\,\tau_1)$, while the capacitance ratio $r^{(N)}$ is found as

$$r^{(N)} = C_0/C_1^{(N)} = \tfrac{1}{2}\,(\pi\,N/2k)^2 \qquad (3)$$

Therefore, $M = Q/r = (4k^2/\pi^3\tau_1)/(f^{(N)}\,N^2)$, which, for $M = 2$, yields the condition $f^{(N)} \cdot N^2 = (2k^2/\pi^3\tau_1)$. The product $f^{(N)} \cdot N^2$ is thus a constant. Solving now for N gives $N^3 = (4k^2/\pi^3\tau_1\,v) \cdot t$ ; hence $N^3 = t/L_0$, where $L_0$ is the characteristic length of the piezoelectric medium:

$$L_0 = (\pi^3/4) \cdot (\tau_1\,v/k^2). \qquad (4)$$

The physical interpretation of $L_0$ is that it is the thickness for which $M = 2$ at the fundamental harmonic. By way of example, for AT-cut quartz, $L_0 \approx 39.2$ nm, or roughly one hundred molecular spacings! The smallness of $L_0$ compared to the usual resonator thicknesses encountered in practice leads one to conclude that substantially higher frequencies are available as far as the intrinsic material constants are concerned. The difficulty in achieving such high frequencies arises from present-day inabilities to fabricate resonators to the requisite thinness so that they can be used at the fundamental harmonic.

Characteristic length $L_0$ can equivalently be expressed in terms of material constants as

$$L_0 = (\pi^3/4) \cdot [\sqrt{(c/\rho)} \cdot \eta\,\varepsilon^S/e^2]. \qquad (5)$$

One sees that $L_0$ contains every relevant acoustic parameter: $\rho$, $\varepsilon^S$, e, c, and $\eta$. That is, $L_0$ is a function of velocity, coupling, and loss. For a given plate thickness t, the maximum usable harmonic is $N_{max} = (t/L_0)^{1/3}$. Of course, $N_{max}$ is to be rounded down to the nearest odd integer. At $N_{max}$, the operating frequency is $f^{(Nmax)} = [(v/2)/(L_0\,t)^{1/3}]$.

The consequences of operating on a particular harmonic may be examined by considering plate resonators of differing thicknesses, such that $N_{max} = 1$, 3, or 5. The fundamental mode resonator has a thickness of $L_0$, while the harmonic resonator thicknesses are $M^3 \cdot L_0$. The frequencies at the intended harmonic are then $f^{(N)} = (v/2L_0) \cdot (1/N^2) = f_0\,/\,N^2$, where the quantity $f_0 = v/2L_0$ denotes the characteristic frequency of the acoustic medium; it is the limiting frequency for which $M = 2$ at the fundamental harmonic. It is clear that, if one desires to attain high frequencies, one pays a severe penalty for using harmonics other than the fundamental. By way of illustration, Table I lists the maximum frequencies, versus harmonic, for quartz and PZT 5A piezoceramic [5,60,64,66,78,79]. Data for various thin-film piezoelectrics are given in Table II [80-83].

Table I. Maximum frequencies at various harmonics

| N | $t/L_o$ | quartz | | PZT 5A | |
|---|---|---|---|---|---|
| | | t (μm) | f (GHz) | t (μm) | f (MHz) |
| 1 | 1 | 0.0392 | 42.3 | 2.75 | 528 |
| 3 | 27 | 1.06 | 4.70 | 74.3 | 58.7 |
| 5 | 125 | 4.90 | 1.69 | 344 | 21.1 |

A figure of merit (FOM) used by filter designers is $(k^2 \cdot Q)$; this is related to $L_o$ as follows. The maximum useable frequency for a resonant device of acoustic velocity v is obtained by operation at the fundamental, and is given by $f_o = v/2L_o = 2k^2/(\pi^3\tau_1)$, where $\tau_1 = 1/(2\pi f_1 Q)$, and Q is the measured quality factor at $f_1$, the nominal frequency. Thus $f_o = (4/\pi^2)$ $(f_1 k^2 Q)$. Put another way, the resonant structure approaches the limit of its usefulness at a normalized frequency $(f_o/f_1)$ approximately 40% of the FOM. A typical CDMA filter with a FOM of 120 at the 1.9 GHz PCS band could be reconfigured so as to remain useful above 20 GHz, insofar as the piezomaterial is concerned.

Table II. Characteristics of selected types of thin-film resonator

| Type | v (km/s) | $\tau_1$ (fs) | k (%) | $L_o$ (nm) | $f_o$ (GHz) |
|---|---|---|---|---|---|
| GaAs | 3.34 | 70 | 6.2 | 471 | 3.54 |
| quartz AT | 3.32 | 11.8 | 8.80 | 39 | 42.3 |
| ZnO | 6.34 | 45 | 28 | 28 | 112 |
| AℓN | 10.4 | 3.2 | 30 | 29 | 1814 [+] |
| LiNbO₃ | 7.40 | 3.0 | 48.7 | 0.73 | 5100 [+] |

+ beyond continuum limit

The issue then clearly focuses on the availability of technology for making thin films, membranes, and similar structures. Technology, not intrinsic material properties, is the real limitation. The use of sol-gel techniques [84-89] for processing ceramic thin films seems particularly promising for producing cost-effective ceramic resonators at UHF and higher frequencies. To be sure, there are certain material-related issues associated with growth, microstructure, surface finish, etc., but manufacturing problems, such as achieving films with adequate parallelism are, in reality, the main difficulty. With suitable attention focused less on material limitations and more on overcoming fabrication shortcomings, the way will be clear for achieving resonators at unprecedented frequencies.

PIEZOELECTRIC ACOUSTIC MATERIALS

The properties of piezoelectric materials for acoustic wave applications have been tabulated for a wide variety of substances [5,60,61,64,74,75,78,79, 90-97]. However, even as measurement methods and apparatus have become increasingly more refined [72,73,77,98,99], there remains a lack of values for the elements of the viscosity tensor. As a consequence, values for $L_o$ and $f_o$ can be deduced only for those orientations and modes of vibration for which Q measurements have been reported. Table III presents piezoacoustic parameters for a number of ceramics and related ferroelectrics.

Table III. Characteristics of selected types of piezoelectrics

| Type | v (km/s) | $\tau_1$ (ps) | k (%) | $L_0$ (µm) | $f_0$ (MHz) |
|------|----------|---------------|-------|------------|-------------|
| PZT sol-gel [+] | 4.45 | 2.19 | 47 | 0.342 | 6.51 GHz |
| PZT 5A | 2.90 | 11 | 30 | 2.75 | 528 |
| PbTiO$_3$ | 4.42 | 31.8 | 50 | 4.36 | 507 |
| fresnoite | 4.70 | 33.9 | 25 | 19.8 | 119 |
| PZT 5A | 4.45 | 236 | 47 | 36.9 | 60.4 |
| PZT/epoxy | 2.12 | 17 | 8 | 43.7 | 24.3 |
| PZT/epoxy | 3.90 | 878 | 57 | 81.7 | 23.9 |
| PVDF | 2.05 | 128 | 12 | 141 | 7.3 |

[+] $PbZr_{0.3}Ti_{0.7}O_3$ on Si substrate; f ~ 1.3 GHz

Figs. 3 and 4 show log-log plots of operating frequency versus plate thickness, with harmonic numbers marked. It is seen that the useable frequency diminishes with harmonic. Fig. 3 plots the behavior of two entries from Table III, while Fig. 4 is plotted for some of the materials and cuts listed in Table II. In the graphs, "TS" refers to thickness-shear motion, and "LE" refers to excitation by a lateral electric field [63]. The lines for a given substance are drawn subject to the constraint M = 2, while allowing the harmonic number N to be a continuous variable. Indicated on each line are the physically meaningful, odd-integer, values of N. Above each curve M < 2, while below each curve M > 2.

The ceramics in Fig. 3 exhibit characteristic frequencies that are in the range used for cellular radio. With advanced growth techniques, it is highly probable that inexpensive resonators capable of use in the GHz region can be fashioned of these materials. The entries in Fig. 4 are seen to be compatible with the frequencies of radar systems such as might be used for collision-avoidance in automobiles, as well as future telecommunication bands. Since the start of the communications industry well over one hundred years ago, the evolution of applications has led to a monotonic increase in frequency limits.

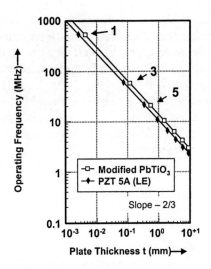

Fig. 3. Maximum operating frequency versus plate thickness for two piezoceramics. For display purposes, the harmonic number is treated as a continuous variable, but odd integer values are indicated. For highest frequency operation, use of the fundamental is required.

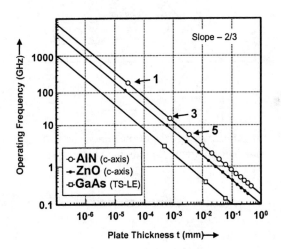

Fig. 4. Maximum operating frequency versus plate thickness for three materials in crystal class 6mm. For display purposes, the harmonic number is treated as a continuous variable, but odd integer values are indicated. For highest frequency operation, use of the fundamental is required.

More generally, Fig. 5 shows the normally encountered ranges of motional time constant $\tau_1$ and piezoelectric coupling factor k for poled ceramics, refractory crystals (such as lithium niobate and tantalate), quartz, and semi-insulating (SI) semiconductors. Also shown are values of the characteristic frequency, $f_o$, found by rewriting (15) as $f_o = (2/\pi^3) \cdot (k^2/\tau_1)$.

Characteristic frequency $f_o$ thus appears in a natural fashion, benchmarking the different generic material classes. With proper attention, the region delimiting the piezoceramics can be extended downward to lower loss values, and consequently higher useful frequency domains.

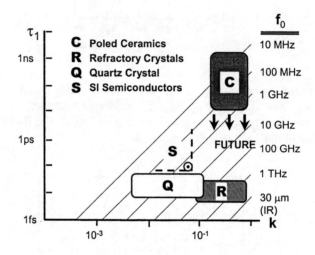

Fig. 5. Properties of generic categories of piezoelectrics plotted in the $\tau_1 - k$ plane. A goal for future piezoceramic work is indicated by arrows.

CONCLUSIONS

We have introduced a new metric for gauging piezoelectric materials for high frequency resonator applications. It is a combination of velocity, coupling, and loss. Use of the measure leads one to conclude that piezoceramics and other ferroelectrics should be useful at frequencies into the GHz region. One concludes that much greater emphasis ought to be devoted in the future to devising advanced growth and fabrication methods [51,52, 100,101] for making such resonator structures commercially manufacturable. Acoustic materials are seen by the foregoing to be intrinsically capable of higher frequency operation than is currently practiced. As scale lengths are reduced, however, other limiting factors are encountered [52]; one such being increased noise levels, due to diminished volume-to-surface ratios.

REFERENCES

[1]W. G. Cady, *Piezoelectricity*, McGraw Hill, New York, 1946; Dover, New York, 1964.

[2]R. A. Heising, *Quartz Crystals for Electric Circuits*, Van Nostrand, New York, Chap. XII, pp. 394-410, 1946.

[3]J. van Randeraat, ed., *Piezoelectric Ceramics*, Eindhoven, The Netherlands: N. V. Philips' Gloeilampenfabrieken, June 1968, 118 pp.

[4]A. Ballato, "Piezoelectric Resonators," in *Design of Crystal and Other Harmonic Oscillators*, by B. Parzen, Wiley and Sons, New York, 1985, pp. 66-122 and 432-436.

[5]B. Jaffe, W. R. Cook, Jr., and H. Jaffe, *Piezoelectric Ceramics*, New York: Academic Press, 1971.

[6]"IEEE Standard definitions of primary ferroelectric terms," ANSI/IEEE Standard 180-1986, New York: IEEE Press, 21pp.

[7]G. H. Haertling, "Rainbow ceramics - a new type of ultra-high-displacement actuator," Am. Ceramic Soc. Bulletin, vol. 73, no. 1, pp. 93-96, January 1994.

[8]L. L. Hench and J. K. West, *Principles of Electronic Ceramics*, New York: John Wiley & Sons, 1990.

[9]R. E. Newnham and G. R. Ruschau, "Smart electroceramics," J. Am. Ceram. Soc., vol. 74, no. 3, pp. 463-480, March 1991.

[10]D. J. Waller and A. Safari, "Piezoelectric lead zirconate titanate ceramic fiber/polymer composites," J. Am. Ceram. Soc., vol. 75, no. 6, pp. 1648-1655, June 1992.

[11]D. H. Turnbull, M. D. Sherar, and F. S. Foster, "Determination of electromechanical coupling coefficients in transducer materials with high mechanical losses," IEEE Ultrasonics Symp. Proc., pp. 631-634, October 1988.

[12]A. Ballato, "Doubly rotated thickness mode plate vibrators," in *Physical Acoustics: Principles and Methods*, (W P Mason and R N Thurston, eds.), Vol. 13, Chap. 5. Academic Press, New York, 1977, pp. 115-181.

[13]"IEEE Standard on Piezoelectricity," IEEE Standard 176-1978, IEEE, New York, 55 pp.

[14]E. A. Gerber and A. Ballato, eds., *Precision Frequency Control*, Vols. 1 and 2, Academic Press, New York and Orlando, 1985.

[15]J. F. Rosenbaum, *Bulk Acoustic Wave Theory and Devices*, Artech House, Boston and London, 1988.

[16]B. A. Auld, *Acoustic Fields and Waves in Solids*, 2nd edition, Vol. I and II, R. E. Krieger Pub. Co., Malabar, FL, 1990.

[17]G. K. Guttwein, A. Ballato, and T. J. Lukaszek, "VHF-UHF piezoelectric resonators," US Patent 3,394,677, issued September 1972.

[18] M. Berté, "Acoustic-bulk-wave resonators and filters operating in the fundamental mode at frequencies greater than 100 MHz," Electron. Lett., vol. 13, no. 9, 28 April 1977, pp. 248-250.

[19] M. Berté, "Acoustic bulk wave resonators and filters operating in the fundamental mode at frequencies greater than 100 MHz," Proc. 31st Ann. Frequency Control Symp., pp. 122-125, June 1977.

[20] A. Ballato, T. J. Lukaszek, and G. J. Iafrate, "Subtle effects in high-stability quartz resonators," Ferroelectrics, vol. 43, nos. 1/2, pp. 25-41, 1982.

[21] K. M. Lakin, G. R. Kline, R. S. Ketcham, A. R. Landin, W. A. Burkland, K. T. McCarron, S. D. Braymen, and S. G. Burns, "Thin film resonator technology," Proc. 41st Ann. Freq. Contr. Symp., pp. 371-381, May 1987.

[22] K. M. Lakin, G. R. Kline, and K. T. McCarron, "High Q microwave acoustic resonators and filters," IEEE MTT-S Intl. Microwave Symp. Digest, vol. 3, pp. 1517-1520, June 1993.

[23] K. M. Lakin, G. R. Kline, and K. T. McCarron, "Overmoded high Q resonators for microwave oscillators," IEEE Intl. Frequency Control Symp. Proc., pp. 718-721, June 1993.

[24] L. Bidart and J. Chauvin, "Direct frequency crystal oscillators," Proc. 35th Ann. Frequency Control Symp., pp. 365-375, May 1981.

[25] R. Stokes and J. D. Crawford, "X-Band thin film acoustic filters on GaAs," IEEE Trans. Microwave Theory Tech., vol. 41, no. 6/7, pp. 1075-1080, June/July 1993.

[26] S. V. Krishnaswamy, "Film bulk acoustic wave resonator technology," IEEE MTT-S Newsletter, no. 130, pp. 21-25, Fall 1991.

[27] E. A. Gerber, T. Lukaszek, and A. Ballato, "Advances in microwave acoustic frequency sources," IEEE Trans. Microwave Theory Tech., vol. MTT-34, no. 10, pp. 1002-1016, October 1986.

[28] K. M. Lakin, "Thin film resonators and filters," IEEE Ultrasonics Symp. Proc. pp. 895-906, October 1999.

[29] K. M. Lakin, G. R. Kline and K. T. McCarron, "High Q microwave acoustic resonators and filters," IEEE Trans. Microwave Theory Tech., vol. 41 no. 12, pp. 2139-2146, December 1993.

[30] T. W. Grudkowski, J. F. Black, T. M. Reeder, D. E. Cullen, and R. A. Wagner, "Fundamental mode UHF/VHF miniature resonators and filters," Appl. Phys. Lett., vol. 39, no. 11, pp. 993-995, November 1980.

[31] K. M. Lakin and J. S. Wang, "Acoustic bulk wave composite resonators," Appl. Phys. Lett., vol. 39, no. 3, pp. 125-128, February 1981.

[32] C. Vale, J. Rosenbaum, S. Horwitz, S. Krishnaswamy, and R. Moore, "FBAR filters at GHz frequencies," Proc. 45th Ann. Frequency Control Symp., pp. 332-336, May 1991.

[33] M. Kitayama, T. Fukuichi, T. Shiosaki, and A. Kawabata," VHF/UHF composite resonator on a silicon substrate," Jap. J. Appl. Phys. vol. 22, Suppl. 22-3, pp. 139-141, 1983.

[34]K. Nakamura, Y. Ohashi and H. Shimizu, "UHF bulk acoustic wave filters utilizing thin ZnO/SiO$_2$ diaphragms on silicon," Jap. J. Appl. Phys. vol. 25, no. 3, pp. 371-375, 1986.

[35]K. M. Lakin, G. R. Kline and K. T. McCarron, "Thin film bulk acoustic filters for GPS," IEEE Ultrasonics Symp. Proc., pp. 471-476, October 1992.

[36]K. M. Lakin, "Modeling of thin film resonators and filters," Proc. IEEE MTT-S Int. Microwave Symp. Dig., pp. 149-152, June 1992.

[37]Q. X. Su, P. B. Kirby, E. Komuro, and R. W. Whatmore, "Edge supported ZnO thin film bulk acoustic wave resonators and filter design," IEEE/EIA Intl. Frequency Control Symp. Proc., pp 434-440, June 2000.

[38]R. Ruby, P. Bradley, J. D. Larson III and Y. Oshmyansky, "PCS 1900 MHz duplexer using thin film bulk acoustic resonator (FBARS)," Electron. Lett. 13 May 1999, vol. 35, no.10.

[39]J. D. Larson, S. M. Ruby, P. Bradley, Y. Oshmyansky, "A BAW antenna duplexer for the 1900 PCS band," IEEE Ultrasonics Symp. Proc. pp. 887-890, October 1999.

[40]P. Osbond, C. M. Beck, D. J. Brierley, M. R. Cox, S. P. Marsh, N. M. Shorrocks, "The influence of ZnO and electrode thickness on the performance of thin film bulk acoustic wave resonators," IEEE Ultrasonics Symp. Proc., pp. 911-914, October 1999.

[41]J. D. Larson III, R. C. Ruby, J. Wen, S. Kok, A. Chien, "Power handling and temperature coefficient studies in FBAR duplexers for the 1900 MHz PCS band," IEEE Intl. Ultrasonics Symp. Proc., pp. 869-874, October 2000.

[42]H. Satoh, Y. Ebata, H. Suzuki, and C. Narahara, "An air gap type piezoelectric composite resonator," Proc. 39$^{th}$ Ann. Frequency Control Symp., pp. 361-366, May 1985.

[43]C. W. Seabury, J. T. Cheung, P. H. Korbin, R. Addison, "High performance microwave air-bridge resonators," IEEE Ultrasonics Symp. Proc., pp. 909-911, November 1995.

[44]W. E. Newell, "Face-mounted piezoelectric resonators," Proc. IEEE, vol. 53, pp. 575-581, June 1965.

[45]K. M. Lakin, K. T. McCarron, and R. E. Rose "Solidly mounted resonators and filters," IEEE Ultrasonics Symp. Proc. pp. 905-908, November 1995.

[46]M. Dubois, P. Muralt, H. Matsumoto, V. Plessky, and S. Kondratiev, "BAW resonator based on aluminum nitride thin films," IEEE Ultrasonics Symp. Proc. pp. 907-910, October 1999.

[47]K. M. Lakin, G. R. Kline and K. T. McCarron, "Development of miniature filters for wireless applications," IEEE Trans. Microwave Theory Tech. vol. 43, no. 12, pp. 2933-2939, December 1995.

[48]K. M. Lakin, K. T. McCarron, J. Belsick, and R. Rose, "Filter banks implemented with integrated thin film resonators," IEEE Intl. Ultrasonics Symp. Proc., pp. 851-854, October 2000.

[49]K. M. Lakin, K. T. McCarron, and J. F. McDonald, "Temperature compensated bulk acoustic thin film resonators," IEEE Intl. Ultrasonics Symp. Proc., pp. 855-858, October 2000.

[50]J. D. Larson III, P. D. Bradley, S. Wartenberg, and R. C. Ruby, "Modified Butterworth-Van Dyke circuit for FBAR resonators and automated measurement system," IEEE Intl. Ultrasonics Symp. Proc., pp. 863-868, October 2000.

[51]US Congress, Office of Technology Assessment, "Miniaturization Technologies," OTA-TCT-514, Washington, DC: US Government Printing Office, November 1991, 48pp.

[52]M. Roukes, "Nanophysics: Plenty of room, indeed," pp. 92-98, 100, in *The Edge of Physics*, Scientific American Special Edition, vol. 13, no. 1, 2003.

[53]"IRE Standards on piezoelectric crystals: Determination of the elastic, piezoelectric, and dielectric constants - The electromechanical coupling factor, 1958," IEEE Standard 178, Proc. IRE, vol. 46, no. 4, pp. 764-778, April 1958.

[54]"IEEE Standard on piezoelectricity," IEEE Standard 176-1987, IEEE Press: New York, 54 pp.

[55]IEC Publication 483: Guide to Dynamic Measurements of Piezoelectric Ceramics (1976). New York: ANSI.

[56]E. S. Ferre-Pikal, M. C. Delgado Aramburo, F. L. Walls, and K. M. Lakin. "1/f frequency noise of 2 GHz high-Q over-moded sapphire resonators," Proc. 2000 IEEE/EIA Intl. Frequency Control Symp. and Exhibition, pp 536-540.

[57]H. E. Bömmel, W. P. Mason, and A. W. Warner, "Experimental evidence for dislocations in crystalline quartz," Phys. Rev., vol. 99, pp. 1894-1896, 1955.

[58]A. W. Warner, "Design and performance of ultraprecise 2.5-mc quartz crystal units," Bell Syst. Tech. J., vol. 39, pp. 1193-1217, September 1960.

[59]G. K. Guttwein, T. J. Lukaszek, and A. Ballato, "Practical consequences of modal parameter control in crystal resonators," Proc. 21st Ann. Frequency Control Symp., pp. 115-137, April 1967.

[60]J. C. Brice, "Crystals for quartz resonators," Revs. Mod. Phys., vol. 57, pp. 105-146, 1985.

[61]J. G. Gualtieri, J. A. Kosinski, and A. Ballato, "Piezoelectric materials for acoustic wave applications," IEEE Trans. Ultrason., Ferro., and Freq. Control, vol. 41, no. 1, pp. 53-59, January 1994.

[62]A. Ballato, "Frequency-temperature-load capacitance behavior of resonators for TCXO application," IEEE Trans. Sonics Ultrason., vol. SU-25, no. 4, pp. 185-191, July 1978.

[63]A. Ballato, E. R. Hatch, M. Mizan, and T. J. Lukaszek, "Lateral field equivalent networks and piezocoupling factors of quartz plates driven in simple thickness modes," IEEE Trans. Ultrason., Ferro., Freq. Control, vol. UFFC-33, no. 4, pp. 385-393, July 1986.

[64]A. Ballato, "Elastic properties of crystalline quartz," in *Handbook of Elastic Properties of Solids, Liquids, and Gases*, (M. Levy, H. E. Bass, and R. Stern, Eds.), Vol. II , Ch. 15, pp. 257-279. Academic Press, San Diego, CA, 2001.

[65]A. Ballato, "Equivalent networks for piezoelectric resonators and transducers," Proc. 5th European Frequency and Time Forum, Besançon, pp. 465-473, March 1991.

[66]J. Lamb and J. Richter, "Anisotropic acoustic attenuation with new measurements for quartz at room temperature," Proc. Roy. Soc. (London), vol. 293A, pp. 479-492, 1966.

[67]A. Seed, "The internal friction of quartz as a function of strain amplitude and frequency," Brit. J. Appl. Phys., vol. 16, pp. 87-91, 1965.

[68]D. B. Fraser, D. M. Dodd, D. W. Rudd, and W. J. Carroll, "Using infrared to find the mechanical Q of $\alpha$-quartz," Frequency, vol. 4, no. 1, pp. 18-21, 1966.

[69]B. Sawyer, "Q capability indications from infrared absorption measurements for $Na_2CO_3$ process cultured quartz," IEEE Trans. Sonics Ultrason., vol. 19, pp. 41-44, 1972.

[70]A. Ballato, "The fluency matrix of quartz," IEEE Trans. Sonics Ultrason., vol. SU-25, no. 2, pp. 107-108, March 1978.

[71]A. Ballato, "Resonance in piezoelectric vibrators," Proc. IEEE, vol. 58, no. 1, pp. 149-151, January 1970.

[72]A. Ballato and J. Ballato, "Measuring modern ferroelectrics accurately," Am. Ceramic Soc. Bulletin, vol. 73, no. 3, p. 224, March 1994; Am. Ceramic Soc. 96th Ann. Meeting Abstracts Book, April 1994, p. 77.

[73]F. K. Priebe and A. Ballato, "Measurement of mode parameters by sweep frequency methods in the frequency range from 20 to 250 MHz," Proc. 20th Ann. Frequency Control Symp., pp. 465-499, April 1966.

[74]J. G. Gualtieri and A. Ballato, "Advances in high-Q piezoelectric materials and devices," Proc. 15th Annual Piezoelectric Devices Conference, pp. 1-12, September 1993. Electronic Industries Association.

[75]A. Ballato and J. G. Gualtieri, "Advances in high-Q piezoelectric resonator materials and devices," IEEE Trans. Ultrason., Ferro., Freq. Control, vol. 41, no. 6, pp. 834-844, November 1994.

[76]A. Ballato, J. G. Gualtieri, and J. A. Kosinski, "Ferroelectric materials for thin-film and membrane resonators," Proc. Ninth IEEE Intl. Symp. on the Applications of Ferroelectrics (ISAF-94), pp. 674-679, August 1994.

[77]A. Ballato, "Interpreting piezoceramic impedance measurements," in *Dielectric Materials and Devices* (K. M. Nair, A. S. Bhalla, T. K. Gupta, S.-I. Hirano, B. V. Hiremath, J.-H. Jean and R. Pohanka, Eds.), pp. 369-410, 2002.

[78]R. Bechmann, "Elastic and piezoelectric constants of alpha-quartz," Phys. Rev., vol. 110, no. 5, pp. 1060-1061, June 1958.

[79]Landolt-Börnstein, Numerical Data and Functional Relationships in Science and Technology, New Series, Group III: Crystal and Solid State Physics, Volumes III/1, 1966; III/2, 1969; III/3, 1969; III/9, 1974; III/11, 1979; III/16a, 1981; III/16b, 1982; and III/17a, 1982. Springer-Verlag, Berlin, New York.

[80]A. Ballato and C. D. Bosco, "Acoustic waves in cubic crystals: networks for semiconducting vibrators, and application to gallium arsenide," Technical Report

DELET-TR-79-9, US Army Electronics R&D Command, Fort Monmouth, NJ, April 1979, 45pp.

[81]J. S. Blakemore, ed., *Gallium Arsenide*, Key papers in physics, No. 1, New York: American Institute of Physics, 1987, 401pp.

[82]S. Adachi, *Physical Properties of III - V Semiconductor Compounds*, New York: Wiley & Sons, 1992.

[83]J. Söderkvist and K. Hjort, "The piezoelectric effect of GaAs used for resonators and resonant sensors," J. Micromech. Microeng., vol. 4, no. 1, pp. 28-34, March 1994.

[84]K. Han, A. Safari, and R. E. Riman, "Colloidal processing for improved piezoelectric properties of flexible 0 - 3 ceramic-polymer composites," J. Am. Ceram. Soc., vol. 74, no. 7, pp. 1699-1702, July 1991.

[85]L. C. Klein, "Sol-gel processing," in *Engineered Materials Handbook, Vol. 4, Ceramics and Glasses*, pp. 209-214, ASM Intl., 1991.

[86]C. Livage, A. Safari, and L. C. Klein, "Sol-gel lead zirconate-titanate thin films: effect of solution concentration," in Proc. Eighth IEEE Intl. Symp. on Appls. of Ferroelectrics (ISAF '92), August 1992, pp. 444-447.

[87]J. B. Wachtman and R. A. Haber, eds., *Ceramic Films and Coatings*, Park Ridge, NJ: Noyes Publications, 1992.

[88]D. Tahan, A. Safari, and L. C. Klein, "The preparation of dielectric ($Ba_{0.8}$, $Sr_{0.2}$) Ti $O_3$ thin films by sol-gel method," in Proc. Sixth US-Japan Seminar on Dielectric and Piezoelectric Ceramics, pp. 47-50, 1993.

[89]H. Schmidt, "The sol-gel process for the synthesis and processing of ceramic powders," Interceram., vol. 43, no. 2, pp. 90, 93, March 1994.

[90]J. G. Gualtieri, J. A. Kosinski, and A. Ballato, "Piezoelectric material constants for surface wave research," Proc. 7th European Frequency and Time Forum, pp. 231-234, March 1993.

[91]J. G. Gualtieri, J. A. Kosinski, and A. Ballato, "Piezoelectric materials for SAW applications," IEEE Ultrason. Symp. Proc., pp. 403-412, October 1992.

[92]A. Ballato and T. Lukaszek, "Microwave acoustic material properties," Microwave Journal, vol. 33, no. 5, pp. 105-114, May 1990.

[93]I. Ueda and S. Ikegami, "Piezoelectric properties of modified $PbTiO_3$ ceramics," Jap. Jour. Appl. Phys., vol. 7, pp. 236-242, 1968. Reprinted in: *Piezoelectricity*, C. Z. Rosen, B. V. Hiremath, and R. Newnham, eds., Key Papers in Physics series, New York: American Institute of Physics, 1992, pp. 175-181.

[94]A. Halliyal, A. S. Bhalla, R. E. Newnham, and L. E. Cross, "Piezoelectric and elastic properties of barium germanium titanate and lithium borosilicate glass-ceramics," IEEE Ultrasonics Symp. Proc., pp. 315-318, October 1981.

[95]C. W. Lee, L. J. Bowen, J. M. Browne, A. Halliyal, A. S. Bhalla, and E. Ylo, "Acoustic wave properties of fresnoite glass ceramics," IEEE Ultrasonics Symp. Proc., pp. 285-289, November 1984.

[96]H. Takeuchi, Y. Ito, S. Jyomura, K. Nagatsuma, and S. Ashida, "New piezoelectric ceramics with zero temperature coefficients for acoustic wave applications," IEEE Ultrasonics Symp. Proc., pp. 400-409, November 1980.

[97]T. Suwannasiri and A. Safari, "Effect of rare-earth additives on electromechanical properties of modified lead titanate ceramics," J. Am. Ceram. Soc., vol. 76, no. 12, pp. 3155-3158, December 1993.

[98]A. Ballato and T. J. Lukaszek, "Shallow bulk acoustic wave progress and prospects," IEEE Trans. Microwave Theory Tech., vol. MTT-27, no. 12, pp. 1004-1012, December 1979.

[99]T. J. Lukaszek and A. Ballato, "Microwave frequency sources employing shallow bulk acoustic wave devices," Microwave Journal, vol. 28, no. 3, pp. 77-99, March 1985.

[100]J. R. Vig, J. W. LeBus, and R. L. Filler, "Chemically polished quartz," Proc. 31st Ann. Frequency Control Symp., pp. 131-143, June 1977.

[101]R. N. Castellano, T. R. Meeker, R. C. Sundahl, and J. C. Jacobs, "The relationship between quartz surface morphology and the Q of high frequency resonators," Proc. 31st Ann. Frequency Control Symp., pp. 126-130, June 1977.

# RECENT DEVELOPMENTS IN LOW-FIRED PIEZOELECTRIC CERAMIC MULTILAYER TRANSFORMER

Longtu Li*, Xiangcheng Chu, and Zhilun Gui
State Key Laboratory of New Ceramics and Fine Processing
Department of Materials Science and Engineering
Tsinghua University, Beijing, 100084, P. R. China

ABSTRACT

The low-fired high performance piezoelectric ceramics used for multilayer piezoelectric transformer (MPT) has been studied. The properties of piezoelectric ceramics sintering temperature lower than $1000\,^{\circ}C$ are as following: $K_p$=0.60~0.70, $d_{33}$≈400 PC/N, $\tan\delta \leqq 50\times10^{-4}$, $\varepsilon^T_{33}/\varepsilon_0$≈2200. The vibration mode and resonance character of MPT were measured by a Laser Doppler Vibrometer. It was found that the resonance impedance is an important influence factor on decreasing temperature rise o f M PT d uring o perating s tate. T he l ow-temperature s intering M PT w ith h igh voltage step-up ratio, high power density, high transfer efficiency, and low cost could be obtained. It reveals a broad a pplication prospect f or back light power of liquid crystal display.

INTRODUCTION

Low-firing multilayer piezoelectric transformer (MPT) was studied in Beijing Tsinghua University on the 1980's [1]. This kind of MPT has high voltage step-up ratio, low driving voltage and small size. Its voltage step-up ratio is ten times higher than that of conventional Rosen type single layer transformer. As known, the sintering temperature of normal piezoelectric ceramics is high up to about $1300\,^{\circ}C$. In order to decrease the consumption of precious metal in internal electrodes, the low

---

* Corresponding author E-mail: LLT-dms@mail.tsinghua.edu.cn

sintering temperature PZT-based piezoelectric ceramics with high performance have been investigated systematically in Tsinghua University [2]. A lot of low-firing high performance piezoelectric ceramics including binary、 ternary and quaternary system compositions have been developed. They can be sintered at 820~1000℃ and obtained with excellent properties [3]. A new kind of quaternary system piezoelectric ceramics PMN-PNN-PZT which can be satisfied used for low firing MPT. Recent years, with increasing requirement of invert of portable computer and other electronic instrument, the MPT has attracted more attention and interested by many researchers and users. A new type invert used for the back-light of liquid crystal display in portable computer has been developed. The MPT and its inverts have many advantages, such as thin shape, small size, high transfer efficiency, anti-interfere for electro-magnetic. The MPT and inverts have been produced industrial scale by Xi'an Konghong Company in China, recently.

LOW-FIRING PIEZOELECTRIC CERAMICS WITH HIGH PERFORMANCE

The chemical grade and analytical grade raw materials $Pb_3O_4$, $TiO_2$, $ZrO_2$, $Nb_2O_5$, $Ni (Ac)_2 \cdot 4H_2O$, $Mg_5(OH)_2(CO_3)_4 \cdot 6H_2O$, $ZnO$, $Li_2CO_3$, $CdO$, $Bi_2O_3$, $MnO_2$, $SrCO_3$ were used and powders were prepared by conventional oxide synthesis processing, samples were formed into discs having a diameter of 15mm and thickness of 1mm under the pressure of about 100Mpa were coated with silver paste and fired. After firing samples were polarized by a DC electric field at 4KV/mm in 120℃ silicon oil. The dielectric and piezoelectric properties were measured by HP4194.

The composition of quaternary system PMN-PNN-PZT ceramics is given as follow:

$$xPb (Mg_{1/3}Nb_{2/3})O_3\text{-}yPb(Ni_{1/3}Nb_{2/3})O_3\text{-}zPb(Zr_uTi_v)O_3+add.w\%.$$

where x+y+z=1; 0≤x≤0.40, 0≤y≤0.35, 0.50≤z≤0.90, u=0.52, v=0.48,  0≤w≤10

The technical route of low temperature sintering is the transition liquid phase sintering [4], low melting additives as initial phase can promote the sintering in the early and middle stages of sintering and as a final phase can form solid solution in the lattic to modify the properties. The suitable amount doping of $ZnO$, $Li_2CO_3$ and $MnO_2$ can be reacted with PbO to form a eutectic phase and advantage to lower sintering temperature. Both benefit of low firing and high performance ceramics can be obtained. The properties of PMN-PNN-PZT doped with Zn, Li and $MnO_2$ are as follows. $K_p$=0.60~0.70, $d_{33}$=(450~500)×PC/N, $\varepsilon^T_{33}/\varepsilon_0$=2000~2500, $Q_m$=400~600, tgδ≤50×10$^{-4}$, sintered at 900℃~1000℃. This kind of piezoelectric ceramics is satisfied used for MPT.

PROPERTIES    OF    LOW-FIRING    MULTILAYER    PIEZOELECTRIC TRANSFORMER

The MPT with Rosen type and central driving type has been studied respectively. The properties of MPT with central driving are listed in the Table I.

Table I. The properties of MPT with central driving

| | Specification | | | |
|---|---|---|---|---|
| | 1503 | 2505 | 3006 | 4509 |
| Resonant Frequency ($\lambda$ /2, KHz) | 110 | 70 | 54 | 36 |
| Step-up ratio (load=100K$\Omega$) | 45 | 60 | 70 | 90 |
| Output power (W) | 1.0 | 3.0 | 4.0 | 8.0 |
| Transfer efficiency (%) | $\geqslant$95 | $\geqslant$95 | $\geqslant$95 | $\geqslant$95 |
| Dimensions (l$\times$w$\times$h)(mm$^3$) | 1.6 | 2.6 | 2.6 | 5.0 |
| Layer thickness$\times$layer numbers | 0.15$\times$13 | 0.20$\times$17 | 0.20$\times$17 | 0.25$\times$15 |
| Sintering Temperature ($^\circ$C) | $\leqslant$1000 | $\leqslant$1000 | $\leqslant$1000 | $\leqslant$1000 |

How to suppress the temperature rise of MPT during operating is very important. Because the transfer efficiency will be decreased with rising of temperature. Many factors can influence on the temperature rise of MPT. The composition of ceramics with low loss, high mechanical quality factor and low resonance impedance can be satisfied for MPT. The fabrication processing of MPT is also very important during the sintering of MPT, the mismatch of densification behavior between metallic internal electrode and ceramic layers can induce the residual internal stress and micro-crack. They can cause defect in the interface between electrode and ceramics. Especially during vibration can generate a dynamic internal stress field and the temperature rise. In addition, the impedance match between the load and the output impedance of MPT is also advantage to reduce temperature rise.

In our study the internal electrode of Ag/Pd=80/15 can be cofired with PMN-PNN-PZT ceramics sintered at about 1000$^\circ$C.

The maximum surface temperature rise is less than 20$^\circ$C at rated output power. It is indicted that the low sintering temperature MPT with high performance can be obtained. It has been used in back-light power for portable computer. These kinds of MPT and their back-light power have been produced in industrial sale by Xi'an Konghong Company in China.

ANALYSIS ON THE RESONANCE CHARACTERISTICS OF MPT

The configuration of MPT is shown in Fig.1, and the Finite Element Analysis on the vibration mode of MPT is shown in Fig.2.

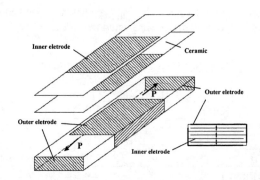

Fig.1 Configuration of MPT

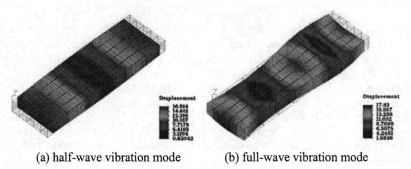

(a) half-wave vibration mode          (b) full-wave vibration mode

Fig.2 Finite Element Analysis for the vibration mode of MPT

Finite Element Analysis (FEA) is a very useful method to obtain the vibration mode. It can be seen the displacement distribution of MPT at resonance state. The maximum displacement occurs at the end of MPT. The nodal position located at the central of MPT for half-wave vibration mode.

Furthermore, the vibration mode was measured by the laser Doppler scanning measurement system. The principle of the Doppler measurement system is illustrated in Fig.3.

The image is generated by interference between object beam and reference beam. The resulting interference signal of the object beam and reference beam is converted into an electrical signal on the photo detector and subsequently decoded in the controller. The mode shapes are obtained by mapping the intensities of speckles on the photo detector. The entire surface of the MPT is irradiated by visible-range light form the helium neon laser. To reduce the amount of background noise in the image, it can be obtained the sum of datum from many images then average the resulting image.

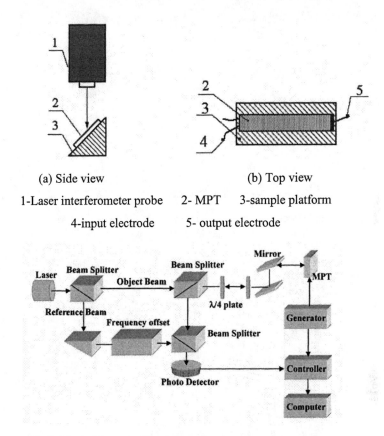

(a) Side view            (b) Top view

1-Laser interferometer probe    2- MPT    3-sample platform

4-input electrode      5- output electrode

Fig.3 Block diagram of laser Doppler measurement system

Input voltage and current for measuring MPT vibration mode using Laser Doppler Vibrometer are listed in the Table II, and the relationship between them is illustrated in Fig.4.

Table II. Input voltage and current for measuring MPT vibration mode using Laser Doppler Vibrometer

| Voltage($V_{p-p}$) | 2 | 4 | 6 | 8 | 10 | 12 | 14 | 16 | 18 | 20 |
|---|---|---|---|---|---|---|---|---|---|---|
| Current($mA_{p-p}$) | 1.54 | 2.96 | 4.59 | 5.8 | 7.01 | 7.73 | 8.15 | 8.34 | 7.98 | 8.64 |

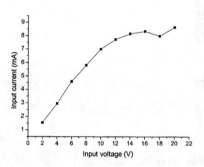

Fig.4 Relationship between input voltage and current for measuring MPT vibration mode using Laser Doppler Vibrometer

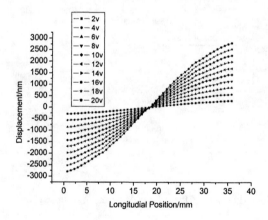

Fig.5 Displacement distribution along the length direction for MPT

The relationship between displacement and input voltage is shown in Fig.5. It can be seen that the largest displacement occur at the end of MPT. The displacement increases with increasing of input voltage. Fig. 6 shows the transformation characteristics of the MPT. The output voltage exhibits excellent linear dependence on the input voltage up to 40V, over which the transformation ratio falls down with the input voltage.

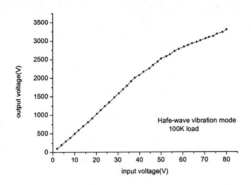

Fig.6 Relationship between input voltage and output voltage
for measuring MPT with 100KΩ load

CONCLUSIONS
    High performance PMN-PNN-PZT ceramics used for the low-fired multilayer piezoelectric transformers (MPT) were developed. The displacement distribution along the length direction for MPT was measured quantitatively by a Laser Doppler Vibrometer. The low temperature sintering MPT with high transfer efficiency, high power density and low cost could be fabricated. It has already used for back light of liquid crystal display. The MPT and its inverts have been commercialized.

REFERENCES
[1] L.L.Tu and D.W.Ti, "Monolithic Piezoelectric Transformer," 37th Electronic Components Conference, 1987 Proceedings, pp.623-625.
[2] Gui Zhilun, Li Longtu, Gao Suhua and Zhang Xiaowen, "Low-temperature Sintering of Lead-based Piezoelectric Ceramics," *Journal of the American Ceramic Society*, 72 [3] 486-91 (1989).
[3] Longtu Li, Zhilun Gui, "Fabrication of Low Firing Piezoelectric Ceramics and Their Applications," *Ferroelectrics*, Vol.262, pp.3-10 (2001).
[4] Gui Zhilun, Li Longtu, Lin Hongqing and Zhang Xiaowen, "Low Temperature

Sintering of Lead Magnesium Nickel Niobate Zirconate Titanate Piezoelectric Ceramic with High Performances," *Ferroelectrics*, Vol.101, pp.93-99 (1990).

[5] K.Uchino, B.Koc, P.Laoratanakul and A.Vazquez Carazo, "Piezoelectric Transformers New Perspective"; pp155-162 in *Piezoelectric Materials in Devices*. Edited by N.Setter.

[6] H.Kadosawa, M.Katsuno, "Development of Piezoelectric Converter," *NEC TOKIN. Technical Review*, vol.29, pp.77-83 (2002).

Microwave Cofiring of Base Metal Electrode Multilayer Capacitors

Y. Fang, D. Agrawal, M. Lanagan,
T. Shrout, C. Randall,
Materials Research Institute
The Pennsylvania State University
University Park, PA 16802

M. Randall, A.
Henderson,
Kemet Corporation
201 Fairview St.
Fountain Inn, SC 29644

ABSTRACT
    Multilayer capacitors (MLCs) with base metal electrodes were cofired by microwave processing. Commercial green chips of MLCs with nickel electrodes were used in the microwave sintering study. Binder burnout was carried out in a conventional furnace. The cofiring experiments were conducted in a multimode microwave cavity operating at 2.45GHz under an inert atmosphere. Microstructure of the microwave processed MLC was studied. The dielectric properties of the microwave sintered MLCs were measured and compared with those sintered by conventional processing. The results show that the properties of the microwave-sintered samples are comparable to or better than the conventional samples. Also the microwave processing was found to have enhanced sintering kinetics and lowered the processing temperature and time substantially.

INTRODUCTION
    Microwave processing of ceramic materials has been widely studied in the past twenty years[1]. The microwave processing lab at Penn State has been working on the microwave sintering of metals, magnetic materials and many kinds of ceramics for over a decade. The use of microwave energy for processing multilayer ceramic capacitors is a rather new development and has great potential to improve productivity and the performance of the products. Several patents such as[2-4] have been filed on utilization of microwave radiation in ceramic processing. The patent by Lauf et al.[4] describes the use of microwave radiation for fabrication of multilayer capacitors (MLCs) with Ag-rich electrodes. However, fabrication of base metal electrode MLCs has not been reported.
    There are many complex processes during the heat treatment of a multilayer ceramic capacitor. First, the binder must be removed at low temperature, leaving no residual carbon in the body before pore closure. In    X7R (a doped-$BaTiO_3$

ceramic material with a core-shell structure) formulated capacitors, chemical modifiers must diffuse from the grain boundary to the grain interior to form the core-shell structure. Finally, the ceramic must be fully sintered at high temperature with no porosity. For base-metal capacitors, the oxidation of the Ni electrodes must also be controlled. Microwave sintering may change the kinetics of these competing processes, which will be important as the grain size decreases for thin-layer X7R capacitors.

The main objective of this study is to apply the microwave technology for processing base metal electrode multilayer ceramic capacitors. The $BaTiO_3$ bulk material is not a good microwave coupler at low temperature. Because of this, susceptors that enhance the microwave absorption of the sintering system must be added around the samples. It has been successfully proven that this kind of sintering system design is suitable for sintering the X7R bulk materials and, more importantly, the X7R-based MLCs.

The newly developed process partitions the microwave energy between the susceptor and the multilayer ceramic capacitors. The principal of this process is based on the interaction between the microwaves and all of the materials in the microwave furnace. The susceptor absorbs part of the microwave energy and radiates thermal energy. Since the susceptor surrounds the MLCs, a more stable and uniform hot zone is maintained. In addition, the thermally heated MLCs will be heated initially from their surfaces. The microwaves also interact directly with the MLCs, in which they are heated as a whole (volumetric heating) and thereby providing very uniform and rapid heating of the sample. The metal powders (Ag-Pd or Ni) in MLCs can be self-heated in a microwave field. The heating rate of the load is dependent upon input power, frequency and the microwave absorption properties of the materials. The energy partition can be controlled by the type and amount of susceptor used in the microwave furnace.

Our previous testing on microwave sintering of Ag-Pd found that the processing was reproducible and the heating was uniform. In the last quarter, we started the initial trials on the target of the project: microwave sintering of BME MLCs. The green chips of the commercial nickel electrode X7R 0603 MLCs with nominal size of 1.52mm x 0.76mm x 0.76mm (0.06" x 0.03"x0.03") were used for the microwave sintering. The focus of this work was on the microstructural development of the X7R BME size 0603 multilayer capacitors in microwave sintering. The preliminary results show that microwave sintering of BME X7R MLCs is promising.

EXPERIMENTAL

The microwave sintering experiments of MLCs were conducted in a 6 KW, 2.45 GHz multimode microwave furnace. An atmosphere control system has been used to control the input gas and flow rate through the applicator. An optical pyrometer has been placed on the top middle of the applicator to monitor the temperature of the sample load. A special susceptor package has been developed to enhance microwave sintering the MLCs in the microwave applicator. This specially-designed susceptor is for the purpose of: a) minimizing the temperature gradient throughout the sintering area at sintering temperature, b) providing very precise temperature control which enables variable holding time at sintering temperature.

The microwave sintering of Ni-electrode MLC chips was carried out in the temperature range of from 1100°C to 1250°C at 2.45 GHz. The total heating time was within 2 h, with about 20 min soak at the peak temperature.

Microwave sintering of BME X7R 0603 MLCs

The sintering experiments were conducted with a sintering package using either SiC or ferrite as a susceptor. The configuration of the susceptor is to fill the space between two mullite tubes with a mixture of coarse SiC and alumina, or pre-sintered crushed coarse ferrite. Both SiC and ferrite are excellent microwave absorbers thus at low temperature the susceptor will be heated first to enhance the heating of the MLC samples. The difference is that SiC can withstand higher temperature than ferrite. The working temperature for SiC can go up to 1400°C or even higher, whereas ferrite is only good up to 1300°C or so. The use of the susceptor is a must to compensate the heat loss from the samples and get uniform temperature distribution.

It was found in this work that the bedding powder is critical to achieve homogeneous sintering by microwave processing. The microwave absorption of the bedding powder should be the same as or close to that of the MLC samples being processed. The bedding powder that is much more or much less absorbing to microwaves than the MLCs could lead to failure in microwave sintering.

In the earlier trials, with a powder that was more absorbing than the samples, we found some samples with burn marks on the surfaces of the sintered MLCs. In order to solve this problem, we chose a bedding powder with microwave absorbing property similar to that of the samples. With this innovation, the heating has been stable and the temperature distribution was more uniform. The sintered chips were uniform and free of burn marks. At about 1200°C, with a soaking period of 20 min or so, and the total heating time in the microwave sintering for about 120 min, the samples were sintered well. Based on literature results for sintering BME capacitors, conventional sintering process of the same materials requires soaking at a peak temperature over 1300°C, and the entire processing takes more than 15h. the microwave process substantially lowered the processing temperature and time significantly.

In this study, an inert atmosphere was used to avoid the oxidation of the Ni electrodes. Before microwave heating, the chamber of the microwave furnace was evacuated to less than 10 Torrs and flushed with ultra-high purity nitrogen. The microwave sintering was carried out in the atmosphere of ultra-high purity nitrogen with or without addition of a small portion of forming gas. The oxygen partial pressure in the microwave-sintering atmosphere was less than $10^{-6}$ atmosphere. For comparison, conventional sintering was also conducted in an atmosphere with oxygen partial pressure $p_{O2} = 1.85 \times 10^{-9}$ atm. The heating rate in the conventional sintering was 2°C/min. The samples were soaked for 2h at 900°C and another 2h at 1320°C.

RESULTS AND DISCUSSION
Overall, BME 0603 MLCs samples microwave sintered at temperature between 1200-1250°C were dense and uniform. The sintered chips were tan or light tan in colors. It was found that when the atmosphere was too reducing, the color of the sintered chips turned dark gray. The geometrical densities of up to 5.81g/cc have been achieved.

State of the Electrodes
The electrodes remained metallic after both microwave and conventional sintering in the controlled atmosphere in this study. X-ray diffraction (XRD) on the as-sintered surface of the microwave sintered samples showed peaks of metallic Ni. No evidence of nickel oxide was observed (Figure 1). Figure 2 shows the powder XRD of the sintered BME X7R 0603 samples with the conventionally sintered sample and the sample with oxidized electrodes as comparison.

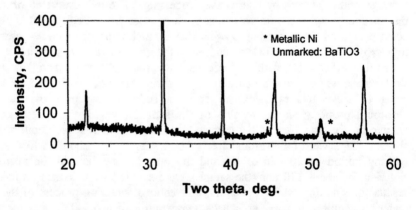

Figure 1. XRD of the as-sintered end surface of the electrodes of the microwave sintered BME 0603 showing that the electrodes maintained metallic after microwave sintering. The XRD pattern was obtained by scanning the as-sintered surface with the exposed electrodes of an array of 64 microwave-sintered chips.

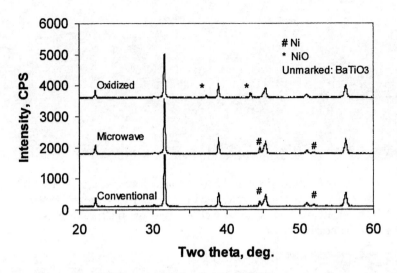

Figure 2. Powder XRD pattern of the BME 0603 microwave sintered at 1250°C, and that of the conventionally sintered sample, with the sample with oxidized electrodes for comparison, indicating that the nickel electrodes of the sintered MLCs remain metallic.

Microstructure
The fracture surface microstructure of the microwave sintered BME (Ni-electrode) chips (cross section) was studied under SEM. Representative SEM micrographs are shown in Figures 3-7.

Figure 3. The as-microwave sintered electrode surface showing that there are no delaminations or cracks during microwave sintering.

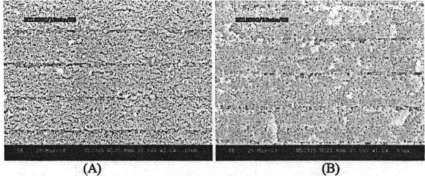

|     |     |
| --- | --- |
| (A) | (B) |

Figure 4. Microstructure of the BME MLC microwave sintered at 1200°C for 10 min showing (A) as-sintered surface, and (B) fracture surface. It is seen that the nickel electrodes have been sintered well whereas the matrix is still porous under this processing condition.

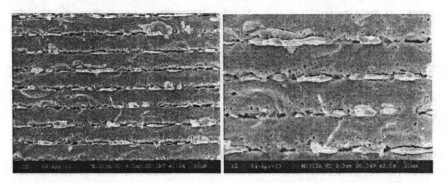

Figure 5. Fracture microstructure of BME 0603 MLC microwave sintered at 1230°C for 20 min.

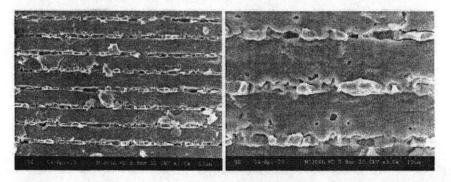

Figure 6. Fracture microstructure of BME 0603 MLC microwave sintered at 1250°C for 10-20 min.

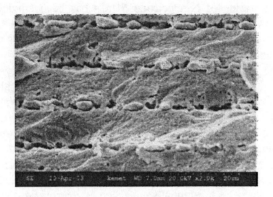

Figure 7. Fracture microstructure of the conventionally sintered BME MLC.

It is seen that for microwave sintering, the densification above 1200°C was very significant. Very dense microstructure could be achieved by microwave sintering. The processing time in the microwave sintering was much shorter than in the conventional sintering, suggesting that the densification kinetics of the BME MLCs has been substantially enhanced in the microwave sintering.

Dielectric Properties

The dielectric properties of a couple representative microwave-sintered BME MLC samples are listed in Table I. Note that the microwave-sintered samples were not re-oxidized before termination and testing, whereas the conventional sample was re-oxidized. The properties could be improved by a few percent after re-oxidation. By comparison, the capacitance and loss of the microwave-sintered samples are close to that of the conventionally sintered sample. Although the standard deviation was higher, further improvement should be expected through optimization of the processing parameters.

Table I. Dielectric properties of the microwave sintered BME 0603 MLCs.

| Firing Conditions | Cap (nF, N= 50) | | DF (%) | | Remarks |
|---|---|---|---|---|---|
| | Avg. | STD (nF) | Avg. | STD | |
| MW 1200°C/20 min. | 86.767 | 9.256 | 1.86 | 0.12 | Not reoxidized |
| MW 1230°C/20 Min. | 93.863 | 3.514 | 1.89 | 0.15 | Not reoxidized |
| Conv. 1320°C/2 h | 100.155 | 3.671 | 2.57 | 0.03 | Re-oxidized |

## SUMMARY AND FUTURE WORK

Microwave sintering of Ni-electrode MLCs has been conducted in an inert atmosphere. It was found that in the temperature range of 1200°C to 1250°C, the X7R 0603 chips were sintered well. The shrinkage of the chips was found to be dense, uniform and free of delaminations or cracks.

It was found that the use of X7R as bedding powder favors the microwave sintering, since the bedding powder has the same microwave absorption as the BME MLCs substrate. By using X7R for bedding, the sintering was stable and the sintered chips were very uniform.

Compared to the conventional process that takes 15h in the whole heating process, the microwave process saves more than 80% in processing time. In addition, to achieve the comparable densification effect, the microwave sintering can be carried out at lower temperature. This indicates that the densification of BME dielectrics has been substantially enhanced by microwave sintering.

The correlation of sintered microstructure and the dielectric properties of the microwave sintered BME MLCs are in process.

## REFERENCES

[1]W.H. Sutton, "Microwave Processing of Ceramic Materials," *Am. Ceram. Soc. Bull.* **68**[2] 376-386 (1989).

[2] C.E. Holcobme et al., US Patent 4,810,846, March 7, 1989.

[3] C.E. Holcobme et al., US Patent 4,880,578, November 14, 1989.

[4]R.J. Lauf, C.E. Holcome, N.L. Dykes, Process for manufacturing multiplayer capacitors, US Patent No. 5,481,428, Jan. 2, 1996, US Patent 5,481,428, 1/1996.

[5]R.J. Lauf, C.E. Holcombe, and C. Hamby, Microwave sintering of multiplayer ceramic capacitors, in Microwave Processing of Materials III, edited by R.L. Beatty, W.H. Sutton, M.F. Iskander, MRS Symposium Proceedings, Vol.269, 1992, MRS, Pittsburgh, PA, pp.223-229

# THE INNER ELECTRODE STRUCTURE OPTIMIZATION OF HIGH VOLTAGE MLCCS

Zhilun Gui*, Yongli Wang, and Longtu Li
State key laboratory of new ceramics and fine processing
Department of Materials Science and Engineering
Tsinghua University, Beijing, 100084, P. R. China

ABSTRACT
Field concentration is considered to be in close relation to the generation of partial discharge and dielectric breakdown in multilayer ceramic capacitors (MLCCs). High voltage multilayer ceramic capacitor (HVMLCC) is provided with special inner electrode structure to depress the field concentration and to ensure their high rated voltage and high reliability. In this paper the inner electrode structure differences between common MLCC and HVMLCC were detailed and the field distribution at some typical positions was analyzed by using finite elements method (FEM). The field distribution was illustrated as a function of the inner electrode structure and the non-linearity characteristics of the dielectric ceramics. The inner electrode structure of high voltage MLCCs was optimized in the view of minimizing the field concentration. A solution of the inner electrode structure for high voltage MLCCs was proposed as a result.

INTRODUCTION

High voltage multilayer ceramic capacitors (HVMLCCs) are one of the most important passive components in advanced large-scale integrated circuits (LSIC). The basic requirement for HVMLCCs is the higher rated voltage (100~5000V) and the stronger shock resistance, although their configurations are desired same to common MLCCs in order to satisfy the surface mounting technology (SMT) specifications. To prevent dielectric breakdown under high voltage load, special inner structures were proposed to depress the field or stress concentration nearby the electrode edges [1-3], which is considered to be in close relation to the

*Corresponding author, E-mail: llt-dms@mail.tsinghua.edu.cn

generation of partial discharge and dielectric breakdown in ceramic capacitors [4,5]. The propositions in literature [1-3] referred the conceit of electric power capacitors and enhanced the breakdown voltage of MLCCs by combining series and parallel capacitances in a single device. However, there are few literatures that have reported more detailed analysis on the improved field distribution in these models.

Typical high performance dielectric ceramics are usually ferroelectric relaxors, BCTZ, PMN-PZN-PT-BT systems for example, which are characterized by nonlinear dielectric response due to the ferroelectric spontaneous polarization. The nonlinearity of ferroelectric materials plays an important role in local field distribution [6]. Klaus Frenken et al. analyzed the field and stress distribution in MLCCs under various electrical and mechanical loads or constraints [7]. The nonlinear dielectric response of ferroelectric ceramics was roughly considered according to the experimental data. Miller et al. reported a phenomenological model for BaTiO$_3$ ferroelectric ceramics [8]. This model works well in fitting the experimental data of polarization versus external field for typical ferroelectric materials, but found some trouble in dealing with relaxor ferroelectrics, which would be detailed in the subsequent section.

The purpose of this paper is focused on the local field inhomogeneity depression and the inner structure optimization in ferroelectric relaxor involved HVMLCCs. An improved phenomenological model was proposed for the nonlinear simulation of ferroelectric relaxor materials, and the field distribution at some typical positions was analyzed using finite elements method (FEM) as a function of the voltage loading, the structural parameters and the nonlinearity of the concerned ferroelectric materials. The inner electrode structure of high voltage MLCCs was optimized in the view of minimizing the field concentration, and a solution of the inner electrode structure for high voltage MLCCs was proposed as a result.

PHENOMENOLOGICAL MODEL OF FERROELECTRIC RELAXORS

Basing on hyperbolic tangent function, Miller et al. have proposed a simple model to fit the experimental polarization-field (P-E) data in ferroelectric capacitors [8], namely

$$P^+(E) = P_{SA} \tanh(\frac{E - E_C}{2\delta}) + \varepsilon_L \varepsilon_0 E \qquad (1)$$

Where
$$\delta \equiv E_C \left[ \ln\left( \frac{1 + \dfrac{P_r}{P_{SA}}}{1 - \dfrac{P_r}{P_{SA}}} \right) \right]^{-1} \qquad (2)$$

$$P^-(E) = -P^+(-E) \qquad (3)$$

Hereinto $P_{SA}$ is the saturated polarization, $P_r$ the remanent polarization, $E_C$ the coercive field and $\epsilon_L$ the relative dielectric constant contributed by the linear polarization mechanism. $P^+(E)$ indicates the P-E relation under ascending electric field, whereas $P^-(E)$ represents that under descending field. The physical representation of these parameters can be found in a typical hysteresis loop, as illustrated in Fig. 1. The first item in the right hand of Equation (1) represents the polarization contribution of spontaneous polarization mechanism while the second one indicates the linear contribution. This model works well when fitting classical ferroelectric materials characterized by relative high coercive field and remanent polarization, as illustrated in Fig. 1. However, equation (1) can not strictly meet the special solution of (P=0, E=$E_C$), especially for the dielectric mediums with relative stronger linear contribution, which is the right case of the materials used in high performance MLCCs. Usually the ferroelectric properties are modified with various dopants and additives to enhance the dielectric constant and lower the loss tangent for capacitor ceramics, which leads to a narrow shape of the hysteresis loop. There exists considerable error between the experimental and the Miller Model fitted curve (see Fig. 1).

Hereon one special factor, namely $\eta$, is introduced into Equation (1) to satisfy the special solution (P=0, E=$E_C$),

$$P^+(E) = P_{SA} \tanh\left( \frac{(1-\eta)E - E_C}{2\delta} \right) + \varepsilon_L \varepsilon_0 E \qquad (4)$$

where
$$\eta = \frac{\ln\left( \dfrac{P_{SA} + \varepsilon_L \varepsilon_0 E_C}{P_{SA} - \varepsilon_L \varepsilon_0 E_C} \right)}{\ln\left( \dfrac{P_{SA} + P_r}{P_{SA} - P_r} \right)} \qquad (5)$$

For a narrow shaped hysteresis loop, the relative dielectric constant under zero bias can be approximated as $\epsilon_r\epsilon_0=P_r/E_c$. The right side of Equation (5) can then be simplified via Taylor expansion:

$$\eta = \frac{2\dfrac{\varepsilon_L\varepsilon_0 E_c}{P_{SA}}\left(1+\dfrac{1}{3}\left(\dfrac{\varepsilon_L\varepsilon_0 E_c}{P_{SA}}\right)^2+\cdots\right)}{2\dfrac{P_r}{P_{SA}}\left(1+\dfrac{1}{3}\left(\dfrac{P_r}{P_{SA}}\right)^2+\cdots\right)} \approx \frac{\varepsilon_L\varepsilon_0 E_c}{P_r}=\frac{\varepsilon_L}{\varepsilon_r} \quad (6)$$

Therefore the factor $\eta$ actually reflects the linear contribution for the whole dielectric response under zero external bias. Hereon we name $\eta$ as the "linearity rate". Fig. 1 shows the experimental data and the fitted curve using Equation (1), (2) and (4). Apparently the latter fitting has higher accuracy. The following field analysis concerning the dielectric nonlinearity in HVMLCCs would take advantage of the $\eta$-modified model.

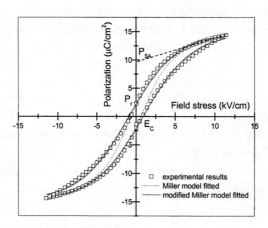

Fig.1 Comparison of the experimental data and the fitting results of the two nonlinear models

INNER STRUCTURE CHARACTERISTICS AND THE CORRESPONDING FEM MODELS FOR HVMLCCs

In comparison with common MLCCs, HVMLCCs have more complex but more symmetrical inner structure. Fig. 2 illustrates the typical structure for common MLCCs and HVMLCCs, according to literature [1-3]. The internal electrodes of HVMLCCs are usually unconnected and spaced regularly in one

Ceramic Materials and Multilayer Electronic Devices

electrode plane, and the unconnected electrodes are desired to be overlapped with the adjacent internal electrodes through the ceramic layer in the thickness direction, affording several series connected capacity takeout portions in one dielectric layer. The number of the capacity takeout portions plays an important role in enhancing the critical voltage load of the capacitor. A plurality of this kind of layers is then connected in parallel by the external electrodes like that in common MLCCs. The shape of the internal electrodes is endowed with rounded rather than rectangle corners in order to lower the flashover possibility.

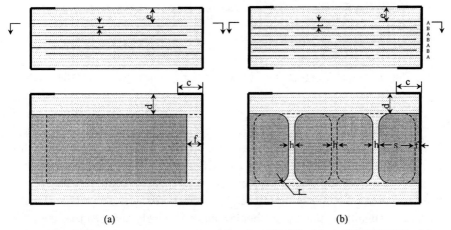

(a)             (b)

Fig. 2 The inner structure schematics for MLCCs (a) and HVMLCCs (b)

Several 2-D FEM models are established to analyze the field concentration at some 'dangerous' locations like the vicinities of the internal electrode edges and the corners, as typically shown in Fig. 3 (a) and (b). In model A, there are two structural sizes: dielectric layer thickness (t) and the distance from the internal electrode end to the external electrode (f) or to the symmetry plane that equally divides the internal electrodes space (h/2). Either 'f' or 'h/2' provides unique boundary electric potential conditions for this model: U1 on the external electrode/symmetry plane and the connected internal ones, and U2 on the opposite internal electrode. For the case of Model B, the structural parameter involves the corner radius and 'f' or 'h/2'. The values of U1 and U2 depend on the voltage load, the number of the series capacity takeout portions, and the location of the concerned region. The potential difference |U1-U2|, however, is definite in spite of the region location in a well-manufactured capacitor. Therefore as calculated local field distribution is universally applicable in one certain HVMLCC.

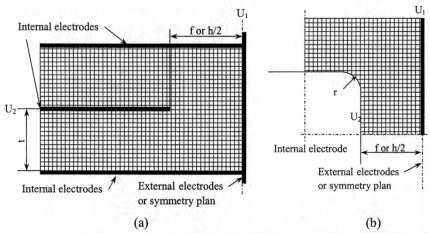

(a)                                      (b)

Fig. 3 Typical 2-D FEM models for the dangerous regions in HVMLCCs

The static field distribution in these regions are calculated as a function of the voltage loading on the capacitor, the nonlinearity of the dielectric material, and the special size parameters for the inner structure of HVMLCCs. Considering that the practical voltage loading on HVMLCCs is possibly high, the potential difference between the model boundaries is set high enough to polarize the ferroelectric medium within the capacity takeout portions to the saturated state. Under this condition, the field inhomogeneity is nearly independent with the external voltage load. Equation (2), (4) and (5) are used in an iterative calculating loop, which is shown in Fig. 4, to determine the local polarization and the permittivity of the ferroelectric material, and consequently the field distribution in the concerned region is calculated according to electromagnetism principles. The related parameters working in Equation (2), (4) and (5) are read from an experimental hysteresis loop of a Y5V style ferroelectric capacitor, as is listed in Table I.

Table I Nonlinearity parameters of concerned Y5V ferroelectric material

| $P_{SA}(\mu C/cm^2)$ | $P_r(\mu C/cm^2)$ | $E_C(kV/cm)$ | $\epsilon_L\epsilon_0(\mu C/kV\cdot cm)$ | $\delta$ | $\eta$ |
|---|---|---|---|---|---|
| 5.57 | 0.16 | 0.11 | 0.299 | 1.914 | 0.243 |

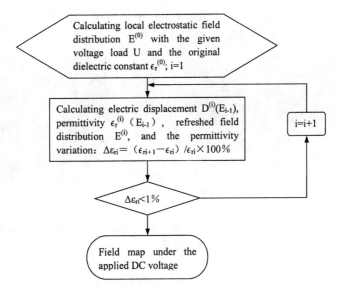

Fig. 4 Iterative loop for the field distribution in nonlinear medium

## FIELD INHOMOGENEITY IN HVMLCC AND THE STRUCTURE OPTIMIZATION

Fig. 5 (a) and (b) exhibit the local field strength and the field changed relative dielectric constant of the ferroelectric medium for Model A. Hereinto the real strength of the local field E, has been divided by that at the homogeneous region between the two opposite internal electrodes, $E_A$, to facilitate comparison and characterization. As evaluated values are defined as relative local field strength $E_r=E/E_A$. Around the electrode terminal the field distorted seriously and the maximum field strength $E_{max}$ is about 3 times that at the homogeneous region ($E_A$). The field strength near the inner angle of the connected electrodes falls below $E_A$, whereas the permittivity at these regions remains a higher level than that at the regions under relative high local field.

It is well agreed that the area of field concentration region and the maximum value of the local field strength play a critical role in the breakdown origination [9]. In the FEM results, the integration $I_C$ synthetically reflected the two factors:

$$I_C = \int_{\Omega} E_r dS \qquad (7)$$

where $\Omega$ corresponds the field concentrated region where $E_r>1$. In this work the value of $I_C$ is to be used to characterize the field distortion extent in the FEM models as well as to evaluate the rationality of the given structural parameters.

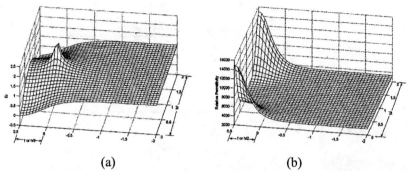

(a)                      (b)

Fig. 5 The distribution of the relative local field strength (a) and the relative dielectric constant of the ferroelectric medium (b) for Model A

Fig. 6 (a) shows the structural parameters dependence of the field distortion. With the increase of f or h/2, the value of $I_C$ and its dependent degree on f or h/2 descends monotonously. The $I_C$ value changes little when f or h/2 is longer than twice of the dielectric layer thickness. Therefore the preferable distance between the external electrodes and the adjacent opposite internal electrode terminals should be longer than 2t, while the space between the coplanar internal electrode-segments should be not shorter than 4t.

The same method has been adapted to process the FEM results for Model B and other 2-D models. The $I_C$ value changing as a function of the corner radius r is illustrated in Fig. 6 (b), and similar depending characteristics is exhibited. It appears that r>0.3t is required to ensure a stable and minimized field distortion. Further analysis gives a series of preferable structural size values in the view of depressing local field concentration. The size values are summarized in Table II as a multiple of the dielectric layer thickness, and their physical indications can be found in Fig 3 (b). Actually Table II gives a solution of the inner electrode structure for HVMLCCs when given the thickness of the dielectric layer, which can be calculated from the desired performance of the capacitor and the electrical properties of the concerned dielectric material within the possible technical scale.

Table II The minimum values of the structural sizes for HVMLCCs

| c | d | e | f | h | r |
|------|------|------|------|------|------|
| f+4t | 4t | 4t | 2t | 4t | 0.3t |

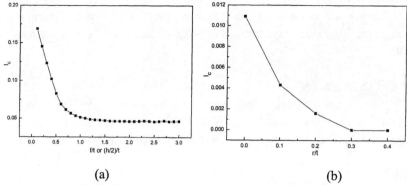

(a)                                    (b)

Fig. 6 The influence of structural sizes on local field concentration
(a) $I_C$ function of f/t or (h/2)/t; (b) $I_C$ function of r/t

Basing on the preferred sizes, one 3-D HVMLCC model as well as one common MLCC model in comparison is established to examine the surface field distribution. It can be found in Fig. 7 that the surface potential contours' distribution on HVMLCC model is more homogeneous in comparison with that on common MLCC model, which is benefit to enhance the voltage loading on the capacitors without causing surface flashover.

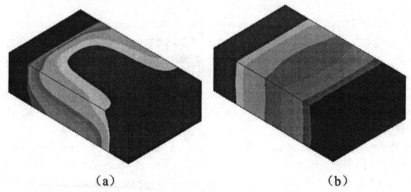

(a)                                    (b)

Fig. 7 Surface potential contour of common MLCCs (a) and HVMLCCs (b)

CONCLUSIONS

In this paper an improved phenomenological model was proposed for the nonlinear simulation of ferroelectric relaxor materials. The local field strength in HVMLCCs was calculated using finite element method as a function of the voltage loading, the inner electrode structural sizes and the nonlinear characteristics of the ferroelectric medium. The inner electrode structure of HVMLCCs was optimized in the view of minimizing the field concentration and a solution of the inner electrode structure for high voltage MLCCs was proposed as a result.

ACKNOWLEDGEMENTS
    This work was supported by the Ministry of Science and Technology of China through 973-project under grant 2002CB613301 and High Technology Research and Development project of P. R. China under grant 2001AA325010.

REFERENCE
[1]Yoichi Kuroda, Chiharu Chikashige, "High voltage multilayer capacitor", U.S. Pat. No. 6134098, Oct. 17, 2000

[2]Yutaka Shimahara, Shozo Takeuchi, "Monolithic capacitor", U. S. Pat. No. 6229686 B1, May, 8, 2001

[3]Patrick hardy, Auxonne, France, "Composite structure resistant to thermal shocks and application thereof to multiple-layer ceramic capacitors", U. S. Pat. No. 5111356, May 5, 1995

[4]Takao Tani, Mitsuru Asai, Kazumasa Takatori, et al. "Evaluation of dielectric strength and breakdown behavior for Sr-, Nb-doped PZT ceramics with various shapes of electrodes", *Journal of the Ceramic Society of Japan*, 105 [4] 308-311 (1997)

[5]Ken Matsuda, Noboru Yoshimura, Tadashi Ogasawara, "Dielectric breakdown of a ceramic-epoxy resin interface on a high voltage ceramic capacitor", Proceeding of the 21st symposium on electrical insulating materials, by Technical Committee on Electrical Insulating materials, IEEJ, 307-310 (1988)

[6]M. Tyunina and J. Levoska, "Dynamic nonlinear dielectric response of relaxor ferroelectric $(PbMg_{1/3}Nb_{2/3}O_3)_{0.68}$-$(PbTiO_3)_{0.32}$ thin films", *Physical Review B*, 65: 132101-132104, (2002)

[7]Klaus Prume, Klaus Franken, Ulrich Böttger, et al. "Modelling and numerical simulation of the electrical mechanical and thermal coupled behaviour of multilayer capacitors (MLCs)", *Journal of the European Ceramic Society*, 22: 1285-1296 (2002)

[8]S. L. Miller, R. D. Nasby, J. R. Schwank, et al. "Device modeling of ferroelectric capacitors", *Journal of Applied Physics*, 68 [12] 6463-6471 (1990)

[9]Jian Ku Shang, Xiaoli Tan, "A maximum strain criterion for electric-field-induced fatigue crack propagation in ferroelectric ceramics", *Materials Science and Engineering*, A301 131-139 (2001)

# FACE-LOADED PIEZOCERAMIC PLATE TRANSDUCERS

**Arthur Ballato**
**US Army Communications-Electronics Command**
**Fort Monmouth, NJ 07703-5201**

## ABSTRACT

Piezoceramic elements are finding increasing uses as cost-effective sensors for a wide variety of measurands. This paper uses a simple, plane bulk acoustic wave model to discuss effects arising from changes occurring at the vibrating surfaces of a piezoelectric transducer, when exposed to coatings having various properties, with a variety of interfacial contact behaviors. Effects of fluid loading on the multi-mode Q values of an obliquely cut piezocrystal are computed for various pressures as an example of mode coupling by mechanical boundary conditions.

## INTRODUCTION

Piezoelectric resonators are used extensively as sensors for a wide variety of measurands [1]-[33], including mass loading [34]-[46], gases [47]-[48], liquids [49]-[69], mass and fluid loadings [70]-[71], viscoelastic/polymer coatings [72]-[79], suspensions/colloids [80]-[84], functionally gradient (non-homogeneous) materials and layers/stacks [85]-[88], and textured surfaces [89]-[91]. The ensuing changes are registered as changes in frequency, phase, and/or impedance level.

In some cases, such as temperature sensing, the bulk resonator material is affected. In other cases, e.g., quartz crystal microbalances, the frequency shift arises from changes occurring at, or near, the vibrating surfaces of the resonator. We consider this latter case. The thrust of the paper is to point out that the system should be treated as a whole: the piezoelectric resonator/actuator/transducer, the mechanical and electrical boundary conditions (BCs) specified at its surfaces, plus the immittance characteristics of the circuit into which the device is incorporated.

## THE PIEZORESONATOR

We consider the case of a laterally unbounded piezoelectric plate supporting plane acoustic waves that have no lateral phase variations; these are the simple thickness modes [86]. The driving electric field may be either along or normal to the plate thickness, and the plate is mechanically loaded on both surfaces by a measurand. The resonator generally supports three modes, but the situation often dealt with in sensor applications is that where only one mode is piezoelectrically driven. For example, a laterally poled thin-film piezoceramic or an AT-cut quartz plate, excited by a field along the thickness, executes pure shear motion. Poling the piezoceramic in the thickness direction, or using an X-cut quartz plate and driving with a thickness field yields pure extensional (longitudinal) motion. For the particular case of a piezoceramic film or plate, or any material with 6mm symmetry, if the polar axis is oblique to the thickness direction, one may piezoelectrically drive all three thickness modes simultaneously (by a lateral field), but one of the shear modes will be pure, and the other two will be coupled [122]. For most other crystal classes, when the plate resonator is fashioned so that its surfaces are oblique to its crystallographic axes, all three modes are piezoelectrically driven, and are coupled in general. Mode coupling should, in any case, be taken into account, particularly for highly piezoelectric materials such as piezoceramics, and refractory oxides such as lithium niobate and lithium tantalate.

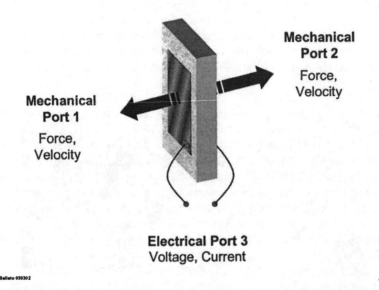

Fig. 1. Piezocrystal plate. Major surfaces constitute the two mechanical ports to which are applied the varieties of boundary loadings discussed in the text. The electrical port consists of attachments to an electrode system by which the vibrational modes are driven via the piezoelectric effect. The electrodes shown apply an electric field in the thickness direction; alternatively, electrodes may be disposed to provide a lateral field.

While the assumption of an unbounded plano-plano plate might seem unrealistic, work on finite and contoured plates with lateral distributions of motion shows that this one-dimensional idealization may very often convey the essence of the observed effects, particularly if the influences of piezoelectricity and circuit loading are properly taken into account [92]-[96].

In order to describe the most general situation where all three thickness modes are coupled, and react with the imposed boundary load, we use the doubly rotated SC-cut of quartz as an example in the sequel.

– Equivalent Circuits

Over the years, many equivalent circuits have been used to model the piezoresonator, and to describe its operation in using circuitry [97]-[119]. Detailed history and associated equivalent networks are found in [115]. The BVD lumped circuit evolved into more elaborate multi-mode, transmission-line networks that place the mechanical boundary loadings and piezoelectric excitation mechanism in series at the surfaces [115, Figs. 8, 10; 116]. Figure 1 shows the plate resonator with attached electrodes, and its three ports. Figure 2 is a schematic representation of how the ports are interconnected by the acoustic, electric, and piezoelectric portions, for the case of a single mode.

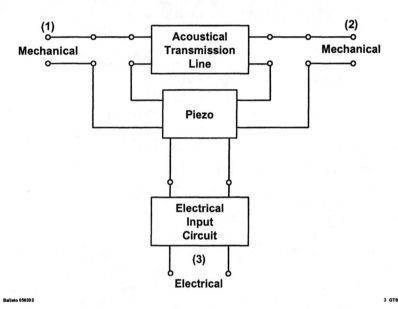

Fig. 2. Schematic representation of how the three ports are interconnected by acoustic, electric, and piezoelectric elements, for the case of a single vibrational mode.

– Piezoelectric Effect

The influence of piezoelectricity in a resonator is manifested in two distinct ways; the first is in so-called piezoelectric stiffening, whereby the elastic stiffnesses $c^E$ governing acoustic wave speeds are augmented to effective stiffness values of the generic form $c = c^E/(1 - k^2)$, where the k are dimensionless quantities known as piezocoupling coefficients.

The second place where piezoelectricity is manifest in resonators is in the driving mechanism, and is often considered only with respect to impedance level and insertion loss. Its influence can be subtler, however. Lawson [120], in his treatment of plate vibrations of a traction-free resonator, found that the "effective thickness" of the plate was greater than the geometrical thickness, and varied with mode and overtone. This is due to the electrical boundary conditions (BCs). Tiersten's exact solution of this problem [121] showed that all three modes are coupled at the boundaries by piezoelectricity. We will see in the SC-cut example below, an instance where mechanical BCs additionally couple all three modes. Mode coupling by these mechanisms must be taken into account for high precision and consistent analyses of sensor behavior, particularly with materials having strong piezocoupling.

## Linear Viscoelastic Lumped Models

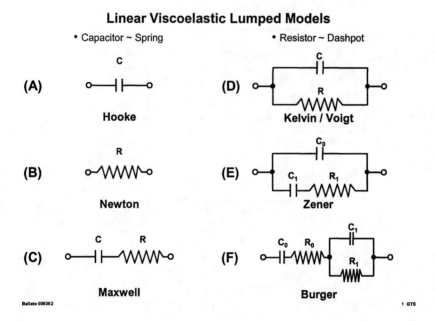

Fig. 3. Linear, viscoelastic lumped circuit models. Capacitors are analogous to springs; resistors are analogous to dashpots.

MECHANICAL SURFACE LOADINGS

Mass deposited uniformly on the surface of a piezoelectric plate resonator lowers its frequency [34]-[46]; the quartz microbalance is based on this principle. This assumes that the mass is in welded contact with the resonator surface, and is represented solely by its inertial character. Dybwad found [123], however, that a microscopic gold sphere lightly dropped on the gold electrode of a thickness shear resonator plate caused the frequency to increase. He modeled the situation as one where the mass of the sphere was attached to the resonator surface by a spring. That is, the attached system possesses both inertial and elastic properties. It may be shown that, depending on the parameters involved, the frequency observed

Ceramic Materials and Multilayer Electronic Devices

may either increase or decrease from the unloaded value. Onoe showed that, in certain instances, electrode mass increased the frequency of contour mode quartz resonators [124]. Mass and electrode stress have been implicated in a number of linear and nonlinear effects [125]-[128].

## Nonlinear Viscoelastic Lumped Models

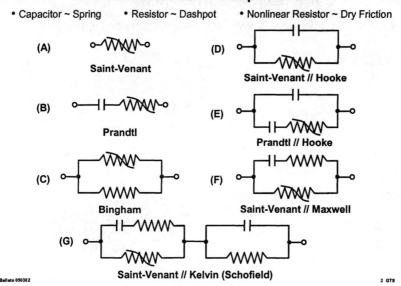

Fig. 4. Nonlinear, viscoelastic lumped circuit models. Nonlinear resistors are analogous to dry friction.

## SOLID-FLUID INTERFACES

Lord Rayleigh, commenting on Stokes' treatment of fluid viscosity, wrote [47, §347]: "The velocity of the fluid in contact with the plane is usually assumed to be the same as that of the plane itself on the apparently sufficient ground that the contrary would imply an infinitely greater smoothness of the fluid with respect to the solid than with respect to itself." We assume this BC.

### – Ideal Fluid

An unbounded ideal fluid in intimate contact with a resonator surface will present to the surface a short circuit for shear waves, and a resistance to longitudinal motion of $R_\ell = A\rho v_\ell$, with A the cross-sectional area, $\rho$ the fluid mass density, and $v_\ell$ the longitudinal acoustic velocity.

### – Newtonian Fluid

An unbounded Newtonian fluid (i.e., a fluid with shear viscosity, $\eta$) in intimate contact with a resonator surface presents to the surface both shear and longitudinal impedances. Shear impedance is $Z_s = A\sqrt{(j\omega\eta\rho)} = R_s + j\omega L_s$; $R_s$ represents shear dissipation, and $L_s$ entrained mass loading. Penetration depth is $\delta$ = $\lambda/2\pi = \sqrt{(2\eta/\rho\omega)}$. Longitudinal impedance consists of $R_\ell = A\rho v_\ell$, plus a small reactance representing wave attenuation.

## SOME TEXTURED INTERFACES

- Realized by micromachining / microtechnology processing

### Slippery Dovetail Array

$T_{22}$, $T_{23}$ Continuous

$T_{12} = 0$

Dovetails may be at an angle in $x_1$-$x_3$ plane

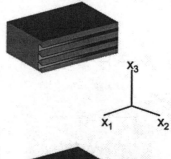

### Slippery Mortise & Tenon Array

$T_{12}$, $T_{23}$ Continuous

$T_{22} = 0$

Ballato 050302                                                          7 GTS

Fig. 5. Examples of textured interfaces, as might be realized by micro-machining, and other microtechnology processes.

– Viscoelastic Lumped Models

Often lumped circuit models can be used to represent viscoelastic materials [72]. Representative networks are shown in Fig. 3 (linear materials) and Fig. 4 (nonlinear materials). The nonlinear resistors of Fig. 4, representing dry friction, may themselves be represented as linear resistors in series with two back-biased diodes in parallel.

– Lubricated Surfaces

Cady [129, §364, pp. 462-463] mentions reduction of friction between an extensional mode (X-cut) quartz plate and a solid surface apparently due to an entrapped layer of air. References [130]-[133] discuss other considerations of lubrication and slip at boundaries.

GENERAL MECHANICAL BCs

One must generally specify conditions on the three components of stress and three components of velocity at surface interfaces. Assuming plate thickness along the $X_2$ axis, one must specify conditions on $T_{12}$, $T_{22}$, and $T_{23}$, plus $v_1$, $v_2$, and $v_3$. Welded conditions correspond to continuity of all six quantities; blockage corresponds to $v_1 = v_2 = v_3 = 0$; transverse slippage corresponds to continuity of $T_{22}$, and $T_{12} = T_{23} = 0$, etc. In general, the six boundary variables are related by an immittance matrix that may be expressed in terms equivalent to those descriptions used in network theory: homogeneous forms of impedance [z] and admittance [y]; mixed forms, [g], [h]; scattering [s]; [ABCD], etc.

### Simplified Interface Network
### CRYSTAL-FLUID

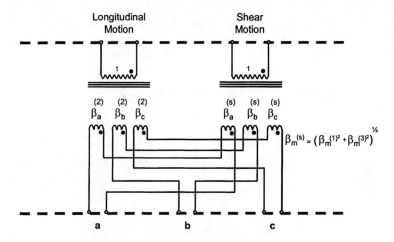

Longitudinal Motion     Shear Motion

$$\beta_m^{(s)} = \left( \beta_m^{(1)^2} + \beta_m^{(3)^2} \right)^{\frac{1}{2}}$$

a     b     c

*Normal - Coordinate Plane Waves in Crystal Plate*

Ballato 050302                                                                5 GTS

Fig. 6. Simplified mechanical interface network describing a crystal – fluid boundary.

**– Textured Interfaces**

With the advent of micro/nano technologies [134]-[136], one is led to consider the possibilities of manufacturing interfaces that impose desired BCs. These may be made in a self-organizing manner [137]. Figure 5 gives two examples.

**– Surface Particles and Bonds**

Particles on the surface of a resonator (particularly quartz) have been a manufacturer's bane for many years, and have been shown to be the cause of various anomalies, e.g., drive level dependence [128]. Loosely applied particles such as lycopodium powder [129, §366, pp. 463-465] can move about from resonator motion; lightly attached particles, such as Dybwad's microspheres [123], might possibly detach with sufficiently high levels of drive. The breaking of molecular bonds by resonator motion, on the other hand, is another matter. One may estimate the possibility of expulsion of attached surface molecules by considering the force required to rupture a bond. Strength of the covalent C-C bond is ~ 10 nN/bond; for other types of bond the range is ~ 1 to 10 nN/bond [134].

As an example, we take the rather extreme case of an unloaded thin-film piezoceramic vibrator in resonance at 220 MHz with piezocoupling of 51%, $R_1 C_1$ time constant of 100 femtoseconds (ten times that of quartz), and 1% surface strain [138]. Amplitude is limited solely by internal friction; the resonator power dissipation is ~ 30 W/mm$^2$, has surface amplitude of ~ 440 Å, and surface acceleration of ~ 8.5 $10^{+10}$ m/s$^2$. A carbon atom of mass 12 amu ~ 2 $10^{-26}$ kg on the resonator surface experiences a force of ~ 1.7 $10^{-15}$ N. This is about six million times less than the classical force required to rupture a bond; consequently, the probability of this happening is vanishingly small.

**DOUBLY ROTATED QUARTZ FLUID SENSOR**

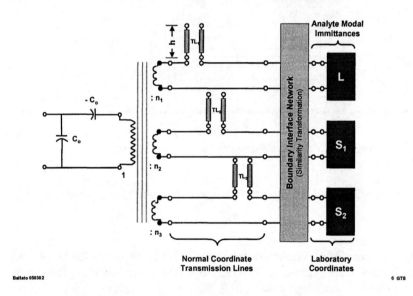

Fig. 7. Doubly rotated quartz resonator used as a fluid sensor. Using a multi-mode resonator permits a larger gamut of analyte properties to be measured.

MODE COUPLING BY A FLUID

In the discussion of solid-fluid interfaces above, expressions are given for the longitudinal and shear impedances presented to the solid resonator surface. The usual sensor configuration consists of a resonator/transducer utilizing a single acoustic mode. Moreover, it is a pure mode, having motion strictly along the thickness direction (e.g., thickness-poled piezoceramic, X-cut quartz, or Z-cut

ZnO), or strictly normal to the thickness (e.g., laterally poled piezoceramic, AT-cut quartz, or X-cut lithium niobate).

In these instances, it is only necessary to consider one of the fluid impedances. In the more general situation where a doubly rotated resonator orientation is utilized [64], as with SC-cut of quartz, or an obliquely poled piezoceramic, the solid surface executes resonant motions that are oblique to its normal at each of the coupled modes (and their overtones). Treating this case requires that both fluid impedances be incorporated; in [64] this was done using the simple, lumped BVD network. It is instructive to do a more involved example, which shows explicitly the mode coupling that takes place via mechanical BCs.

AIR-LOADED SC-CUT QUARTZ

The SC quartz cut is doubly rotated, meaning that the plate axes are oblique to the crystallographic axes. Its properties, and corresponding numerical data are given in [86] and Table I. In Table I, the plate thickness is taken as t = 0.1797 mm, in order to fix the nominal c-mode fundamental resonance frequency at 10 MHz, according to $f_m = v_m/2t$. $Q_m = (2\pi f_m \tau_m)^{-1}$ are the mechanical quality factors, and $\tau_m$ are the motional time constants [86]. The piezocoupling coefficients are $k_m$, the $f_{Rm}$ are the relaxation frequencies, at which the modal $Q_m$ values become unity. $|\varphi_d^{(m)}|$ and $|\theta_d^{(m)}|$ are the angles specifying the modal displacements [86]; departures from zero indicate coupled modes.

Table I. Acoustic Properties of SC-cut Quartz

| Quantity | Unit | Mode a | Mode b | Mode c |
|---|---|---|---|---|
| $f_m$ | MHz | 18.820 | 11.001 | 10.000 |
| $v_m$ | km/s | 6.764 | 3.954 | 3.594 |
| $\tau_m$ | fs | 10.5 | 6.35 | 11.7 |
| $k_m$ | % | 3.33 | 4.71 | 4.99 |
| $|\varphi_d^{(m)}|$ | degree | 12.9 | 4.28 | 8.57 |
| $|\theta_d^{(m)}|$ | degree | 6.31 | 9.57 | 13.7 |
| $Q_m$ | $10^{+6}$ | 0.805 | 2.278 | 1.360 |
| $f_{Rm}$ | THz | 15.2 | 25.1 | 13.6 |

We take the right-handed orthogonal plate (laboratory) coordinates as follows: $X_1$ along the digonal crystal axis, and $X_2$ along the plate thickness. In this cut, all three simple thickness modes are excited by an electric field in the $X_2$ direction. The appropriate electrical equivalent circuit is that given in [115, Fig. 10]. Appearing at the six mechanical ports, however, are the mechanical variables of stress and velocity referred to the normal (internal, eigenfunction) coordinates within the plate. The connection between these systems is represented in network form by the ideal transformer circuit given in [115, Fig. 15], attached to each plate surface. Algebraically, the impedance presented at each interface in the laboratory coordinates is converted by a similarity transformation to impedance referred to the normal (internal) coordinates. The transformation is

$$Z_{\text{internal}} = \beta^T \bullet Z_{\text{laboratory}} \bullet \beta, \tag{1}$$

where $\beta$ is the modal matrix. A network representation is given in Fig. 6.

### MODE c (SC cut)

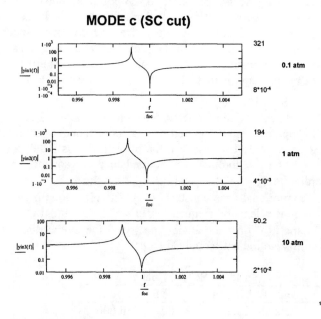

Fig. 8. Normalized admittance versus normalized frequency in the vicinity of c-mode resonance for an SC-cut quartz plate of 10 MHz nominal frequency for three values of ambient air loading pressure.

– Immersion in Air Ambient

For simplicity rather than necessity, we assume that both surfaces of the SC-cut quartz plate are exposed to unbounded reservoirs of air at the same pressure. The equal surface loadings render the configuration symmetric about the midsection of the crystal, and permit bisection of the network [139]-[141]. The result is shown in Fig. 7. "Analyte modal immittances" are, in this case, the longitudinal (L) and shear ($S_1 = S_2$) impedances of air, considered as a Newtonian fluid. Three modal acoustic transmission lines (TLs) represent quasi-longitudinal ("a" mode), fast quasi-shear ("b" mode), and slow quasi-shear ("c" mode) motions. The TL lengths equal the geometrical half-thickness of the plate, with doubled acoustic admittances, due to bisection. The three $n_m$ are piezoelectric transformer turns ratios (m = a, b, or c mode), permitting the voltage impressed at the electrical port to drive the resonator. Values $n_m$ are proportional to the corresponding piezocoupling factors of the modes [86].

Ceramic Materials and Multilayer Electronic Devices

– Fluid Impedance Matrix

For the present case, $Z_{laboratory}$ is $Z_{fluid}$, where

$$Z_{fluid} = \begin{pmatrix} Z_{shear} & 0 & 0 \\ 0 & Z_{long} & 0 \\ 0 & 0 & Z_{shear} \end{pmatrix}, \tag{2}$$

with $Z_{shear} = Z_s = A\sqrt{(j\omega\eta\rho)}$, and $Z_{long} = R_\ell = A\rho v_\ell$. The modal matrix $\beta$ is

$$\beta = \begin{pmatrix} \beta_1^{(c)} & \beta_1^{(a)} & \beta_1^{(b)} \\ \beta_2^{(c)} & \beta_2^{(a)} & \beta_2^{(b)} \\ \beta_3^{(c)} & \beta_3^{(a)} & \beta_3^{(b)} \end{pmatrix}. \tag{3}$$

Superscripts denote modes; mode "c", the slow quasi-shear, has particle motion predominantly along the $X_1$ axis, etc. Although $Z_{fluid}$ is diagonal, the similarity transformation with $\beta$ produces a symmetric impedance matrix in the normal coordinate system that contains no zeros. For the SC-cut of quartz, $\beta$ has the following numerical values:

$$\beta = \begin{pmatrix} +0.9605 & +0.2217 & -0.1681 \\ -0.2364 & +0.9689 & -0.0730 \\ +0.1467 & +0.1099 & +0.9831 \end{pmatrix}. \tag{4}$$

– Acoustic Properties of Air

Table II contains values of pertinent acoustic properties of air at 300° K, at three pressures [142]-[143]. Penetration depth $\delta$ is for 10 MHz, the nominal frequency of the SC-cut c-mode example. Rayleigh [47, p. 313] remarks: "Both by theory and experiment the remarkable conclusion has been established that within wide limits the force *[viscosity]* is independent of the density of the gas. For air at 0° Centigrade Maxwell found *[η]* = .0001878 (1 + .00366 θ) …". The modern MKS value is listed.

– Resonator Input Admittance

The impedance matrix of air is referred back to the normal coordinate frame via

$$Z_{normal} = \beta^T \bullet Z_{fluid} \bullet \beta, \tag{5}$$

attached to the modal TLs as in Fig. 7, and the result is solved for the input admittance at the electrical port. Input admittance, normalized to that of the resonator static capacitance $C_o$ at $f_{oc}$ = 10 MHz, is graphed in Fig. 8 for three values of ambient pressure. The frequency scale is normalized to c-mode frequency $f_{oc}$. Resonances become increasingly blunted with pressure.

Table II. Acoustic Properties of Air at 300° K

| Pressure | Density | Velocity | Viscosity | Depth $\delta$ |
|---|---|---|---|---|
| (atm) | (kg/m$^3$) | (m/s) | ($\mu$Pa-s) | ($\mu$m) |
| 0.1 | 0.11767 | 347.23 | | 2.24 |
| 1.0 | 1.1769 | 347.33 | 18.464 | 0.707 |
| 10 | 11.799 | 348.49 | | 0.223 |

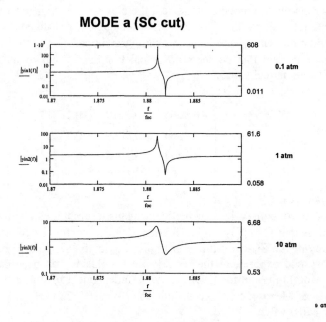

Fig. 9. Normalized admittance versus normalized frequency in the vicinity of a-mode resonance for an SC-cut quartz plate of 10 MHz nominal frequency for three values of ambient air loading pressure.

Similar curves obtain for the other modes, but the effect is particularly marked for the quasi-longitudinal "a" mode, as is to be expected; Fig. 9. When reflecting boundaries, parallel to the plate surfaces, replace the unbounded reservoirs, the resulting finite layers of air form additional resonant structures and yield modulations of the curves in Fig. 8 and Fig. 9 [69].

Table III provides the quality factors $Q_m$ for each mode of the SC-cut quartz plate, assuming that loss arises solely from air loading. Also given are the intrinsic Q values for an unloaded resonator, assuming acoustic viscosity in quartz [86], and the fundamental modal frequencies; the plate is 0.1797 mm thick.

CONCLUSIONS

Optimum performance of a sensor, actuator, or transducer is achieved when it is treated, along with using circuitry, as a complete system. To do this, the interplay of various effects must be taken into account. This paper has discussed a number of these, relating to piezoelectricity, equivalent circuits, boundary effects, and mode coupling. An air-loaded SC-cut quartz plate resonator is treated as an example.

Table III. Quality Factors of Air-Loaded SC-cut Quartz

| Pressure | $Q_a$ | $Q_b$ | $Q_c$ |
|---|---|---|---|
| (atm) ↓ | $10^{+3}$ | $10^{+3}$ | $10^{+3}$ |
| 0.1 | 209 | 524 | 370 |
| 1 | 20.9 | 162 | 89.3 |
| 10 | 2.12 | 44.0 | 14.1 |
| $Q_{intrinsic}$ → | 805 | 2,278 | 1,360 |
| $f_{om}$ (MHz)→ | 18.820 | 11.001 | 10.000 |

REFERENCES

[1]V. Mecea and R. V. Bucur, "The mechanism of the interaction of thin films with resonating quartz crystal substrates: The energy transfer model," Thin Solid Films, vol. 60, pp. 73-84, 1979.

[2]E. Benes, "Improved quartz crystal microbalance technique," J. Appl. Phys., vol. 56, no. 3, pp. 608-626, 1 August 1984.

[3]H. Nowotny and E. Benes, "General one-dimensional treatment of the layered piezoelectric resonator with two electrodes," J. Acoust. Soc. Am., vol. 82, no. 2, pp. 513-521, August 1987.

[4]T. Nakamoto and T. Moriizumi, "A theory of a quartz crystal microbalance based upon a Mason equivalent circuit," Jap. J. Appl. Phys., vol. 29, no. 5, pp. 963-969, May 1990.

[5]H. Nowotny, E. Benes, and M. Schmid, "Layered piezoelectric resonators with an arbitrary number of electrodes (general one-dimensional treatment)," J. Acoust. Soc. Am., vol. 90, no. 3, pp. 1238-1245, September 1991.

[6]G. Hayward, "Viscous interaction with oscillating piezoelectric quartz crystals," Analytica Chimica Acta, vol. 264, pp. 23-30, 1992.

[7]E. A. Klavetter, S. J. Martin, and K. O. Wessendorf, "Monitoring jet fuel thermal stability using a quartz crystal microbalance," Energy & Fuels, vol. 7, no. 5, pp. 582-588, 1993.

[8]M. A. Grundy, W. E. Bolek, W. T. Coakley, and E. Benes, "Rapid agglutination testing in an ultrasonic standing wave," J. Immunol. Methods, vol. 165, pp. 47-57, 1993.

[9]H. Drobe, A. Leidl, M. Rost, and I. Ruge, "Acoustic sensors based on surface-localized HPSWs for measurements in liquids," Sensors and Actuators, vol. A 37-38, pp. 141-148, 1993.

[10]V. M. Mecea, "Loaded vibrating quartz sensors," Sensors and Actuators, vol. A40, pp. 1-27, 1994.

[11]V. M. Mecea, "Vibrating piezoelectric sensors," Sensors and Actuators, vol. A41-42, pp. 630-637, 1994.

[12]G. L. Hayward and G. Z. Chu, "Simultaneous measurement of mass and viscosity using piezoelectric quartz crystals in liquid media," Analytica Chimica Acta, vol. 288, pp. 179-185, 1994.

[13]R. W. Cernosek, S. J. Martin, K. O. Wessendorf, M. D. Terry, and A. N. Rumpf, "Quartz resonator fluid monitors for vehicle applications," Proc. Sensors Expo, pp. 527-539, Cleveland, OH, September 1994.

[14]T. W. Schneider and S. J. Martin, "Influence of compressional wave generation on thickness-shear mode resonator response in a fluid," Anal. Chem., vol. 67, no. 18, pp. 3324-3335, September 15, 1995.

[15]T. W. Schneider, G. C. Frye, S. J. Martin, and J. J. Spates, "Investigation of the quartz resonator as an industrial cleaning monitor," Analytica Chimica Acta, vol. 309, pp. 53-62, 1995.

[16]E. Benes, M. Gröschl, W. Burger, and M. Schmid, "Sensors based on piezoelectric resonators," Sensors and Actuators, vol. A48, pp. 1-21, 1995.

[17]J. R. Vig and R. L. Filler, "Chemical sensor based on quartz microresonators," J. Microelectromech. Syst., vol. 5, no. 2, pp. 138-140, June 1996.

[18]C. Zhang and G. Feng, "Contributions of amplitude measurement in QCM sensors," IEEE Trans. Ultrason., Ferroelect., Freq. Contr., vol. 43, no. 5, pp. 942-947, September 1996.

[19]V. M. Mecea, J. O. Carlsson, and R. V. Bucur, "Extensions of the quartz-crystal-microbalance technique," Sensors and Actuators, vol. A53, pp. 371-378, 1996.

[20]E. Benes, M. Gröschl, F. Seifert, and A. Pohl, "Comparison between BAW and SAW sensor principles," IEEE Intl. Freq. Contr. Symp. Proc., pp. 5-20, May 1997.

[21]J. M. Hammond, R. M. Lec, X. J. Zhang, D. G. Libby and L. A. Prager, "An acoustic automotive engine oil quality sensor," IEEE Intl. Freq. Control Symp. Proc., pp. 72-80, May, 1997.

[22]R. Thalhammer, S. Braun, B. Devcic-Kuhar, M. Gröschl, F. Trampler, E. Benes, H. Nowotny, M. Kostal, M. Hruskovic, and J. Hrbik, "Viscosity sensor based upon an angular momentum compensated piezoelectric thickness shear sandwich resonator," IEEE Intl. Freq. Contr. Symp. Proc., pp. 105-113, May 1997.

[23]C. Behling, R. Lucklum, and P. Hauptmann, "Direct method for shear moduli calculation from quartz crystal resonator measurements," IEEE Intl. Freq. Contr. Symp. Proc., pp. 823-830, May 1998.

[24]E. Benes, M. Gröschl, F. Seifert, and A. Pohl, "Comparison between BAW and SAW sensor principles," IEEE Trans. Ultrason., Ferroelect., Freq. Contr., vol. 45, no. 5, pp. 1314-1330, September 1998.

[25]R. Thalhammer, S. Braun, B. Devcic-Kuhar, M. Gröschl, F. Trampler, E. Benes, H. Nowotny, and M. Kostal, "Viscosity sensor utilizing a piezoelectric thickness shear sandwich resonator," IEEE Trans. Ultrason., Ferroelect., Freq. Contr., vol. 45, no. 5, pp. 1331-1340, September 1998.

[26]A. Menon, R. Zhou, and F. Josse, "Coated-quartz crystal resonator (QCR) sensors for on-line detection of organic contaminants in water," IEEE Trans. Ultrason., Ferroelect., Freq. Contr., vol. 45, no. 5, pp. 1416-1426, September 1998.

[27]C. Behling, R. Lucklum, and P. Hauptmann, "Fast three-step method for shear moduli calculation from quartz crystal resonator measurements," IEEE Trans. Ultrason., Ferroelect., Freq. Contr., vol. 46, no. 6, pp. 1431-1438, November 1999.

[28]R. Lucklum, C. Behling, and P. Hauptmann, "Signal amplification with multilayer arrangements on chemical quartz-crystal-resonator-sensors," Proc. Joint Meeting of the 13th European Freq. and Time Forum and the 1999 IEEE Intl. Freq. Control Symp., pp. 987-990, April 1999 and IEEE Trans. Ultrason., Ferroelect., Freq. Contr., vol. 47, no. 5, pp. 1246-1252, September 2000.

[29]P. Hauptmann, R. Borngraeber, J. Schroeder, and J. Auge, "Application of novel sensor electronics for quartz resonators in artificial tongue," IEEE Intl. Freq. Contr. Symp. Proc., pp. 100-105, June 2000.

[30]A. Arnau, T. Sogorb, and Y. Jiménez, "A new method for continuous monitoring of series resonance frequency and simple determination of motional impedance parameters for loaded quartz-crystal resonators," IEEE Trans. Ultrason., Ferroelect., Freq. Contr., vol. 48, no. 2, pp. 617-623, March 2001.

[31]R. Lucklum and P. Hauptmann, "Thin film shear modulus determination with quartz crystal resonators: A review," IEEE Intl. Freq. Contr. Symp. Proc., pp. 408-418, June 2001.

[32]R. M. Lec, "Piezoelectric biosensors: Recent advances and applications," IEEE Intl. Freq. Contr. Symp. Proc., pp. 419-429, June 2001.

[33]R. Lucklum, P. Hauptmann, and R. W. Cernosek, "Thin film material properties with quartz crystal resonators," IEEE Intl. Freq. Contr. Symp. Proc., pp. 542-550, June 2001.

[34]G. Sauerbrey, "Verwendung von Schwingquarzen zur Wägung dünner Schichten und zur Mikrowägung," Z. Physik, vol. 155, pp. 206-222, 1959.

[35]J. G. Miller and D. I. Bolef, "Sensitivity enhancement by the use of acoustic resonators in cw ultrasonic spectroscopy," J. Appl. Phys., vol. 39, no. 10, pp. 4589-4593, September 1968.

[36]J. G. Miller and D. I. Bolef, "Acoustic wave analysis of the operation of quartz-crystal film-thickness monitors," J. Appl. Phys., vol. 39, pp. 5815-5816, 1968.

[37]C. –S. Lu and O. Lewis, "Investigation of film-thickness determination by oscillating quartz resonators with large mass load," J. Appl. Phys., vol. 43, no. 11, pp. 4385-4390, November 1972.

[38]A. Ballato and T. Lukaszek, "Mass effects on crystal resonators with arbitrary piezo-coupling," Proc. 27th Annual Freq. Control Symp., pp. 20-29, June 1973.

[39]A. Ballato and T. Lukaszek, "Mass-loading of thickness-excited crystal resonators having arbitrary piezo-coupling," IEEE Trans. Sonics Ultrason., vol. SU-21, no. 4, pp. 269-274, October 1974.

[40]E. C. van Ballegooijen, "Simultaneous mass and temperature determination using a single quartz wafer: An optimized crystal cut," J. Appl. Phys., vol. 50, no. 1, pp. 91-101, January 1979.

[41]Applications of Piezoelectric Quartz Crystal Microbalances (C. Lu and A. W. Czanderna, Eds.), Volume 7 of Methods and Phenomena: Their Applications in Science and Technology, Elsevier, Amsterdam, 1984.

[42]W. Stöckel and R. Schumacher, "In situ microweighing at the junction metal/electrolyte," Ber. Bunsenges. Phys. Chem., vol. 91, pp. 345-349, 1987.

[43]P. J. Cumpson and M. P. Seah, "The quartz crystal microbalance; radial/polar dependence of mass sensitivity both on and off the electrode," Meas. Sci. Technol., vol. 1, pp. 544-555, 1990.

[44]A. S. Way, "Quartz resonator techniques for simultaneous measurement of areal mass density, lateral stress, and temperature in thin films," Vacuum, vol. 44, nos. 3-4, pp. 385-388, 1993.

[45]R. V. Bucur, J. –O. Carlsson, and V. M. Mecea, "Quartz-crystal mass sensors with glued foil electrodes," Sensors and Actuators, vol. B37, pp. 91-95, November 1996.

[46]M. Nakazawa, "Analysis of thickness dependence on electrical equivalent circuit model for AT-cut resonators," IEEE Intl. Ultrasonics Symp. Proc., pp. 925-930, October 1998.

[47]J. W. S. Rayleigh, The Theory of Sound, Vol. 2, second revised edition, (1896), Dover, New York, 1945.

[48]R. Lucklum, B. Henning, P. Hauptmann, K. D. Schierbaum, S. Vaihinger, and W. Göpel, "Quartz microbalance sensors for gas detection," Sensors and Actuators, vol. A25-27, pp. 705-710, 1991.

[49]W. P. Mason, "Viscosity and shear elasticity measurements of liquids by means of shear vibrating crystals," J. Colloid Sci., vol. 3, pp. 147-162, 1948.

[50]S. Bruckenstein and M. Shay, "Experimental aspects of use of the quartz crystal microbalance in solution," Electrochimica Acta, vol. 30, no. 10, pp. 1295-1300, 1985.

[51]K. K. Kanazawa and J. G. Gordon II, "The oscillation frequency of a quartz resonator in contact with a liquid," Analytica Chimica Acta, vol. 175, pp. 99-105, 1985.

[52]K. K. Kanazawa and J. G. Gordon II, "Frequency of a quartz microbalance in contact with liquid," Anal. Chem., vol. 57, pp. 1771-1772, 1985.

[53]H. Muramatsu, E. Tamiya, and I. Karube, "Computation of equivalent circuit parameters of quartz crystals in contact with liquids and study of liquid properties," Anal. Chem., vol. 60, no. 19, pp. 2142-2146, October 1, 1988.

[54]B. A. Martin and H. E. Hager, "Velocity profile on quartz crystals oscillating in liquids," J. Appl. Phys., vol. 65, no. 7, pp. 2630-2635, 1 April 1989.

[55]E. Benes, M. Schmid, and V. Kravchenko, "Vibration modes of mass-loaded planoconvex quartz crystal resonators," J. Acoust. Soc. Am., vol. 90, no. 2, part 1, pp. 700-706, August 1991.

[56]W. Wei, Z. Mo, and S. Yao, "Multi-component analysis in solution using piezoelectric quartz sensors," Analytica Chimica Acta, vol. 251, pp. 143-148, 1991.

[57]Z. Lin, C. M. Yip, I. S. Joseph, and M. D. Ward, "Operation of an ultrasensitive 30-MHz quartz crystal microbalance in liquids," Anal. Chem., vol. 65, no. 11, pp. 1546-1551, June 11, 1993.

[58]S. J. Martin, G. C. Frye, and K. O. Wissendorf, "Sensing liquid properties with thickness-shear mode resonators," Sensors and Actuators, vol. A44, pp. 209-218, 1994.

[59]Z. Lin and M. D. Ward, "The role of longitudinal waves in quartz crystal microbalance applications in liquids," Anal. Chem., vol. 67, no. 4, pp. 685-693, February 15, 1995.

[60]M. Rodahl, F. Höök, A. Krozer, P. Brzezinski, and B. Kasemo, "Quartz crystal microbalance setup for frequency and Q-factor measurements in gaseous and liquid environments," Rev. Sci. Instrum., vol. 66., no. 7, pp. 3924-3930, July 1995.

[61]B. Devcic-Kuhar, D. Harrer, R. Thalhammer, M. Gröschl, E. Benes, H. Nowotny, and F. Trampler, "Three layer thickness extensional mode piezoelectric resonator for determining density and sound velocity of liquids," IEEE Intl. Freq. Contr. Symp. Proc., pp. 81-89, May 1997.

[62]M. Thompson and G. L. Hayward, "Mass response of the thickness-shear mode acoustic wave sensor in liquids as a central misleading dogma," IEEE Intl. Freq. Control Symp. Proc., pp. 114-119, Orlando, FL, May, 1997.

[63]S. J. Martin, J. J. Spates, K. O. Wessendorf, T. W. Schneider, and R. C. Huber, "Resonator/oscillator response to liquid loading," Anal. Chem., vol. 69, no. 11, pp. 2050-2054, June 1, 1997.

[64]Y. Kim, J. R. Vig, and A. Ballato, "Sensing the properties of liquids with doubly rotated resonators," IEEE Intl. Freq. Contr. Symp. Proc., pp. 660-666, May 1998.

[65]A. Püttmer and P. Hauptmann, "Ultrasonic density sensor for liquids," IEEE Intl. Ultrason. Symp. Proc., pp. 497-500, October 1998.

[66]R. Thalhammer, B. Devcic-Kuhar, D. Harrer, F. Trampler, E. Benes, M. Gröschl, and H. Nowotny, "Piezoelectric sandwich resonator for sensing viscosity, sound speed, and density of liquids," 194th Meeting of The Electrochemical Society, Z1 – Acoustic Wave-based Sensors, November 1998, 1p.

[67]R. Borngraeber, J. Schroeder, R. Lucklum, and P. Hauptmann, "Is an oscillator based measurement adequate in a liquid environment?," IEEE Intl. Freq. Contr. Symp. Proc., pp. 443-448, June 2001.

[68]C. Zhang and J. Vetelino, "A bulk acoustic wave resonator for sensing liquid electrical property changes," IEEE Intl. Freq. Contr. Symp. Proc., pp. 535-541, June 2001.

[69]P. C. Y. Lee and R. Huang, "Effects of a liquid layer on thickness-shear vibrations of rectangular AT-cut quartz plates," IEEE Trans. Ultrason., Ferroelect., Freq. Contr., vol. 49, no. 5, pp. 604-611, May 2002.

[70]S. J. Martin, V. E. Granstaff, and G. C. Frye, "Characterization of a quartz crystal microbalance with simultaneous mass and liquid loading," Anal. Chem., vol. 63, no. 20, pp. 2272-2281, October 15, 1991.

[71]C. Zhang, F. Feng, and S. Sui, "A new approach to the development of quartz crystal sensors distinguishing between mass loading and liquid damping," IEEE Trans. Instrum. Meas., vol. 47, no. 5, pp. 1234-1238, October 1998.

[72]W. C. Sperry, "Rheological-model concept," J. Acoust. Soc. Am., vol. 36, no. 2, pp. 376-385, February 1964.

[73]R. A. Crane and G. Fischer, "Analysis of a quartz crystal microbalance with coatings of finite viscosity," J. Phys. D: Appl. Phys., vol. 12, pp. 2019-2026, 1979.

[74]H. Ohigashi, T. Itoh, K. Kimura, T. Nakanishi, and M. Suzuki, "Analysis of frequency response characteristics of polymer ultrasonic transducers," Japanese J. Appl. Physics, vol. 27, no. 3, pp. 354-360, March 1988.

[75]C. E. Reed, K. K. Kanazawa, and J. H. Kaufman, "Physical description of a viscoelastically loaded AT-cut quartz resonator," J. Appl. Phys., vol. 68, no. 5, pp. 1993-2001, 1 September 1990.

[76]B. Hartmann, G. F. Lee, and J. D. Lee, "Loss factor height and width limits for polymer relaxations," J. Acoust. Soc. Am., vol. 95, no. 1, pp. 226-233, January 1994.

[77]S. J. Martin, G. C. Frye, and S. D. Senturia, "Dynamics and response of polymer-coated surface acoustic wave devices: Effect of viscoelastic properties and film resonance," Anal. Chem., vol. 66, no. 14, pp. 2201-2219, July 15, 1994.

[78]J. M. Carcione, "On energy definition in electromagnetism: An analogy with viscoelasticity," J. Acoust. Soc. Am., vol. 105, no. 2, part 1, pp. 626-632, February 1999.

[79]D. K. Gramotnev and M. L. Mather, "Anomalous absorption of bulk shear acoustic waves by an ultra-thin layer of a non-Newtonian fluid," J. Acoust. Soc. Am., vol. 106, no. 5, pp. 2552-2559, November 1999.

[80]M. Gröschl, "Ultrasonic separation of suspended particles – Part I: Fundamentals," Acta Acustica, vol. 84, pp. 432-447, 1998.

[81]M. Gröschl, "Ultrasonic separation of suspended particles – Part II: Design and operation of separation devices," Acta Acustica, vol. 84, pp. 632-642, 1998.

[82]M. Gröschl, W. Burger, B. Handl, O. Doblhoff-Dier, T. Gaida, and C. Schmatz, "Ultrasonic separation of suspended particles – Part III: Application in biotechnology," Acta Acustica, vol. 84, pp. 815-822, 1998.

[83]F. T. Schulitz, Y. Lu, and H. N. G. Wadley, "Ultrasonic propagation in metal powder-viscous liquid suspensions," J. Acoust. Soc. Am., vol. 103, no. 3, pp. 1361-1369, March 1998.

[84]R. M. Lec and J. Sorial, "The study of colloidal systems with TSM piezoelectric sensors," IEEE Intl. Freq. Contr. Symp. Proc., pp. 838-845, June 2001.

[85]M. Onoe and K. Okada, "Analysis of contoured piezoelectric resonators vibrating in thickness-twist modes," Proc. 23rd Annual Frequency Control Symp., pp. 26-38, May 1969.

[86]A. Ballato, "Doubly rotated thickness mode plate vibrators," In *Physical Acoustics: Principles and Methods*, (W. P. Mason and R. N. Thurston, Eds.) Vol. 13, Ch. 5, pp. 115-181, 1977. Academic Press, New York. ISBN 0-12-477913-1.

[87]J. Ballato, R. Schwartz, and A. Ballato, "Network formalism for modeling functionally gradient piezoelectric plates and stacks and simulations of rainbow ceramic actuators," IEEE Trans. Ultrason., Ferroelect., Freq. Contr., vol. 48, no. 2, pp. 462-476, March 2001.

[88]R. Lucklum and P. Hauptmann, "Generalized acoustic parameters of non-homogeneous thin films," Proc. 2002 IEEE Intl. Freq. Control Symp. and PDA Exhibition, pp. 234-241, May 2002.

[89]S. J. Martin, K. O. Wessendorf, C. T. Gebert, G. C. Frye, R. W. Cernosek, L. Casaus, and M. A. Mitchell, "Measuring liquid properties with smooth- and textured-surface resonators," IEEE Intl. Freq. Control Symp. Proc., pp. 603-608, June, 1993.

[90]S. J. Martin, G. C. Frye, A. J. Ricco, and S. D. Senturia, "Effect of surface roughness on the response of thickness-shear mode resonators in liquids," Anal. Chem., vol. 65, no. 20, pp. 2910-2922, October 15, 1993.

[91]C. Zhang, S. Schranz, R. Lucklum, and P. Hauptmann, "Mass effects of quartz resonant sensors with different surface microstructures in liquids," IEEE Trans. Ultrason., Ferroelect., Freq. Contr., vol. 45, no. 5, pp. 1204-1210, September 1998.

[92]L. Wimmer, S. Hertl, J. Hemetsberger, and E. Benes, "New method of measuring vibration amplitudes of quartz crystals," Rev. Sci. Instrum., vol. 55, no. 4, pp. 605-609, April 1984.

[93]S. Hertl, L. Wimmer, and E. Benes, "Investigation of the amplitude distribution of AT-cut quartz crystals," J. Acoust. Soc. Am., vol. 78, no. 4, pp. 1337-1343, October 1985.

[94]J. R. Vig and A. Ballato, "Comments about the effects on nonuniform mass loading on a quartz crystal microbalance," IEEE Trans. Ultrason., Ferroelect., Freq. Contr., vol. 45, no. 5, pp. 1123-1124, September 1998.

[95]H. Nowotny, N. Finger, E. Benes, and M. Gröschl, "Vibration modes of piezoelectric plates with small spatial thickness variation," Proc. Joint Meeting 13th European Freq. and Time Forum and the 1999 IEEE Intl. Freq. Control Symp., pp. 501-504, April 1999.

[96]B. K. Sinha, "Doubly rotated contoured quartz resonators," IEEE Trans. Ultrason., Ferroelect., Freq. Contr., vol. 48, no. 5, pp. 1162-1180, September 2001.

[97]G. Arlt, "Resonance-antiresonance of conducting piezoelectric resonators," J. Acoust. Soc. Am., vol. 37, no. 1, pp. 151-157, January 1965.

[98]T. R. Meeker, "Thickness mode piezoelectric transducers," Ultrasonics, vol. 10, no. 1, pp. 26-36, January 1972.

[99]M. Brunot, "Structures piézoélectriques à couches multiples," Ann. Télécommunic., vol. 31, nos. 1-2, pp. 45-73, 1976.

[100]M Schmid, E. Benes, and R. Sedlaczek, "A computer-controlled system for the measurement of complete admittance spectra of piezoelectric resonators," Meas. Sci. Technol., vol. 1, pp. 970-975, 1990.

[101]M. Schmid, E. Benes, W. Burger, and V. Kravchenko, "Motional capacitance of layered piezoelectric thickness-mode resonators," IEEE Trans. Ultrason., Ferroelect., Freq. Contr., vol. 38, no. 3, pp. 199-206, May 1991.

[102]V. E. Granstaff and S. J. Martin, "Characterization of a thickness-shear mode quartz resonator with multiple nonpiezoelectric layers," J. Appl. Phys., vol. 75, no. 3, pp. 1319-1329, 1 February 1994.

[103]M. Valentin and C. Filiâtre, "Application of the impedance transformation on transmission lines to electrochemical microbalance," Jour. de Physique III, vol. 4, pp. 1305-1319, July 1994.

[104]C. Filiâtre, G. Bardèche, and M. Valentin, "Transmission-line model for immersed quartz-crystal sensors," Sensors and Actuators, vol. A44, pp. 137-144, 1994.

[105]A. Ballato and J. Ballato, "Networks for piezoceramic resonators," J. Acoust. Soc. Am., vol. 98, no. 5, pt. 2, p. 2877, November 1995.

[106]A. Ballato and J. Ballato, "Modern piezoceramic equivalent networks," IEEE Intl. Ultrasonics Symp. Proc., pp. 683-686, November 1995.

[107]A. Ballato and J. Ballato, "Accurate electrical measurements of modern ferroelectrics," Ferroelectrics, vol. 182, nos. 1-4, pp. 29-59, 1996.

[108]A. Ballato and J. Ballato, "High frequency piezoceramic equivalent circuit," J. Am. Ceram. Soc., vol. 79, no. 5, pp. 1413-1415, May 1996.

[109]J. Messina and A. Ballato, "Dependence of strain amplitude on loss mechanisms in plate resonators," IEEE Intl. Frequency Control Symp. Proc., pp. 366-370, June 1996.

[110]A. Ballato and J. R. Vig. "Piezoelectric Devices," in *Encyclopedia of Applied Physics*, G. Trigg, ed., Vol. 14, pp. 129-145. VCH Publishers, New York, 1996.

[111]T. R. Meeker, "Piezoelectric resonators and applications," in *Encyclopedia of Applied Physics*, G. Trigg, ed., Vol. 14, pp. 147-169, VCH Publishers, New York, 1996.

[112]A. Ballato, "Influence of air loading and dissipation on plate transducer amplitude," J. Acoust. Soc. Am., vol. 103, no. 5, pt. 2, p. 2832, May 1998; Proc. ASA/ICA, Vol. II, pp. 735-736. ISBN 1-56396-816-9.

[113]R. W. Cernosek, S. J. Martin, A. R. Hillman, and H. L. Bandey, "Comparison of lumped-element and transmission-line models for thickness-shear-mode quartz resonator sensors," IEEE Intl. Freq. Contr. Symp. Proc., pp. 96-104, May 1997, and IEEE Trans. Ultrason., Ferroelect., Freq. Contr., vol. 45, no. 5, pp. 1399-1407, September 1998.

[114]E. Benes, M. Schmid, M. Gröschl, P. Berlinger, H. Nowotny, and K. C. Harms, "Solving the cable problem between crystal sensor and electronics by use of a balanced bridge oscillator circuit," Proc. Joint Meeting of the 13th European Freq. and Time Forum and the 1999 IEEE Intl. Freq. Control Symp., pp. 1023-1026, April 1999.

[115]A. Ballato, "Modeling piezoelectric and piezomagnetic devices and structures via equivalent networks," IEEE Trans. Ultrason., Ferroelect., Freq. Contr., vol. 48, no. 5, pp. 1189-1240, September, 2001.

[116]A. Ballato, "Piezoelectric resonators loaded with viscoelastic and nonuniform media," IEEE Intl. Frequency Control Symp. Proc., pp. 191-201, May 2002.

[117]A. Arnau, Y. Jiménez, and T. Sogorb, "An extended Butterworth-Van Dyke model for quartz crystal microbalance applications in viscoelastic fluid media," IEEE Trans. Ultrason., Ferroelect., Freq. Contr., vol. 48, no. 5, pp. 1367-1382, September 2001.

[118]Y. Deblock, P. Campistron, M. Lippert, and C. Bruneel, "Electrical characterization of plate piezoelectric transducers bonded to a finite substrate," J. Acoust. Soc. Am., vol. 111, no. 6, pp. 2681-2685, June 2002.

[119]A. C. Bartlett, "A class of equivalent electrical networks," Phil. Mag., ser. 6, vol. 49, no. 292, pp. 728-739, April 1925.

[120]A. W. Lawson, "The vibration of piezoelectric plates," Phys. Rev., vol. 62, pp. 71-76, July 1942.

[121]H. F. Tiersten, "Thickness vibrations of piezoelectric plates," J. Acoust. Soc. Am., vol. 35, no. 1, pp. 53-58, January 1963.

[122]A. Ballato, "Lateral and thickness excitation of obliquely poled ferroelectric ceramic plates," in *Ceramic Transactions*, Vol. 106, pp. 309-332, 2000. ISBN 1-57498-098-X.

[123]G. L. Dybwad, "A sensitive new method for the determination of adhesive bonding between a particle and a substrate," J. Appl. Phys., vol. 58, no. 7, pp. 2789-2790, 1 October 1985.

[124]M. Onoe, "Effects of evaporated electrodes on quartz resonator vibrating in a contour mode," Proc. IRE, vol. 45, no. 5, p. 694, May 1957.

[125]L. Dworsky and R. G. Kinsman, "A simple single model for quartz crystal resonator low level drive sensitivity and monolithic filter intermodulation," IEEE Trans. Ultrason., Ferroelect., Freq. Contr., vol. 41, no. 2, pp. 261-268, March 1994.

[126]E. P. EerNisse, "An analysis of drive level sensitivity in thickness shear quartz resonators," IEEE Intl. Freq. Control Symp. Proc., pp. 346-356, June, 1996.

[127]S. –Y. Liu, Y. –H. Kao, Y. O. Su, and T. –P. Perng, "Stresses induced by hydrogen absorption and desorption in Pd nanofilms," J. Alloys and Compounds, vol. 316, pp. 280-283, 2001.

[128]E. P. EerNisse, E. Benes, and M. Schmid, "The role of localized rotational imbalance in drive level dependence phenomena," Proc. 2002 IEEE Intl. Freq. Control Symp. and PDA Exhibition, pp. 2-7, May 2002.

[129]W. G. Cady, *Piezoelectricity*, McGraw-Hill, New York, 1946; Dover, New York, 1964.

[130]H. J. Bernstein and V. F. Weisskopf, "About liquids," Am. J. Phys., vol. 55, no. 11, pp. 974-982, November 1987.

[131]F. Ferrante, A. L. Kipling, and M. Thompson, "Molecular slip at the solid-liquid interface of an acoustic-wave sensor," J. Appl. Phys., vol. 76, no. 6, pp. 3448-3462, 15 September 1994.

[132]S. Granick, "Soft matter in a tight spot," Physics Today, vol. 52, no. 7, pp. 26-31, July 1999.

[133]R. Lucklum and G. McHale, "Treatment of slip in a generalized acoustic concept," IEEE Intl. Freq. Contr. Symp. Proc., pp. 40-46, June 2000.

[134]K. E. Drexler, *Nanosystems: Molecular Machinery, Manufacturing, and Computation*, Wiley-Interscience, New York, 1992. ISBN: 0-471-57518-6.

[135]Proc. IEEE, vol. 86, no. 8, pp. 1529-1812, August 1998. Special Issue on Integrated Sensors, Microactuators, and Microsystems (MEMS).

[136]The AMPTIAC Newsletter, Spring 2002, vol. 6, no. 1, pp. 1-65. Advanced Materials and Processes Technology Information Analysis Center (AMPTIAC), 201 Mill Street, Rome, NY 13440-6916. Special Issue: Nanotechnology.

[137]O. Holland and C. Melhuish, "Stigmergy, self-organization, and sorting in collective robotics," Artificial Life, vol. 5, no. 2, pp. 173-202, 1999.

[138]A. Ballato, "Resonant strain levels in modern ceramic plate actuators," In *Am. Ceramic Soc. Trans.: Dielectric Materials*, Vol. 100 (K. M. Nair and A. S. Bhalla, eds.), pp. 443-454, 1999. ISBN 1-57498-066-1.

[139] A. C. Bartlett, "An extension of a property of artificial lines," Phil. Mag., ser. 7, vol. 4, no. 24, pp. 902-907, November 1927.

[140] A. C. Bartlett, *The Theory of Electrical Artificial Lines and Filters*, John Wiley & Sons, New York, 1930, p. 28.

[141] O. Brune, "Note on Bartlett's bisection theorem for 4-terminal electrical networks," Phil. Mag., ser. 7, vol. 14, no. 93, pp. 806-811, November 1932.

[142] J. Hilsenrath, C. W. Beckett, W. S. Benedict, L. Fano, H. L. Hoge, J. F. Masi, R. L. Nuttall, Y. S. Touloukian, and H. W. Woolley, "Tables of Thermal Properties of Gases," NBS Circular 564, National Bureau of Standards, Washington, DC, November 1955.

[143] J. Hilsenrath, "Thermodynamic Properties of Gases," in *American Institute of Physics Handbook*, 2nd ed., D. E. Gray, Ed., McGraw-Hill, New York, 1963.

# HIGH STRAIN PNN-PT-PZ PIEZO CERAMICS AND APPLICATIONS TO MULTILAYER ACTUATORS

K. Niwa, M. Kondo, M. Hida and K. Kurihara
Fujitsu Laboratories, Ltd.
10-1 Morinosato-Wakamiya, Atsugi 243-0197, Japan

## ABSTRACT

In order to explore high piezoelectric constant and lower sintering temperature for co-firing with Ag electrodes, effect of composition on piezoelectric constant and sinterability has been studied using $Pb(Ni_{1/3}Nb_{2/3})O_3$-$PbTiO_3$-$PbZrO_3$ (PNN-PT-PZ) ceramics. A ceramic with a large piezoelectric constant ($d_{33}$ = 1100 pm/V) was obtained at the composition of PNN-PT-PZ 50/34.5/15.5. We also found that excess lead oxide (PbO) addition improves sinterability of PNN-PT-PZ ceramic, and that the sintering temperature could be decreased to around 900°C when 1 mol% of excess PbO was added. We fabricated piezoelectric multiplayer actuators by co-firing PbO-rich PNN-PT-PZ ceramic with silver internal electrodes. Its displacement was the same as that of an actuator fabricated of stoichiometric ceramic powder and silver-palladium alloy electrodes, sintered at 1050°C. PNN-PT-PZ ceramic is thus a promising piezoelectric material for use in multilayer actuators with silver internal electrodes because it can be sintered at a low temperature. In this paper, we will also describe applications of PNN-PT-PZ ceramics to the piezoelectric micro actuators for precision head positioning of HDD.

# INTRODUCTION

Piezoelectric actuators are critical components in precision positioners, such as ultrasonic ac motors using resonating strain [1]. There are many designs for these ceramic actuator devices, though they all utilize the strain induced in the ceramic longitudinally or transversely to the applied electric field [2]. The multilayer actuator belongs to the first category (the strain is induced longitudinally) and is one of the typical designs for piezoelectric ceramic actuators. Single crystals of lead-containing perovskites have excellent piezoelectric constant ($d_{33}$ = 1570 pC/N) [3]. Those of piezoelectric ceramics, such as Pb(Zr, Ti)$O_3$ (hereafter PZT) and modified PZT, are smaller ($d_{33}$ is around 650 pC/N) due to the grain boundary in the ceramic [4]. However, piezoelectric ceramics do have advantages. For example, they are applicable to large piezoelectric devices, and their preparation costs are much less than those of single crystals. What they lack is performance comparable to that of single crystals.

PZT ceramics are normally obtained by firing the green body of the powder at around 1250°C [5]. This temperature is slightly higher for multilayer applications co-fired with electrode materials. Decreasing the sintering temperature provides several advantages in the preparation of a multilayer device. For example, the composition of the internal electrode is an important factor in determining the manufacturing cost of a multilayer actuator. The melting point of the material of internal electrodes should be higher than the firing temperature, and the electrode material should have low reactivity with PbO in PZT ceramics. Therefore, platinum or silver-palladium alloys are commonly used for the internal electrodes. Another merit is the ability to control the ceramic composition. The vaporization of PbO decreases with decreasing temperature. Sol-gel processing is one effective method to decrease the sintering temperature of a powder [6]. However, it is difficult to prepare a large amount of powder by the sol-gel process, and the raw materials, such as organic metals, are more expensive than powders prepared by a solid-solution method.

The Pb(Ni$_{1/3}$Nb$_{2/3}$)O$_3$-PbTiO$_3$-PbZrO$_3$ (hereafter PNN-PT-PZ) ceramic is an attractive material for many piezoelectric applications because it has a large electromechanical coupling coefficient for ceramics (k$_{33}$ = 0.8) [7-9]. Another feature of PNN-PT-PZ ceramics is that they can be sintered at relatively low temperatures. We previously investigated the effect of excess lead oxide (PbO) on sintering behavior and on the surface microstructure of PNN-PT-PZ ceramics and found that ceramics with excess PbO could be liquid-phase sintered at below 950°C [10]. This firing temperature indicates that silver electrodes (melting point 962°C) could be used as an internal electrode in a co-fired multilayer. We have already reported that the multilayer actuator made of PNN-PT-PZ ceramic with silver internal electrodes could be successfully fabricated by sintering at 900°C [11, 12].

We have now investigated the composition dependence on the piezoelectric constant in PNN-PT-PZ system to prepare the ceramic with large longitudinal piezoelectric constant. We also investigated the preparation and the basic reliability of the multilayer actuator with silver internal electrode.

EXPERIMENTAL PROCEDURE

First, we investigated the piezoelectric constant with the ceramic composition in the vicinity of morphotropic phase boundary (MPB) [9]. Figure 1 shows the investigated composition area. Next, we investigated the influence of excess PbO content on the piezoelectric constant and sinterability of PNN-PT-PZ ceramics. The investigated compositions were Pb$_{1+x}$(Ni$_{0.33}$Nb$_{0.67}$)$_{0.5}$Ti$_{0.35}$Zr$_{0.15}$O$_{3+x}$ (x = -0.02, 0, 0.01 or 0.05). We designate these compositions as 2 mol% PbO-less, stoichiometric, 1 mol% PbO-rich and 5 mol% PbO-rich, respectively. The details of the preparation and evaluation of calcined PNN-PT-PZ powder are described elsewhere [9,10].

Multilayer actuators were prepared using the conventional tape-casting method. Pastes consisting of 100% silver powder (Ag) or coprecipitation powder of silver-30mol%palladium (Ag-Pd) were used as internal electrode materials. The laminated green bodies were sintered at 900 °C in the sample with Ag internal electrode and at 1050°C with Ag-Pd electrode for 6 h. The number of driving layers was 11, and each layer had a thickness of 36 μm.

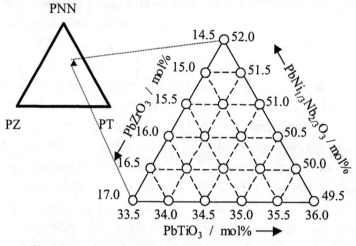

Fig.1 Investigated compositeon area in this study.

The relative density was determined using the Archimedean method. A value of 8.31 g/cm$^3$ for the theoretical density of the PNN-PT-PZ ceramic was derived from the lattice parameter and the composition. The microstructure of the fractured surface of the multilayer ceramic was observed with a field-emission-scanning electron microscope (FE-SEM, SH-100, Hitachi, Japan). The ceramic crystallinity was determined by X-ray diffraction method (XRD, Rigaku, RAD-IIIR, Japan). The piezoelectric constant was derived from the slope of the strain-electric field curve. The strain was measured using strain measurement apparatus (Toyoseiki, Japan). These measurements were taken using specimens sintered sufficiently at 1050°C for 3 h. The capacitance, dielectric permittivity, and resonance frequency were measured with an impedance analyzer (HP4194A, Hewlett-Packard). The piezoelectric constant was also calculated by resonant-antiresonant method. The displacement of the multilayer actuator was measured using the laser Doppler method. The detail evaluation procedure was described in the previous paper. [11]. To evaluate reliability, the multilayer actuators were driven at 7.2 kHz for $6 \times 10^{10}$ cycles in an environment of 40°C and 90% humidity.

**RESULTS AND DISCUSSION**

Figure 2 shows the change of piezoelectric constant ($d_{33}$) of the ceramic with the composition and X-ray diffraction pattern with 2theta-theta measurement of PNN-PT-PZ50/35/15 and 50/34/16.

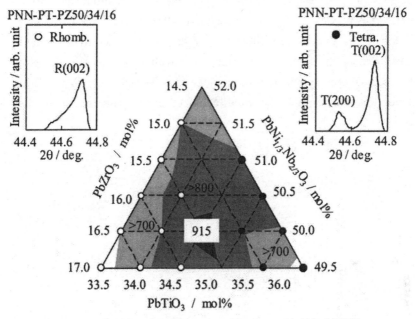

Fig.2 Change in the piezoelectric constant ($d_{33}$) and XRD pattern with the PNN-PT-PZ composition.

The (200)/(002) peaks of the XRD patterns of PNiNb-PT-PZ 50/35/15 and 50/34/16 show tetragonal and rhombohedral phas, respectively. The open and close circles in the map indicate the composition with the tetragonal and the rhombohedral peak pattern. Thus, this figure indicates the MPB exists within these compositions. This area was identical with the MPB positions derived from electromechanical coupling coefficient ($k_{33}$) and dielectric permittivity ($\varepsilon^T_{33}/\varepsilon_0$), as shown in previous paper [9]. The $d_{33}$ reached the maximum value of 915 pC/N on PNN-PT-PZ 50/34.5/15.5.

Figure 3 shows the change of piezoelectric constant of the ceramic as a function of PT content (PNN=50 mol%). The $d_{33}$ calculated from the results of resonant-antiresonant method was 915 pC/N in PNN-PT-PZ 50/34.5/15.5, as shown in Fig.2. The $d_{33}$ derived from the strain measurement was 1100 pm/V in PNN-PT-PZ 50/34.5/15.5 [12]. This difference is due to the difference of driving voltage. In the strain measurement, the domain wall should move with an applied electric field, because the driving voltage is close to the coercive field (around 5kV/cm). Thus, this difference is the contribution of the domain motion in the ceramics.

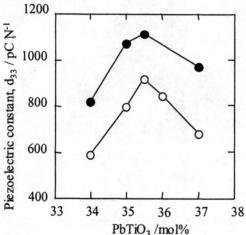

Fig.3 Change in the piezoelectric constant ($d_{33}$) derived from resonance and strain measurement of PNN-PT-PZ ceramics.

Figure 4 shows the shrinkage of the 2 mol% PbO-less, stoichiometric, 1 mol% PbO-rich and 5 mol% PbO-rich green disks as a function of temperature.   The starting and ending temperatures of the densification decrease as PbO content increases.   The 2 mol% PbO-less disk was insufficiently sintered at 1200°C.   However, both the PbO-rich disks could be sintered at lower temperature than the stoichiometric one. The 1 and 5 mol% PbO-rich disks shrank rapidly around 900 and 840°C, respectively.   This figure suggests the addition of PbO promotes the sintering by liquid-phase sintering [10].

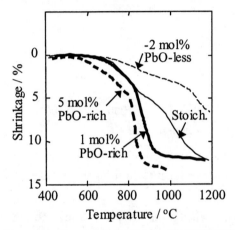

Fig.4 Change in the shrinkage of the PNN-PT-PZ green bodies with PbO content.

Figure 5 shows the change in the relative density of PNiNb-PT-PZ ceramic as a function of temperature. The relative density of a stoichiometric disk reached 98% of the theoretical density at 1000°C. The stoichiometric disk was insufficiently sintered at 950 °C. The relative density of 1 mol% PbO-rich disk reached 95% of the theoretical density at 850°C and 98% at 900°C. The change of the relative density of 5 mol% PbO-rich was almost same behavior as that of 1 mol% PbO-rich. The sintering temperature thus decreased by about 150°C with the addition of excess PbO. This high sinterability of PNiNb-PT-PZ ceramics with the excess PbO addition enables the preparation of a multilayer actuator with internal silver electrodes.

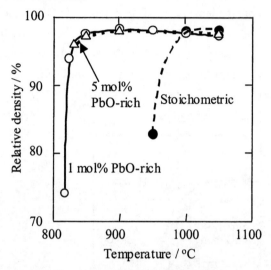

Fig.5 Change in relative density of PNN-PT-PZ ceramics with different PbO content as a function of firing temperature.

Figure 6 shows the change in the piezoelectric constant ($d_{33}$) and relative density of ceramics sintered at $1050^{\circ}C$ as a function of the excess PbO content. The maximum $d_{33}$ value was obtained on the stoichiometric composition. The $d_{33}$ decreased monotonically with the increase of excess PbO content. This decrease is not due to the decrease of the density, because the relative density is almost constant near theoretical density. However, the decrease in the piezoelectric constant with the excess PbO content of 1 mol% was relatively small, and the value remained above 750 pC/N. The results illustrated in Figs. 5 and 6 indicate that in terms of the sintering and piezoelectric properties, an excess PbO content of around 1 mol% is the best choice for fabricating a multilayer actuator with silver internal electrodes.

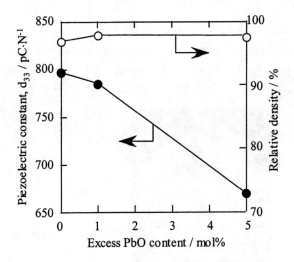

Fig.6 Change in the piezoelectric constant ($d_{33}$) and relative density of PNN-PT-PZ ceramics as a function of excess PbO content.

Figure 7 shows the microstructures of the fractured surfaces of a multilayer actuator fabricated from PNiNb-PT-PZ ceramic with silver internal electrodes. The co-firing temperature was 900°C. Since there were few pores between the grains, the ceramic-electrode interfaces did not have delaminations. The silver electrodes did not melt, and the multilayer ceramic was sufficiently densified at 900°C. We thus succeeded in developing a multilayer actuator with silver internal electrodes by using low-temperature sintering of PNiNb-PT-PZ ceramic. We have already reported that the displacement of the multilayer actuator with Ag internal electrode was same as that with Ag-Pd electrode in previous paper [11].

Figure 8 shows the results of the long-term change in the displacements of the multilayer actuators with Ag electrodes and Ag-Pd electrodes. The co-firing temperatures of multilayer actuators with Ag and Ag-Pd electrodes were 900 and 1050°C, respectively. These actuators were driven with an ac bias at 7.2 kHz, in an environment with a humidity of 90% and a temperature of 40°C. The displacements of both actuators did not change even after 6 x 10^10 pulses. High-performance and reliability of a multilayer actuators can thus be fabricated using PNiNb-PT-PZ ceramic and silver internal electrodes.

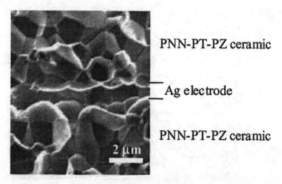

PNN-PT-PZ ceramic

Ag electrode

PNN-PT-PZ ceramic

2 µm

Fig.7 Microstructure of the fractured surface of multiplayer actuator co-fired with Ag electrodes at 900 °C.

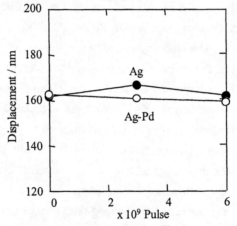

Fig.8 The long-term change in the displacements of multiplayer actuators with Ag electrodes and Ag-Pd electrodes. The sintering temperature of Ag and Ag-Pd electrodes samples was 900 and 1050 °C, respectively.

## APPLICATION TO HDD MICROACTUATORS

In recent years, the areal density of magnetic disk drive has increased by 70% to 100% every year, mainly based on the improvement of recording heads and mediums. There have been an increasing demand of wider servo band to achieve stable operation at a higher track density. However, the servo bandwidth of voice-coil motor (VCM) systems, which are widely used for positioning the magnetic head, is limited by the mechanical resonances of the carriage, coil, and suspension. One possible solution respond to a higher track density is dual-stage actuator system using piezoelectric micro actuator which drives head slider directory.

Figure 9 shows a schematic structure of our new piezoelectric micro actuator system[13]. Two piezoelectric multilayer actuators made of PNN-PT-PZ ceramics are placed between a head slider and a suspension. Those actuators are bonded diagonally to a slider and suspension. The unique feature of the actuator system is a symmetrical structure. Because of conformation of a center of gravity and an axis of rotation, excitation of resonance of suspension will be minimized. This is an important concept of our new actuator system. Another feature of the actuator system is very simple structure, especially using simple shaped piezoelectric actuator elements which are the same as widely used rectangular shaped ones.

In this study, design targets are wide slider moving stroke of $1 \mu$m at 30V operation and high resonance frequency over 20kHz for wider servo band width. FEM analysis was performed in order to get a suitable design which cover the design specifications. The model used in this study is whole HGA consisting of 30% pico-slider, two piezoelectric micro actuator elements and suspension. The suspension also consists of a gimbal and loadbeam. The air springs are also taken into account because the slider is flying above a rotating disk. The detailed design was fixed by comparing results of static analysis, modal analysis, and frequency response analysis.

Figure 10 shows a result of displacement distribution by FEM analysis of the HGA. The displacement of the head element is $0.93 \mu$m at 30V applied. This is very close to our displacement target of $1\,\mu$m at 30V applied.

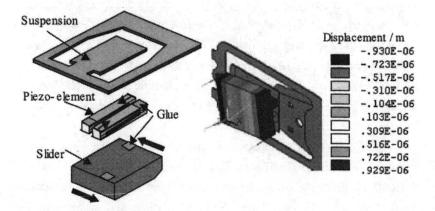

Fig.9 Schematic structure of micro actuator system.

Fig.10 FEM simulation result of displacement distribution.

Figure 11 shows a simulation result of frequency response. Main resonance frequency of the actuator is 26.3 kHz that is higher than our target of 20 kHz. Note that excitation of the suspension near 14 kHz is very small compared to that of the actuator. The reason of this small resonance is a unique feature of our symmetrical actuator structure.

The measured displacement at head edges (head element side and carriage side) at 30V applied were $0.91\,\mu$m and $0.89\,\mu$m respectively. Those are very close to calculated value of $0.93\,\mu$m. Figure 12 shows a measured frequency response of the fabricated HGA using piezoelectric micro actuator. The resonance frequency of the actuator is 25.1 kHz. This is also very close to the calculated values. Measured peaks near 14 kHz that is excitation of the suspension are very small compared to the resonance of actuator.

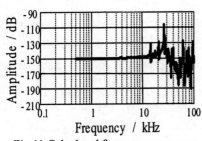
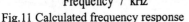

Fig.11 Calculated frequency response

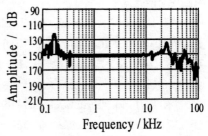

Fig.12 Measured frequency response

## CONCLUSION

We investigated the piezoelectric properties and sinterability of Pb(Ni$_{1/3}$Nb$_{2/3}$)O$_3$-PbTiO$_3$-PbZrO$_3$ (PNN-PT-PZ) ceramics for actuator application. Compositions near MPB strongly affect piezoelectric properties. A ceramic with a large piezoelectric constant ($d_{33}$ = 1100 pm/V) was obtained on the MPB composition of PNN-PT-PZ 50/34.5/15.5.

We also investigated the effect of excess lead oxide (PbO) content on the sinterability of PNN-PT-PZ ceramic. We found that the sintering temperature could be decreased to around 900°C when 1 mol% of excess PbO was added. We fabricated piezoelectric multilayer actuators by co-firing PbO-rich PNN-PT-PZ ceramic with silver internal electrodes. Its displacement was the same as that of an actuator fabricated of stoichiometric ceramic powder and silver-palladium alloy electrodes, sintered at 1050°C. PNN-PT-PZ ceramic is thus a promising piezoelectric material for use in multilayer actuators with silver internal electrodes because it can be sintered at a low temperature.

Piezoelectric micro actuator systems for HDD were fabricated using PNN-PT-PZ ceramics. Results of FEM analysis and measured data of fabricated HGA are in good agreement and show large displacements and excellent vibration characteristics.

# REFERENCES

[1]K. Uchino, "The trend of micro-mechatronics and piezoelectric / electrostrictive actuators"; pp. 1-12 in *Piezoelectric actuators and ultrasonic motors*, 2nd ed. Edited by H. L. Tuller, Kluwer Academic Publishers, Boston, 1997.

[2]K. Uchino, "Structures and fabrication process of ceramic actuators"; pp. 121-1256 in *Piezoelectric actuators and ultrasonic motors*, 2nd ed. Edited by H. L. Tuller, Kluwer Academic Publishers, Boston, 1997.

[3]J. Kuwata, K. Uchino and S. Nomura, "Dielectric and Piezoelectric Properties of $0.91Pb(Zn_{1/3}Nb_{2/3})O_3$-$0.09PbTiO_3$ Single Crystals", *Japanese Journal of Applied Physics*, 21 1298-1302 (1982).

[4]Y. Yamashita, "Large Electromechanical Coupling Factors in Perovskite Binary Material System", *Japanese Journal of Applied Physics*, 33 [9B] 5328-5331 (1994).

[5]D .A. Buckner and P. D. Wilcox, "Effects of Calcining on Sintering of Lead Zirconate-Titanate Ceramics", *Ceramic Bulletin*, 51 [3] 218-222 (1972) .

[6]P. Duran and C. Moure, "Sintering at near theoretical density and properties of PZT ceramics chemically prepared", *Journal of Material Science* 20 827-833 (1985).

[7]M. Kondo, M. Hida, M. Tsukada, K. Kurihara and N. Kamehara, "Piezoelectric Properties of $PbNi_{1/3}Nb_{2/3}O_3$-$PbTiO_3$-$PbZrO_3$ Ceramics Near the MPB", *Journal of Ceramic Society of Japan*, 105 [8] 719-721 (1997).

[8]M. Kondo, M. Hida, M. Tsukada, K. Kurihara and N. Kamehara, "Piezoelectric Properties of $PbNi_{1/3}Nb_{2/3}O_3$-$PbTiO_3$-$PbZrO_3$ Ceramics", *Japanese Journal of Applied Physics*, 36 [9B] 6043-6045 (1998).

[9]M. Kondo, M. Hida, M. Tsukada, K. Kurihara, M.Kutami and N. Kamehara, "Piezoelectric Properties and Phase Transitions of $PbNi_{1/3}Nb_{2/3}O_3$-$PbTiO_3$-$PbZrO_3$ Ceramics", pp. 311-314, in *Proceedings of the 11th IEEE International Symposium on the Applications of Ferroelectrics*, Edited by E. Colla, D. Damjanovic and N. Setter, IEEE

Ultrasonic, Ferroelectrics and Frequency Control Society, New Jersey, 1998.

[10]M. Kondo and K. Kurihara, "Sintering Behavior and Surface Microstructure of PbO-rich $PbNi_{1/3}Nb_{2/3}O_3$-$PbTiO_3$-$PbZrO_3$ Ceramics", *Journal of American Ceramic Society*, **84** 2469-2474 (2001).

[11]M. Kondo and K. Kurihara, to be submitted in *Sensors and Actuators A* (2003)

[12]M. Kondo and K. Kurihara, "Piezoelectric Properties and Applications of $PbNi_{1/3}Nb_{2/3}O_3$-$PbTiO_3$-$PbZrO_3$ Ceramics" to be pressed in *Key Engineering Materials*, **230-231** (2003).

[13]T. Mita, K. Kurihara, M. Hida and S. Koganezawa, "Abstract of Spring Meeting of Jpn. Soc. for Precision Eng.", (Jpn. Soc. for Precision Eng., Tokyo, Japan, 2002) p. 115.

# GELATIN-MODIFIED SURFACES IN SELECTED ELELECTRONIC COMPONENTS

Stane Pejovnik,[†] Marjan Bele, Miran Gaberšček, Robert Dominko, Jernej Drofenik, and Janko Jamnik

National Institute of Chemistry, Hajdrihova 19, SI-1000 Ljubljana, Slovenia

The importance of uniform conducting coatings on non-conducting substrate is discussed. The uniformity of coating is achieved through substrate pretreatment with appropriate polymer molecules, which are easily adsorbed on various surfaces (e.g. gelatin). While the uniform coatings are not essential for average electronic conductivity of the surface, they are shown to be of vital importance in applications where they take part in diffusion-limited processes, like in electrochemical solid-state diffusion typical for lithium batteries. Uniform coatings consisting of carbon black particles can improve the electrochemical performance (capacity) of cathodes for as much as 50 %, if compared to uncoated cathode particles.

## I.    Introduction

Preparation electronically conducting layers on non-conducting surfaces/interfaces is a matter of great technological and scientific interest. For example, electroless metal deposition has a wide use in microelectronics, especially in printed wiring board applications.[1] The need for new techniques which allow a reduction in environmental problems has led to new deposition methods, like the water-based deposition of conductive coatings formed by densely packed mesoscopic particles of carbon black onto printed wiring board laminates. Typically, these conductive coatings are used during the through-hole metalization process in printed wiring board laminates, where the outer copper layers of a printed wiring board are electrically connected to the inner layers by the deposition of a thin layer of carbon black. This serves as a thin electrically conductive layer, over which a thicker copper layer is electroplated.[2,3]

[†]Permanent address: Faculty of Chemistry and Chemical Technology, University of Ljubljana, Askerčeva 5, SI-1000, Ljubljana, Slovenia.

The basic requirement for a high performance coating is that the primary conductive coating has substantial electrical conductivity. This can be achieved if the primary coating is densely packed and has a thickness of several hundreds of nanometers. In previous work[4,5,6] we have shown that such coatings can be efficiently produced by deposition of carbon black onto polymer-modified solid surface. The deposition of carbon particles proceeds via a substrate-induced deposition and has two steps. In the first step, a polymer is adsorbed on the surface from a water-solution. In the second step, i.e. after dipping the substrate into a water-based carbon black suspension, the surface-adsorbed polymer triggers a substrate-induced deposition of conductive carbon black particles. A typical example of a water-soluble polymer, which yields good results, is gelatin, a denatured protein. The adsorbed film of gelatin provides a "hairy" interface, with polymer loops and tails sticking out into solution, which extends approximately 0.5 μm into the water solution.[7] Now the substrate can attract many kinds of particles because gelatin contains many kinds of active groups: cationic, anionic and nonionic. Bridging properties of gelatin have been confirmed using the Atomic Force Microscopy.[7] However, for successful deposition of carbon black coatings, which are dense enough to conduct electrical current along the particles, gelatin properties are not enough. Beyond the conditions of gelatin adsorption, it is also necessary to optimize the properties of carbon black dispersion. On one hand, the water dispersion of carbon black particles has to be stable. For this purpose, surfactants are used, which adsorb onto the surfaces of particles. Due to dissociation, these surfactants become charged in aqueous solution and the resulting electrostatic repulsive forces between equally charged surfaces lead to stabilization of dispersion against van der Waals attraction.[8,9] On the other hand, the electrostatic properties of particles in dispersion have to be near the point where the particles can approach the polymer surface to a certain minimum distance, so that deposition and adsorption onto a surface can occur. This point is controlled by the appropriate addition of a salt,[5,7] which screens the electric field of the surfaces and allows particles to approach closer to the surface during their Brownian motion. Under such conditions, the deposition can only occur on coated substrate surface, but not on other surfaces and, of course, coagulation cannot occur in the bulk dispersion.

In the present work, we briefly report the use of a similar coating procedure on a completely different problem. The positive electrode in lithium rechargeable batteries consists of transition metal oxides ($LiCoO_2$, $LiMn_2O_4$, etc.),[10] which, however, exhibit very low electronic conductivity ($10^{-5}$ to $10^{-4}$ Scm$^{-2}$). In order to increase the electrode average conductivity and, hence, to increase its power density, the oxide particles are usually mixed with a certain amount of conducting powder (mostly graphite-based, also metallic etc.) and polymer binder.[11] We have shown[12] that such a technology is quite ineffective as it leads to particle agglomeration rather than to systematic particle ordering. Here we show that a slightly modified coating technology (the so called **Novel Coating Technology – NCT**)[13] leads to a much more uniform arrangement of sub-micrometer conductive carbon particles around oxide particles, which in this case serve as a sort of substrate. The more ordered particle arrangement results in an electrode with higher energy and power density.

## II.    Materials and Methods

*(1) Raw Materials*

Type A gelatin (Fluka No. 48722; Fluka, Buchs, Switzerland) with medium gel power 180 Bloom was used as a surface modifier (the initiator of deposition) and a binder. Gelatin (type A) derived from pigs skin typically contains 79.4 mol% non-ionizable peptide units (glycine, alanine, proline, valine, etc.), 12% acidic amino acids (aspartic acid, glutamic acid, etc.) and 8.6% basic amino acids (lysine, hydroxylysine, arginine, histidine, etc.). The isoelectric point (pH$_{IEP}$) of gelatin used is 9,2.[4] As a conductive agent, carbon black designated as Printex XE2 supplied by Degussa AG (Frankfurt, Germany) was used. Printex XE2 are a highly conductive carbon blacks with a 950m$^2$/g BET (The Brunauer–Emmett–Teller) surface area and an average primary particle size of 30 nm, according to Degussa. The cationic surfactant cetyltrimethylammonium bromide (CTAB, Aldrich No. 85,582-0, Aldrich, Milwaukee, WI, USA), and sodium acetate (NaAc) Nr.6268 from Merck KgaA, (Darmstadt, Germany) was used for preparation of carbon black dispersion. The active cathode particles were obtained from Merck (LiCoO$_2$ "SC15 Selectipur® 1.01183, Merck"). Metallic lithium foil (0.75 mm thick) was obtained from Alfa Aesar (Johnson Matthey, Karlsruhe, Germany).

*(2) Preparation of composite cathode materials and electrodes.*

Deposition of carbon black onto active cathode particles from dispersion takes place only after gelatin-pre-treatment of the active cathode particles. Preparations of gelatin solution and carbon black dispersion used in this procedure are described in more details in our previous work.[4,5,9]

The essential steps in the NCT of the composite cathode preparation are shown in Fig.1. In the first step the active particles were immersed into gelatin solution. The amount of added gelatin in this step was bellow 1 wt. % in total. After mixing, the slurry was dried at 60 °C. In the second step, a desired amount of carbon black from dispersion was added to the gelatin-pretreated active particles. To the obtained mixture, an additional amount of gelatin solution was added (third step) to bind the carbon black-covered active particles. The amount of added gelatin in this step was proportional to the amount of added carbon black. At the end the slurry was partially dried and pressed on an aluminum substrate to yield electrodes of a thickness of 70-110 µm (mass of active material was about 3-5 mg). Prior to use, the electrodes were dried in vacuum at 110 °C for at least 24 h.

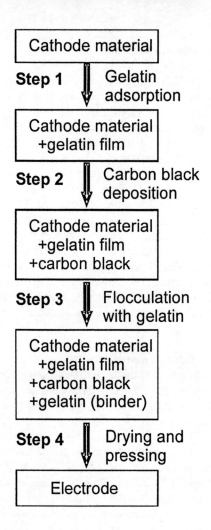

Fig. 1

*Figure 1: Schematic diagram of the composite cathode preparation using novel coating technology (NCT).*

To compare the effects of the NCT on cathode performance, reference cathodes based on the same active material were made using the conventional procedure.[14] The active material was thoroughly mixed with a PTFE slurry (Aldrich 44,509/6) and carbon black (Printex XE2) so that the proportions between active material, PTFE and carbon black in the final composites were the following: (90-x):10:x, where x varied from 0 to 10. Further treatment of the slurry was the same as in the NCT procedure.

For specific conductivity measurements[15] pellets, about 2-4 mm thick, with surface area 0.5 cm$^2$ (diameter 8 mm) were prepared from the same cathode composite materials as described above. On both pellet surfaces, conductive silver paint (Demetron Leitsilber 200, 27/96) was deposited to serve as electrical contact.

*(3) Characterization of composite electrodes*

The electrochemical tests were performed using a laboratory-made three-electrode testing cell as described elsewhere.[16,17] The working electrode was a composite cathode electrode prepared as described above while the counter and the reference electrodes were made of metallic lithium. The electrolyte used was 1 M solution of LiPF$_6$ in EC:DMC (1:1 ratio) as received (Merck KgaA, Darmstadt, Germany). The galvanostatic electrochemical measurements were carried out using a Solartron 1286 Electrochemical Interface (Solartron Mobrey Ltd, Berks, U. K.). The constant current during cell cycling was ±80 μA (corresponding to C/5). Composites were characterized using scanning electron microscopy (JEOL JSM-T220 Scanning Electron Microscope). Specific conductivity was measured by impedance spectroscopy using Helwett Packard 4284A in frequency range from 10$^4$ Hz to 10 Hz.

## III. Results and Discussion

Deposition of carbon black particles onto printed wiring board substrate, as discussed in Introduction, results in a conducting coating of a thickness of several hundreds of nanometers. This provides good surface conductivity at a range of several mm, i.e., one can say that such a laminate is wired on a millimeter scale. By contrast, a similar conducting coating formed on the cathode (positive electrode) particles with micrometer dimensions, obviously, results in wiring at a micrometer scale. Furthermore, the goal of conductive coating on the printed wiring boards is only to provide good conductivity on the surface, while the role of coating on cathode particles is more complex. On one hand, the coating may serve as a simple "provider" of electrons from the current collector to the given cathode particle (this is typical for both conventional and NCT procedure) while on the other hand, the coating, if perfect enough, may also serve as a "creator" of an equipotential surface around each cathode particles. At least in theory, formation of equipotential surfaces should facilitate uniform electrochemical insertion/deinsertion which, in turn, should be reflected in a better electrochemical performance of cathode.

The mutual arrangement of carbon black and active cathode particles has been observed in several ways.[13,18,19] In the present paper, we use scanning electron microscopy (SEM) to directly observe the distribution of carbon black in cathode composites prepared at various conditions. Figures 2a and 2b show carbon black distribution in two composite cathode materials prepared according to the conventional procedure and according to NCT procedure, respectively. In the latter case, the distribution of carbon black is much more uniform than in the former. Obviously, if carbon black is simply mixed with the active particles, there is no agent present in the system to force carbon black particles to distribute uniformly among the active particles.

Ceramic Materials and Multilayer Electronic Devices

Fig. 2a

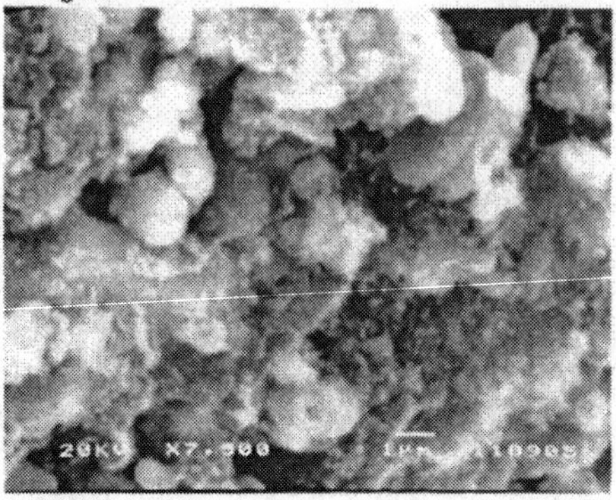

Fig. 2b

*Figure 2: Scanning electron micrographs of LiCoO₂ cathode materials containing 5 wt % of carbon black. Carbon black particles are the sub-micrometer particles. The larger particles are LiCoO₂. a) Composite obtained using conventional procedure, b) composite obtained using NCT procedure.*

The average bulk electronic conductivity of the composite material was obtained by measuring the impedance response of dry pellets prepared from cathode material. From the impedance data, the bulk resistance was determined and, knowing the geometry of pellets, the conductivity was calculated. Fig. 3 shows that the average conductivity of pellets increases significantly in the range from 0 up to 2-3 wt.% of carbon black for both procedures. The differences between the procedures are observable but not very important, if it is taken into account that the conductivity changes by several orders of magnitude. In both cases, above 3 wt.% carbon black pathways are completely formed and the conductivity reaches a plateau value. Hence, in terms of average conductivity it is not very important that, for example, each particle is surrounded by carbon black. It is enough that carbon black pathways extend from one side of the pellet to the other, while the detailed structure of these pathways in obviously not important. However, the local distribution of carbon black becomes important, if the electrochemical performance of cathodes is tested. Figure 4 shows cathode capacity as a function of current density. The capacities obtained by NCT procedure are higher in the whole range bellow 10 wt.% of added carbon black.

This can be explained in terms of the aforementioned equipotential surfaces, which are formed in the case of NCT but not in the case of conventional cathode technology. Namely, the existence of equipotential surface around each cathode particles means that electrochemical insertion of lithium ion/electron couple can take place at the same time at all spots on the surface of given particle. This maximizes the current at given potential or, in other words, minimizes the polarization (i.e. losses). At the end of cathode charging or discharging process, all particles are completely charged with lithium or completely empty, respectively. This is not the case for the conventional procedure. There the charging/discharging cannot proceed at all points on the surface but only in places, which are in contact with carbon black. Being so, the charging/discharging now leads to significant lithium gradients nor only in the radial but also in every other direction in the particle. Because diffusion in solids is a slow process, the charging/discharging process is completed before these gradients are equilibrated, i.e. before the particles are completely filled with lithium or empty, respectively. Hence, the practical capacities at, for example, 2 wt.% of carbon black obtained by the conventional procedure, is only 50% of the value obtained by NCT.

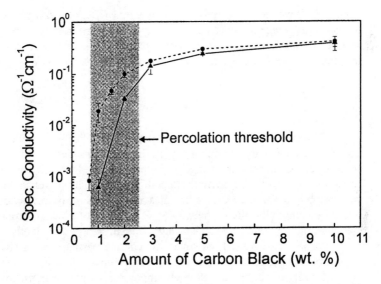

*Figure 3: Dependence of specific conductivity of LiCoO₂ composite cathodes on carbon black content. Solid circles: composites prepared according to the NCT procedure, solid triangles: composites prepared according to the conventional procedure using the same active material and 10 wt % of PTFE.*

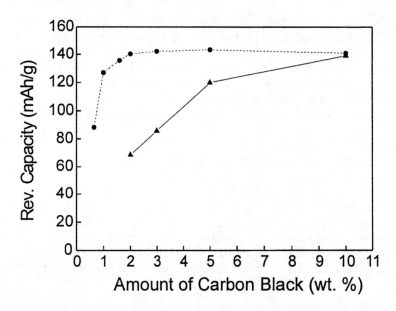

*Figure 4: Dependence of reversible capacity of LiCoO₂ composite cathodes on carbon black content. Solid circles: composites prepared according to the NCT procedure, solid triangles: composites prepared according to the conventional procedure using the same active material and 10 wt % of PTFE.*

## IV.   Summary

The surface of a non-conducting material is easily made conducting if the material is coated by conducting particles, such as carbon black (the coating process can be successfully triggered by pre-adsorbed polymer molecules). These holds equally well for particle-shaped non-conducting substrates as for flat macroscopic non-conducting substrates. If one is only interested in average surface conductivity, the uniformity of coating is not of vital importance. Rather than that, other parameters, such as layer thickness or, equivalently, the content of conductor are decisive. If, however, the coating participates in diffusion-limited kinetic processes, such as insertion of ions/electrons into a solid-state substrate, the uniformity of coating is extremely important. Only a uniform coating provides equipotential conditions all over the surface of substrate and, hence, leads to a uniform solid state diffusion. This was clearly demonstrated on an example of cathodes for lithium batteries. The uniformly coated oxide particles exhibited a much better electrochemical kinetics than the non-uniformly coated substrate.

### Acknowledgements

This research is sponsored by NATO's Scientific Affairs Division in the framework of the Science for Peace Programme. The financial support from the Ministry of Science and Technology of Slovenia is also fully acknowledged.

# References

[1] G.O. Mallory and J.B. Hajdu Editors, *Electroless Plating: Fundamentals and Applications* American Electroplaters and Surface Finishers Society, Orlando, FL, 1990.

[2] P. Pendleton, *IPC-Inst. Interconnecting and Packaging Electron. Circuits*, Lincolnwood, IL, USA, Technical Papers. IPC 32nd Annual Meeting 776/1-20, Lake Buena Vista, FL, USA, p 610 (1989).

[3] J.O. Besenhard, O.Claußen, H.P.Gausmann, H. Meyer, and H. Mahlkov, "Method for Coating Surfaces with Finely Particulate Materials", *United States Patent*, 5,705,219 (1998).

[4] M. Bele, S. Pejovnik, J.O. Besenhard, and V. Ribitsch, "Substrate-induced Coagulation of Carbon Black on Gelatin-modified Printed Wiring Board Surfaces; Part 1. Gelatin Adsorption on to Printed Wiring Board Surfaces", *Colloids Surf A*, 143 [1] 17–26 (1998).

[5] M. Bele, K. Kocevar, I. Musevic, J. O. Besenhard, and S. Pejovnik, "Substrate-Induced Deposition of Carbon Black Particles from Aqueous Dispersion on Gelatin-modified Surface", *Colloids Surf A*, 168 [3] 231–239 (2000).

[6] M. Bele, J.O. Besenhard, S. Pejovnik, and H. Meyer, "Solution for Pretreatment of Electrically Non-conductive Surfaces, and Method of Coating the Surfaces with Solid Material Particles", *United States Patent*, 6,235,182 (2001).

[7] M. Bele, K. Kocevar, S. Pejovnik, J. O. Besenhard, and I. Musevic, "Molecular Bridging Between Water-dispersed Particles and Gelatin-coated Surfaces", *Langmuir*, 16 [22] 8334-8342 (2000).

[8] R.J. Hunter, *Foundations of Colloid Science*, Clarendon Press: Oxford, 1989.

[9] M. Bele, A. Kodre, I. Arcon, J. Grdadolnik, S. Pejovnik, and J.O. Besenhard, "Adsorption of Cetyltrimethylammonium Bromide on Carbon Black from Aqueous Solution", *Carbon*, 36 [7-8] 1207-1212 (1998).

[10] H. Tukamoto, and A.R. West, "Electronic Conductivity of $LiCoO_2$ and its Enhancment by Magnesium Doping", *J. Electrochem. Soc*, 144 [9] 3164-3168 (1997).

[11] Z. Liu, J.Y. Lee, and H.J. Linder, "Effects of Conducting Carbon on the Electrochemical Performance of $LiCoO_2$ and $LiMn_2O_4$ Cathodes", *J. Power Sources*, 97-98, 361-365 (2001).

[12] M. Bele, M. Gaberscek, R. Dominko, J. Drofenik, and S. Pejovnik, "Method for the Preparation of a Cathode for Lithium ionic Batteries", *International patent application no. PCT/SI01/00030, filing date 12 November 2001 : applicant's or agent's file reference 301-P14PC/01*. [S.l.]: Patent Cooperation Treaty (PCT), 2001.

[13] R. R. Dominko, M. Gaberscek, J. Drofenik, M. Bele, and S. Pejovnik, "A Novel Coating Technology for Preparation of Cathodes in Li-ion Batteries", *Electrochem. Solid State Lett.*, 4 [11] A187-A190 (2001).

[14] S.E. Cheon, C.W. Kwon, D.B. Kim, S.J. Hong, H.T. Kim, and S.W. Kim, "Efect of Binary Conductive Agents in $LiCoO_2$ Cathode on Performance of Lithium Ion Polymer Battery", *Electrochim. Acta*, 46 [4] 599-605 (2000).

[15] A.S. Skapin, S. Pejovnik, and J. Jamnik, "Determination of the Local Electrical Properties in Ceramic Materials Gained by Microcontact Impedance Spectroscopy", *J. Eur. Ceram. Soc.*, **21** [10] 1759-1762 (2001).

[16] M. Gaberscek, M. Bele, J. Drofenik, R. Dominko, and S. Pejovnik, "Improved Carbon Anode for Lithium Batteries - Pretreatment of Carbon Particles in a Polyelectrolyte Solution", *Electrochem. Solid State Lett.*, **3** [4] 171-173 (2000).

[17] J. Drofenik, M. Gaberscek, R. Dominko, M. Bele, and S. Pejovnik, "Carbon Anodes Prepared from Graphite Particles Pretreated in a Gelatin Solution", *J. Power Sources*, **94** [1] 97-101 (2001).

[18] Z. Liu, A.Yu, J.Y. Lee, "Cycle Improvement of LiMn$_2$O$_4$ Cathode in Rechargeable Lithium Batteries", *J. Power Sources*, **74** [2] 228-233 (1998).

[19] A. Momchilov, A. Trifonova, B. Banov, B. Purecheva, and A. Kozawa, "Nonaqueous UFC Suspensions, used as Conductive Additive in Cathodes for Lithium Batteries", *J. Power Sources*, **81-82,** 566-570 (1999).

# MULTIMODE UNDERWATER TRANSDUCERS

R. E. Newnham and D.C. Markley
The Materials Research Laboratory
The Pennsylvania State University
University Park, PA 16802

R.J. Meyer Jr. and W.J. Hughes
The Applied Research Laboratory
The Pennsylvania State University
University Park, PA 16802

A.-C. Hladky-Hennion
C.N.R.S., I.S.E.N,
41, Boulevard Vauban
59046 Lille CEDEX, France

J. K. Cochran Jr.
Georgia Institute of Technology
771 Ferst Drive, N.W.
Atlanta, GA 30332-0245

ABSTRACT

A quiet revolution is taking place in ultrasound technology and much of it is centered on multimode transducers. During the past few years, a number of complex nonlinear phenomena are being studied for use in harmonic imaging, parametric arrays, elastography and sonoelasticity, and time-reversed acoustics. In these applications the transducer may be called upon to transmit at one frequency and receive at another, or to simultaneously transmit at two frequencies and receive at a sum or difference frequency, or to interrogate at one frequency and deliver focused high power at another, or to interrogate at high frequency while being continually repositioned at a much lower frequency, or to transmit in narrow beam patterns while receiving in an omnidirectional mode. Robust designs are needed for transducers that carry out two or more disparate functions, often at different frequencies, different amplitudes and different phases.

In our current research program, our goal is to develop a family of small, low-cost, underwater and biomedical transducers based on extrusion technology. Some of these designs resemble traditional Class IV and Class VII flextensional transducers and will expand their useful operating range. Others incorporate features of tonpilz and vector sensor transducers. Miniature versions of these high-power, low frequency transducers are being optimized to produce broadband transmit and receive response, engineered vibration modes, and optimized acoustic beam patterns. Transducer topologies with various shapes, cross-sections, and symmetries can be fabricated through high volume, low-cost ceramic and metal extrusion processes. Dimensions of the pieces can be as small as one millimeter and as large as 10 cm, which provide resonance frequencies from above 1 MHz to below 10 kHz. The acoustic vibration modes, resonance frequencies and radiation patterns of these transducers are controlled through the symmetry of the transducer material and its external shape, poling pattern, the driving and receiving electrode geometries and driving conditions. Finite element analysis methods are used extensively in our research to design these transducers, analyze their response, and refine the geometries based on experimental results.

## INTRODUCTION

Traditional flextensional transducers are widely used for fish-finding, oil exploration, sonar systems, and low-frequency biomedical applications in the 1-100 kHz range. As shown in Figure 1, they generally consist of a piezoelectric transducer (the electromechanical driving element) and a vibrating shell which emits and receives acoustic waves. The shell is not piezoelectric. We are currently making flextensional transducers with active shells. Our approach is to extrude the green ceramic through a die that makes monolithic Class IV or Class VII flextensional transducers. Both the internal driving element and the shell are made from a poled piezoelectric ceramic such as PZT.

Class IV and Class VII flextensionals are illustrated in Figure 1. Previously we have patented designs for small Class V (the "Moonie" and the "Cymbal" and the Class VI (the "Double Dipper") flextensionals. These transducers consist of metal shells bonded to ceramic disks or rings. The "Moonie" patent has been commercially successful in towed arrays for oil prospecting, and the "Cymbal" is be tested in transdermal drug delivery, especially for the diabetes market.

Bandwidth is the name of the game in acoustics, just as in optics. This is especially true in nonlinear acoustic applications such as harmonic imaging, parametric arrays, elastic imaging, and time-reversed acoustics. Many medical and underwater ultrasound transducers utilize small inexpensive broadband transmitters and receivers that function well in the low frequency range for long-range penetration and at higher frequencies for improved resolution at short range [1,2,3]. Transducers with these properties are normally obtained using an array of narrow-band transmitters, each operating at a different frequency, or by mass loading a narrow-band transducer. Combining the functions of two or more narrow-band transducers in one monolithic structure provides the benefits of more imaging information at a lower cost. The basic concept is illustrated schematically in Figure 2.

Long-range underwater profiling of the ocean floor provides an interesting example. A multimode projector emits two acoustic beams of frequency $f_1$, and $f_2$. The waves will combine in a nonlinear medium such as seawater, to produce sum $f_1 + f_2$ and difference $f_1 - f_2$ waves. Seawater preferentially absorbs high frequency acoustic waves. Therefore the difference wave at frequency $f_1 - f_2$ will have the longest range. Low-frequency waves such as this are used to probe geologic strata underneath the ocean in the search for oil and mineral deposits.

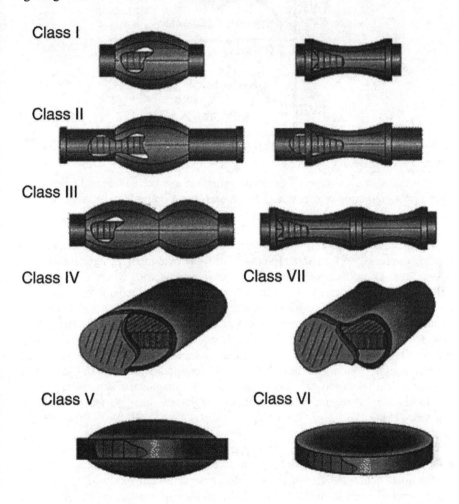

Figure 1. Standard flextensional transducers. Each of the designs consists of a metal shell driven by a stack of poled piezoelectric ceramics. In our method, we replace both the shell and the stack with a monolithic poled ceramic capable of generating multiple vibrations.

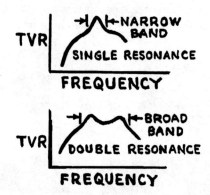

Figure 2. Graphical representation of a single resonance device and a device having two radiating resonances. Multimode operation leads to broader system bandwidth in transmit voltage response (TVR).

Recently, several doubly resonant transducer designs have been put forward to provide improved performance. Examples of these dual mode designs include: (i) A two layer transducer prepared from relaxor ferroelectrics where the operating frequency of the device can be switched from f to 2f by reversing the polarity of the DC bias [4]. (ii) A tonpilz design with three masses and two piezoelectric stacks that has two distinct mechanical resonances [5]. (iii) A standard double mass loaded longitudinal vibrator, for low frequency operation, with a head mass composed of a small array of high frequency transducers [6]. (iv) A laminated tonpilz design, which operates both in the longitudinal and radial modes to provide a dual operation frequency [3]. And (v) a magnetostrictive-piezoelectric hybrid transducer where each section of the hybrid has its own mechanical resonance [1].

In addition to bandwidth, the shape of the acoustic radiation pattern and directional response of transducers are also important parameters in ultrasonic applications. When the size of the transducer is small compared to the acoustical wavelength of interest, the transducer behaves almost as an acoustical monopole with omnidirectional response. However, this omnidirectional characteristic may create significant problems when a transducer is intended to be used as a projector, or used in an array that is to radiate in only one direction. Often, large baffles are used, or rows of transducers are spaced and phased carefully to give the desired beam patterns. This can be an expensive, time consuming and cumbersome solution. A method has been developed for radially poled hollow cylindrical and spherical transducers with segmented electrodes driven together or individually in order to: (i) transmit and receive in certain directions by driving these sections with phase differences, (ii) engineer the shape of the acoustic radiation beam patterns, (iii) identify the direction of incoming acoustic waves [7,8,9]. This idea was most recently applied to miniature cymbal flextensional transducers to obtain unidirectional transducers with cardioid beam patterns [10].

Transducers with broad bandwidth and shaped beam patterns will find applications in conventional ultrasound, but there are also emerging applications that utilize the nonlinear properties of the medium in which the acoustic wave is traveling. These applications also require a broadband, multimode transducer. Four such applications are harmonic imaging, parametric transducer arrays, elastic imaging, and time-reversed acoustics.

TRANSDUCER DESIGNS

Miniaturization is the general trend in biomedical and underwater transducers, but this poses certain performance problems. If the radiating dimensions of a projector are less than a wavelength (ka«1), a large displacement is required to generate sufficient volume velocity to achieve high source levels. Since the typical strain that can be obtained from a bulk piezoelectric ceramic is limited to 0.1 %, amplification mechanisms are required to obtain the necessary large displacements for low frequency projectors. Flextensional transducers with flexing, compliant shells provide such a mechanism with the required volume displacements and 70 to 90 % efficiencies; however, the shells need to accommodate both the hydrostatic stresses and the AC drive stresses [11]. Such mechanical amplification schemes add complexity to the design, cost to the fabrication, and raise reliability issues in the long-term use of the transducers.

The goal of our program is to develop novel monolithic piezoelectric ceramic transducer designs with internal displacement or stress amplification mechanisms that will allow us to engineer resonance frequencies, vibration modes and acoustic beam patterns with broadband transmit and receive response. A few of the monolithic ceramic extrusions with different shapes and symmetries are shown in Figure 3.

In all of these designs, electrodes are painted on the inside and outside surfaces of the thin ceramic shells, and in the case of flat arms, to the parallel surfaces of the arms. Ceramics are poled through the wall thickness. As a result, at lower frequencies, transducers operate using the $d_{31}$ piezoelectric coefficient. Similar to the hollow spheres, shells have a radius to thickness ratio (r/t) as their amplification factor.

In the first design (Figure 3.(a)), the small tube at the center of the transducer is inactive, and intended mainly as a means to carry a stress bolt or a cable for power and driving circuits. The outer shell and the arms can be activated simultaneously, or independently. The outer shells can be poled and driven from inside to outside or vice versa. On the other hand, the arms in the second design

(Figure 3.(b)) are inactive and serve only to connect two cylindrical, active shells and transfer the displacement and the vibration of the inner shell to the outer one. Such a design would provide two separate radial vibration modes. The resonance frequencies of these two modes can then be engineered by changing the radius of the cylinders.

The number of arms can also be increased to give the transducer a more robust design with possibly higher pressure tolerance at the expense of sensitivity, or the number of arms can be decreased to have a more complaint structure. The designs in Figure 3.(c) and 3.(d) show two pipe-shaped handles that can be used to carry the power cables, or keep the transducers oriented parallel to the sea-bottom during operation. Figure 3.(e) is a mixture of class IV and class VII flextensional transducers and can be used in double drive mode to obtain cardioid beam patterns. The principles of double drive operation are explained in next section. Figure 3.(f) is another design to tap into more than one vibration mode (breathing mode of the side pipes, flextensional mode of the connecting arms, etc.). It can also provide directional response in a plane parallel to the axisymmetry axis of both pipes.

In the Figure 3.(g) through Figure 3.(n), the shapes resemble those of the Class IV and Class VII flextensional transducers, respectively, but note that the entire structure (the shell and the arms) is composed of ceramic and the transducer does not contain any metallic shell. By poling and driving different sections of these transducers separately, new vibration modes can be obtained and acoustic radiation beam patterns can be engineered.

## MULTIMODE EXCITATION AND MULTIDRIVE BEAM FORMING

As discussed in the introduction section, most of the ultrasound applications require broad bandwidth, and in some cases dual operating frequencies. In addition, certain applications require highly directional acoustic radiators, or the ability to steer an acoustic radiation beam. The methods that we use to achieve these goals in our transducer designs are presented in this section.

Complementing active arms with active shells provides several vibration modes, such as the radial mode of the shells, transverse mode of the arms, length modes of the entire structure, thickness mode of the walls, and cross-coupled

Ceramic Materials and Multilayer Electronic Devices

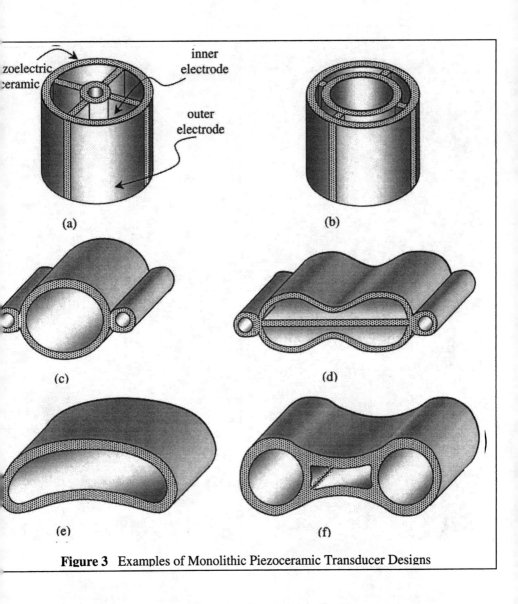

**Figure 3** Examples of Monolithic Piezoceramic Transducer Designs

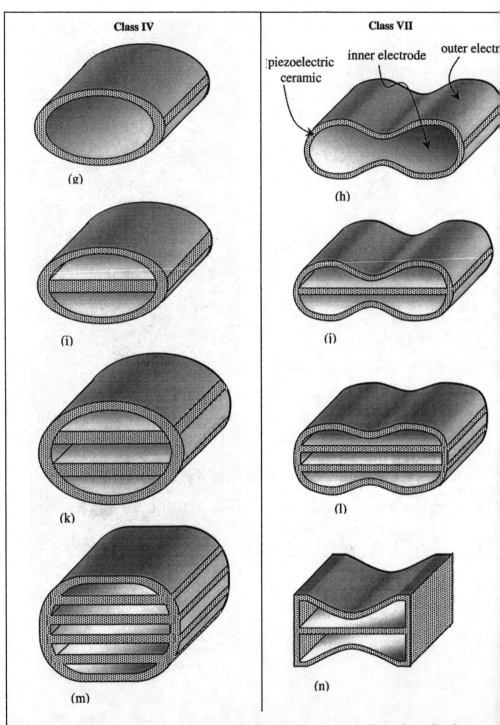

**Figure 3** (cont.) Examples of Monolithic Piezoceramic Transducer Designs

modes. All of these modes can be controlled through the dimensions of the structure and the way they are poled, activated, and driven. The resonance frequencies of these modes can be brought closer together to obtain a multi-frequency broadband transducer, or a transducer with dual operating frequencies, such as f and 2f. For example, possible driving alternatives for the Figure 3.(a) wagon wheel design are shown in Figure 4. The bold arrows indicate the electric field direction. As in this example, all of the other designs can be driven in various ways to tap into new vibration modes.

In addition to the geometrical and dimensional modifications, different sections of the transducer can be driven with a phase difference and with different voltages to provide engineered acoustic radiation beam patterns. A directional beam pattern can be achieved through cancellation of sound pressure in one direction and addition in the opposite direction. One method was initially developed by Erlich [7] for hollow cylindrical transducers with a plurality of electrodes to obtain dipole beam patterns. It was later applied to hollow spheres [8] and most recently to miniature flextensional cymbal transducers by Zhang [10] to obtain cardioid beam patterns.

The principles of the double-drive operation are explained here using the Figure 3.(g) design as an example (Figure 5). The inside electrode is used as the ground electrode. When the back and front outside electrodes are driven in phase with the same electric field ($V_b=V_f$) as shown in Figure 5.1, a pure breathing mode will be excited and an omnidirectional beam pattern (monopole) will be obtained (Figure 5.2). If the two outside electrodes are driven under electric fields with the same amplitude but a phase difference of 180°, then a dipolar beam pattern will be obtained (Figure 5.3). In the dipole mode, the transmit voltage response (TVR) shows two maxima in the front and back of the transducer, but their phase is opposite. If the output from the dipole mode is added to the output of an omnidirectional mode with equal TVR, a cardioid beam pattern with only one maxima can be obtained (Figure 5.4). The formulation for the cancellation procedure can be given as follows [10]:

$V_f$ is the electric field applied to the front side and $V_b$ is the electric field applied to the back side. $V_m$ and $V_d$ are driving fields associated with the monopole and dipole drive conditions.

$$V_f = V_m + V_d \tag{1}$$

$$V_b = V_m - V_d \tag{2}$$

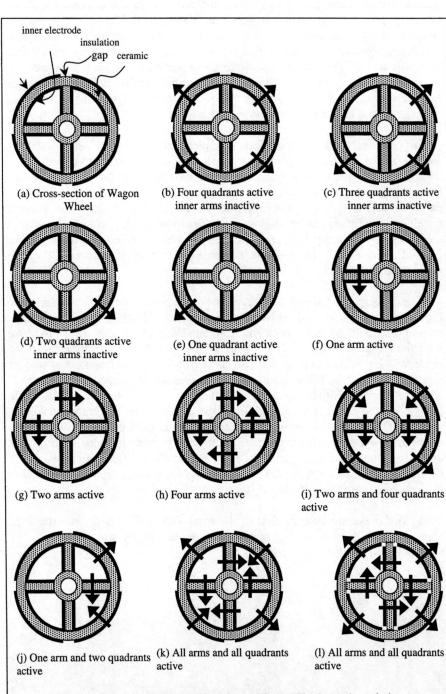

**Figure 4.** Possible driving conditions for the Wagon Wheel transducer design

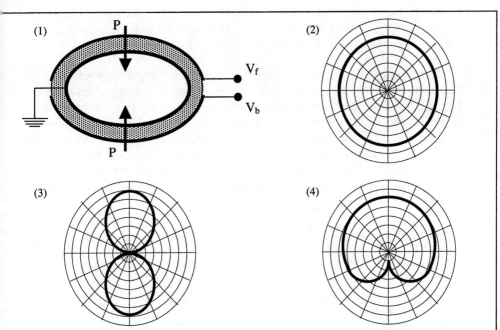

**Figure 5**    The driving scheme of the oval double driver transducer and resultant beam patterns.

(1). Cross-section of the transducer with separated outer electrodes and common ground inside electrode

(2). Monopole – omnidirectional mode ( $V_b = V_f = V_m$ , $\varphi = 0°$ )

(3). Dipole mode ($V_b = -V_d$ , $V_f = V_d$   $\varphi = 180°$  )

(4).    Cardioid mode $\left( \dfrac{V_b}{V_f} = \dfrac{(1-R)}{(1+R)} \right)$ , where $R = \dfrac{TVR_m}{TVR_d}$ and $0° < \varphi < 180°$

$$\frac{V_b}{V_f} = \frac{1-r}{1+r} \qquad \text{where } r = \frac{V_d}{V_m} \qquad (3)$$

TVR (transmit voltage response) is related to the voltage by

$$TVR_b = \frac{p_b}{V_b} \quad \text{and} \quad TVR_f = \frac{p_f}{V_f} \qquad (4,5)$$

where p is the measured sound pressure. To cancel the sound pressure completely in the back side, the pressure amplitudes should be equal, leading to :

$$\frac{V_b}{V_f} = \frac{1-R}{1+R} \qquad \text{where } R = \frac{TVR_m}{TVR_d} \qquad (6)$$

Ceramic Materials and Multilayer Electronic Devices

The complex ratio R is determined from the measured monopole and dipole constant voltage transmitting responses. The equation gives the ratio of the voltages and the phase lag $\varphi$ on each side of the transducer.

The procedure defined above is for the simplest case where there are only two electrodes involved in a simple structure. These same ideas can be applied to the Figure 1.(a) design, driving two of the quadrants (1 & 2) together as front electrodes and the other two (3 & 4) as back. By switching the coupled electrodes (i.e. 2 & 3 as front and 1 & 4 as the back electrodes and so on) we can steer the cardioid beam pattern around the circumference of the cylinder. Incorporating the double drive idea into the more complex designs while driving their arms will give us even more leverage to engineer the shape of the acoustic radiation beam patterns.

TRANSDUCER FABRICATION AND TESTING

The monolithic ceramic transducer designs presented in the previous section can be prepared from lead titanate zirconate (PZT - $Pb(Zr,Ti)O_3$) based piezoelectric ceramic compositions by extrusion. The feed material is prepared by mixing ceramic powders with organic binders in a high-shear mixer, or for a more homogeneous material, by mixing as a slurry and filter-pressing to form a plastic filter cake. Extrusion stages are (i) material feeding, (ii) consolidation and flow of the feed material in the barrel, (iii) flow through a tapered die or orifice, (iv) flow through a finishing tube of constant or nearly constant cross-section and (v) ejection. After forming the green ceramic bodies are taken through a polymer burnout process in the temperature range between 300°C and 700°C, followed by a sintering step at higher temperatures ranging between 1200°C and 1400°C. For lead containing compositions, the ceramic must be fired in a closed container in a lead-rich atmosphere to reduce lead loss from the ceramic body. After firing, the appropriate surfaces are coated with electrode metal through sputtering, painting or dipping. Lead wires are then attached to the electrodes. The ceramic is poled by subjecting it to high electric field at elevated temperatures in the range between 100 and 200°C.

A schematic for the extrusion die used to make the PZT wagon-wheel design discussed, is illustrated in Figure 6. Feed holes 2.5 mm in diameter conduct the fine-grained PZT paste to the die where the final shaping is carried out. Shape forming uses a paste containing the calcined powder in an organic-water system to impart the plasticity required for extrusion. Extrudability of the paste is primarily controlled by the water/binder content, solids loading, and particle size distribution.

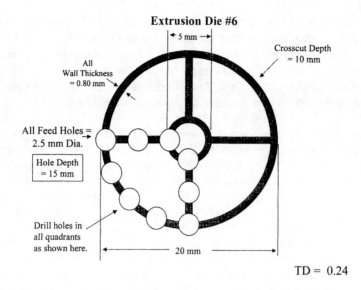

Figure 6. Extrusion Die Design for Wagon Wheel Shape

To produce fine geometry with good precision, fine-grained powder with sizes about 1-2% of the feature dimensions are necessary. By using fine powders in the micron and submicron range, extruded articles with 100 μm features are feasible.

Following the processing and fabrication procedure laid out in the previous sections, the next step is to determine the resonant vibration modes experimentally using impedance spectroscopy. The impedance spectrum of a transducer provides information on the resonance and antiresonance frequencies, their associated coupling coefficients and quality factors. The displacement shapes and symmetry of the vibration modes will be identified analytically using the ATILA® finite element analysis (FEA) code. ATILA is an FEA code developed for the modeling of sonar transducers. It can provide information concerning prestresses, and the behavior under hydrostatic pressure (static analysis), together with the resonant frequencies of various modes and their associated coupling factors (modal analysis), the in-air or in-water impedance and displacement field, the transmitting voltage response, free field voltage sensitivity and the directivity beam patterns (harmonic analysis) [12].

In an initial experiment, a wagon wheel design (Fig 1a) with an average outer tube diameter ($\phi_o$) of 17.5 mm, inner tube diameter ($\phi_i$) of 5.0 mm and wall thickness (t) of 1.0 mm was fabricated from soft PZT-5A material by extrusion. Ceramic pieces with various lengths were cut from the green piece and fired at regular binder burnout and sintering conditions (550°C for 60 minutes and

1285°C for 90 minutes) under PbO rich atmosphere in a closed crucible. The dimensions after the sintering shrinkage are as follows: $\phi_o \approx 14.8$ mm, $\phi_I \approx 4.0$ mm, $t \approx 0.65$ mm, length (l) $\approx 12.5$ mm. The fired pieces were dip coated with air-dry silver electrode and poled through the wall thickness at 120°C for 20 minutes under an electric field of 20 kV/cm. In this initial test, only the outer shell was driven and the arms were inactive, as depicted in Figure 4 (b).

In our development work on various unique transducer designs we use the ATILA® finite-element program. ATILA was created by the Institute Supérieur d'Électronique du Nord, (ISEN) France and is specifically designed to solve problems of elastic, piezoelectric, magnetostrictive, and electrostrictive materials radiating in a fluid. A finite element analysis of the extruded structure was undertaken in order to identify its associated vibration modes. A three dimensional model of the wagon-wheel structure was created using the dimensions obtained from the sintered piece. Taking advantage of the symmetry of the structure, only $1/8^{th}$ of the transducer was meshed. ATILA mathematical solutions show excellent correlation to measured results for the transducer in-air (Figure 7). Because ATILA also allows for modeling in water performance, outputs can include impedance and admittance spectra in air or water, transmit and receive sensitivities, beam patterns, stresses, and displacements. Displacements can be animated with the program to characterize resonance modes.

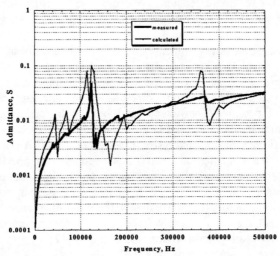

Figure 7. Measured vs. calculated admittance spectra of the wagon-wheel extrusion in air.

## VECTOR SENSORS AND PROJECTORS

In a number of underseas applications, it is desirable that a hydrophone possesses directivity characteristics so that the direction of the source of acoustic energy can be determined. Directional acoustic sensors have been in operation since 1969 as antisubmarine warfare platforms. Airborne (DIFAR) and activated sonobuoy (DICASS) systems both make use of pressure gradient sensors.

The wagon wheel monolith in Figure 8 is similar to the cylindrical designs used in activated sonobuoys. As explained earlier, it is made by extruding a slurry of PZT (lead zirconate titanate) through a patterned die. After firing, both the inner and outer surfaces are electroded with silver. The outer shell and four spokes are all piezoelectric after poling. This design can be used both as a projector and a receiver.

Figure 8. The extruded "Wagon Wheel" transducer made from piezoelectric PZT with silver electrodes. It is intended for use as a directional receiver or transmitter

With four leads attached to the inner surfaces (Figure 5), each quadrant can be driven independently by adjusting the phase, frequency, and amplitude of the applied voltage. For each quadrant, two resonant modes occur in the 40-50 kHz ranges. Combining these modes in the optimum manner provides a useful method of controlling the acoustic beam pattern. The procedure is similar to that carried out earlier with the Double-Driver oval design. An advantage of the wagon-wheel and other multimode monolithics is that beam patterns can be controlled in two-dimensions. The earlier work is mainly one-dimensional. One application envisaged for the multimode monolithic transducer is in the unmanned underwater vehicles and automated sonobuoys needed for harbor and fleet security.

Directionality is important in reception as well as transmission. Acoustic pressure gradient sensors are under development in several laboratories. The wagon wheel is one of the multimode monolithics that appears to be useful in measuring pressure gradients. By monitoring the pressure-wave signals received on all four quadrants, both the direction and the gradient can be determined. Summing the four measurements gives the average pressure. Directional sensors and projectors are but two of the many interesting applications for monolithic multimode transducers.

Compared to the standard flextensional (Figure 1), the multimode monolithics are much less expensive because no assembly is required and there are no glue bonds. They can be extruded to any length, giving a wide range of resonant frequencies. But most important of all, carefully designed dies make multimode operation possible for wider bandwidth, beam shaping, and many interesting applications in nonlinear acoustics.

ACKNOWLEDGEMENTS
The authors would like to acknowledge the support of Jan Lindberg (Code 321) at the Office of Naval Research (N00014-01-1-0872).

REFERENCES
1. S.C. Butler, and F.A. Tito, "A Broadband Hybrid Magnetostrictive/Piezoelectric Transducer Array," *Proceedings of the MTS/IEEE Oceans 2000 Conference and Exhibition*, 3 1469 –1475 (2000).

2. T.R. Howarth, and R.Y. Ting, "Development Of A Broadband Underwater Sound Projector," *Proceedings of the MTS/IEEE Oceans 1997 Conference and Exhibition*, 2 1195-1201 (1997).

3. J. Lan, and S.G. Boucher, "Dual Frequency Mode Transducer" *Proceedings of the MTS/IEEE Oceans 1996 Conference and Exhibition*, 2 763-766 (1996).

4. T.R. Gururaja, A. Shurland and J. Chen, "Medical Ultrasonic Transducers With Switchable Frequency Bands Centered About $f_0$ And $2f_0$," *Proceedings of the 1997 IEEE Ultrasonics Symposium*, **2** 1659–1662 (1997).

5. S.C. Thompson, M.P. Johnson, E.A. McLaughlin and J.F. Lindberg, "Performance And Recent Developments With Doubly Resonant Wideband Transducers; pp. 239-249 in *Transducers for Sonics and Ultrasonics*, Technomic Publishing Co., Inc., Lancaster, PA, 1993.

6. J.F. Lindberg, "Parametric Dual Mode Transducer," U.S. Pat. No. 4,373,143, Feb. 8, 1983.

7. S.L. Erlich, "Sonar Transducer," U.S. Pat. No. 3,290,646, 1966

8. S.L. Erlich, "Spherical Acoustic Transducers," U.S. Pat. No. 3,732,535 1973.

9. S.H. Ko, G.A. Brigham and J.L. Butler, "Multimode Spherical Hydrophone," *Journal of the Acoustical Society of America*, **56**, [6] 1890-1898 (1974).

10. J. Zhang, A.-C. Hladky-Hennion, W.J. Hughes and R.E. Newnham, "A Miniature Class V Flextensional Cymbal Transducer With Directional Beam Patterns: The Double Driver," *Ultrasonics*, **39** 91-95 (2001).

11. E.F. Rynne, *Innovative Approaches For Generating High Power, Low Frequency Sound in Transducers for Sonics and Ultrasonics*; pp. 38-49 Technomic Publishing Co., Inc., Lancaster, PA, 1993.

12. A.-C. Hladky-Hennion, and J.N. Decarpigny, "Finite Element Modeling Of Active Periodic Structures: Application To 1-3 Piezocomposites," *Journal of the Acoustical Society of America*, **94** 621-635 (1993).

# PRE-STRESSED CIRCULAR ACTUATORS

Karla Mossi
Virginia Commonwealth University
School of Engineering, Rm. 314
601 West Main Street P.O. Box 843015
Richmond, VA 23284-3015

Robert G. Bryant
NASA LaRC, MS 226
Hampton, VA 23681

## ABSTRACT

Circular pre-stressed Unimorph-type actuators are used in a variety of transducer applications. However, a main disadvantage of using these actuators, for applications other than resonators, is limited because of durability, power consumption, resistance to harsh environments, and relatively low displacements when clamp-mounted as required for a particular application. This paper presents a comparative study between three types of actuators; thin Unimorph pre-stressed actuators, Bimorphs, and radial field diaphragms. The performance parameters of these actuators were conducted under the same boundary conditions (clamped about the perimeter), at low frequencies, using no-load conditions. The end objective of this study is to provide the tools to design an air pump that satisfies three conditions, low capacitance, hence lower power consumption and smaller drive electronics, displaces the most air volume, hence producing a high mass flow rate, at a wide range of frequencies.

## INTRODUCTION

Piezoelectric actuators have been in existence for several years, however, their application as part of complete mechanisms, machines, or devices are rare. One of the main reasons for failure to find a suitable application for these devices are the boundary conditions dictated by the environment that the device would be used[1,2]. Piezoelectric actuators such as moonies[3], rainbows[4,5], unimorphs[6], thunders[7,8,9], and bimorphs[10,11] have been investigated and their properties and behavior are well documented. Predicting their performance in an application however, is still not available, especially when working with circular actuators. A new type of circular actuator that utilizing inter-digitized electrodes, radial field diaphragms, RFD, has been designed[12,13]. Preliminary work shows that RFDs have properties that may be key in an application design.

The overall objective of the project is to use these active diaphragm in a synthetic jet cavity no larger than 7.62 cm x 7.62 cm x 2.54 cm (3 inx3 inx1 in). However, relevant parameters need to be measured before the design of the final pump is started. In order to accomplish this objective, three types of actuators were selected to measure maximum displacement, and other properties at different operating frequencies and voltages: a Bimorph, a Thunder, and a Radial Field Diaphragm. These three types of actuators were chosen for this study because of their particular shape, circular. Even thought the three devices are very different in nature, the objective here is to compare their performance when utilized in a specific application, an air pump.

## EXPERIMENTAL SETUP

The elements used for testing consisted on three different groups, bimorphs, pre-stressed curved Unimorphs, Thunder, and Radial Field Diaphragms, RFD. All of the devices had a diameter of 63.5 mm (2.5 inches). The bimorph utilized consisted of two bonded piezoelectric layers manufactured by Piezo Systems, Inc. model number T216-A4NO-573X. The device is manufactured with Type 5A material with nickel electrodes and a total thickness of 4.1 mm (16 mil) and each PZT layer 1.9 mm thick. The Thunder® devices manufactured by Face International Corporation consisted of layers of stainless steel type 304, 0.254 mm thick, PZT type 5A, 0.254 mm thick, and copper, 0.0254 mm thick, laminated using SI adhesive in between each layer. The last group was the radial field diaphragms, RFD, manufactured by NASA Langley Research center. These devices consist of one PZT layer laminated in between Kapton film with an inter-digitized electrode patterned printed on it. Distance between electrodes for this set has been optimized from previous results[2]. A schematic of the layout of these three types of devices is shown in Figure 1a, 1b, and 1c.

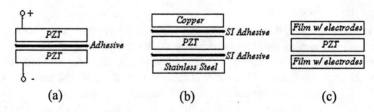

(a)  (b)  (c)

**Fig. 1**. Schematic of (a) Bimorph, (b) Thunder, and (c) RFD

*Clamping Mechanisms:* It has been proven that the boundary conditions that a piezoelectric actuator is going to be subjected to in an application have a significant impact on the final performance of the device. For instance, Liew states that different boundary conditions and applied voltages affect the shape control of piezo-laminated composite beams[2]. For this reason the characterization of circular devices becomes crucial for the design of an application. The basic layout for the three types of devices consists of a circular cavity on a rectangular plate, where the top and bottom layer are held together with screws Figure 2a. A specifically designed clamping mechanism for each device type was utilized within the structure shown in Figure 2a for each device. For the bimorph device, because of the fragility of the device and the absence of a layer of extension that can be clamped freely, a groove was machined on the cavity, which was reinforced with neoprene rubber to provide a cushion and a seal at the same time, see a schematic in Figure 2b. The thunder device has a small tab made of stainless steel (the bottom layer of the device is larger than the rest of the layers), 1.27 mm around the perimeter of the device. These devices can be clamped easily between the top and bottom layers of the holder. Approximately 3 mm thick silicon rubber was used to provide a seal between the top and bottom clamping layers. The RFD provided the easier clamping method of all the pieces, since the film can be clamped easily without the need to utilize any sealing material or specially made cavities. These devices were simply fastened between the top and bottom layer of the cavity.

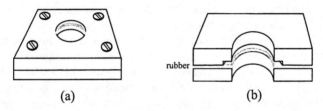

(a)                                (b)

**Fig. 2** Clamping Devices, (a) RFD and Thunder, (b) Bimorph

*Dielectric Properties:* The reactance and capacitance variations with frequency of these three types of devices were measured using an impedance analyzer, HP 4194A and a data acquisition system. From these measurements, resonant frequency can be measured as well as to provide a tool for the quality of the pieces within each group[14]. Capacitance measurements can be used for the design of the power supply.

*Surface Mapping:* In order to better identify the shapes of the diaphragms at rest and when activated, measurements mapping the displacement direction of the devices while clamped were performed. This was accomplished by using a non-contact laser, Nais LM10 for measuring the surface at different angles along the radius of each device, and a Trek PZD700 voltage amplifier. These measurements were performed at intervals of 0, 22.5, 45, 67.5, and 90 degrees segments at intervals of 3.175 mm (0.125") along the radius of each device. The results were then processed to create a surface map of the devices at rest and with applied DC voltages.

*Displacement Measurements:* Displacement performance for each device was measured using two types of devices, a fiber optic for the higher frequencies, and a LVDT for frequencies below 10 Hz. The higher frequency measurements were performed using a non-contacting fiber optic sensor manufactured by Opto-Acoustic Sensors. An extended working range adapter was added to the tip of the fiber optic cable increasing the maximum measurable displacement to 3.048 mm. The lower frequencies were measured using a Newport 850F LVDT and the devices were powered using a Trek Model 1010B.

## RESULTS AND DISCUSSION

All the measurements were performed with the devices clamped to ensure the results provide accurate data for the final pump design. The first set of measurements consisted of the dielectric properties of the materials. All of the devices are built using the same type of piezoelectric material, a PZT 5A type material, however electrode patterns are different as well as poling fields and total material thickness, hence the stress levels on each device type differ and needs to be measured and documented for the proper design of drive electronics. Because the capacitance of the elements seems to highlight the differences more than impedance or reactance alone, capacitance results only are shown and only for one sample of each group to ensure clarity. These results shown in Figure 3 below showed that the capacitance of the RFD devices is constant across the measured frequency range, and its values are approximately 5 times lower than a Thunder device and .a Bimorph. This property provides RFD with a significant advantage over Bimorphs and Thunder devices since providing power to a highly capacitive load requires more complex drive electronics. Also note that the bimorph produces a resonant frequency peak, 400 Hz, lower than the other two devices in addition to the continuous peaks observed at higher frequencies.

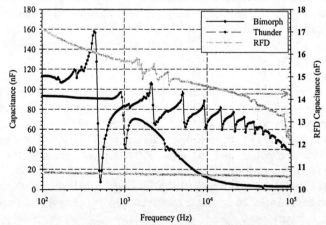

**Fig. 3** Capacitance variations with Frequency

*Surface Mapping*: These measurements were performed using the non-contact laser with the devices at zero VDC, and applying a DC voltage with varying magnitudes depending on the device. The results then were fitted using an appropriate function. The results showed that a bimorph and the RFD seem to have a Gaussian distribution curve shape at rest as well as when activated. The thunder devices however, have a parabolic shape. For the bimorphs and for the radial field diaphragms, a function of the form shown in equation (1) was used. This equation was used as a tool to visualize the movement of the devices under applied voltage, since the shape of the device is one important factor to be considered when designing the pump for optimal conditions.

$$f(x,y) = a \cdot e^{-\frac{1}{2}\left[\left(\frac{x-x_o}{b}\right)^2 + \left(\frac{y-y_o}{c}\right)^2\right]} \tag{1}$$

where a, b, c, $x_o$, and $y_o$ are constants and f (x, y) represents the displacement at points x and y. The results are shown in a mesh plot in figure 4a and in a contour plot in figure 4b for zero VDC, and +180VDC. Note that the displacement performance here is very circular and uniform across the radius of the device. The maximum positive voltage recommended by the manufacturer was used to drive the device, for purposes of clarity, results for the –180 VDC are not shown.

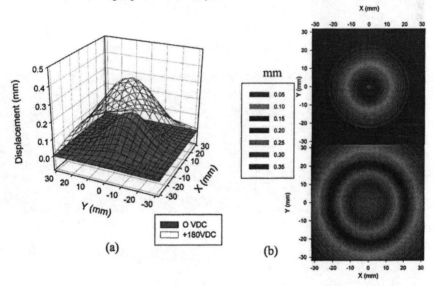

**Fig. 4** Bimorph Displacement Results (a) Surface Mapping (b) Contour Plots

Applying equation 1 for the radial field diaphragms a mesh plot can be constructed, shown in Figure 5. This plot clearly demonstrates the changes on shape of the RFD under 0 VDC and the maximum voltage applied, +1000 VDC.

Since visualization becomes a problem on a 3D map, contour plots at voltages varying from 0 VDC to +1000 VDC are shown in Figure 6. Note that the highest displacement is concentrated into a small area of the device's surface. Negative voltage is not shown for purposes of visualization.

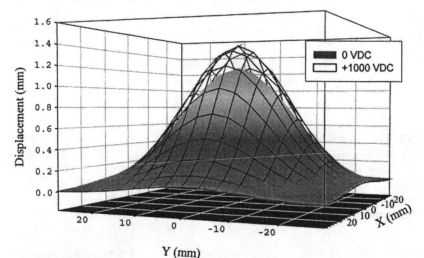

**Fig. 5** Surface Mapping of an RFD Device

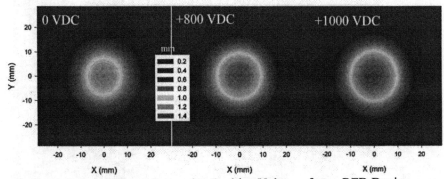

**Fig. 6** Contour Plots at Increasing Positive Voltages for an RFD Device

This fact is emphasized since the next 3D surface map curve fitting, did not fit the shape of the thunder devices. Instead a parabolic shape was used. See equation 2 below.

$$f(x, y) = y_o + a \cdot x + b \cdot y + c \cdot x^2 + d \cdot y^2 \qquad (2)$$

where $y_0$, a, b, c, d are constants, x, and y are the coordinates of the device's surface, and f (x, y) is the displacement obtained. Because of the characteristics of this equation, the mesh plot has to be limited to the dimensions of the device, and the data does not extend to the complete device's surface. A better view is obtained with the contour plots, shown in Figure 7 a thru c. Note that in this case the displacement is not circular such as the one displayed by the bimorph and the RFD. This effect may be due to the initial shape of the devices and the pre-stressed nature of the element. Performing some simple mathematical approximations, the volume displaced by each device can be calculated and it shows that the bimorph device displaces the most volume followed closely by the thunder device, and finally the radial field diaphragm. This shape needs to be taken into account when designing any type of application.

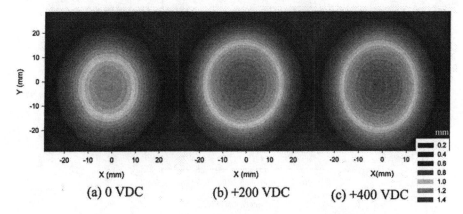

(a) 0 VDC    (b) +200 VDC    (c) +400 VDC

**Fig. 7** Contour Plots of the Displacement of a Thunder Device

*Displacement Loops:* Displacement was measured at different frequencies and voltages for all of the devices. A typical voltage displacement loop at 1 Hz and different voltages for each device type is shown in Figures 8.

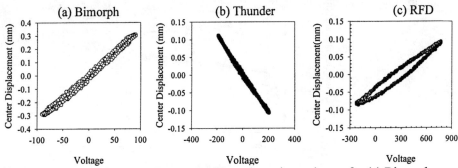

**Fig. 8** Voltage Displacement Loops at 1 Hz and varying voltages for (a) Bimorph, (b) Thunder, and (c) RFD

Since this data is difficult to compare because of the different applied fields, different capacitance values, and different thickness, the loops shown above are used just to provide peak displacement data. A better illustration of the variations of displacement with frequency at particular voltages is shown in Fig 9 for the Bimorph, figure 10 for the Thunder device, and figure 11 for the RFD device. Note that for the bimorph device the maximum frequency that could be measured was 140 Hz, since deformed voltage displacement loops indicated depoling of the device. The same phenomenon was observed on the RFD devices in addition to excessive heating observed but not measured in this study. The only devices that continue to work toward resonant frequency, almost 350 Hz were the Thunder devices, however, heat produced was not measured.

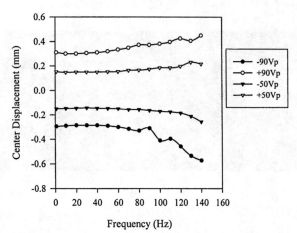

**Fig. 9** Displacement Variations with Frequency for a Bimorph Device

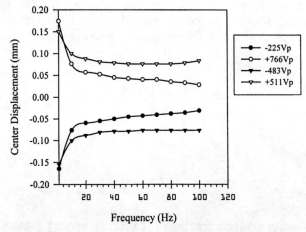

**Fig. 10** Displacement Variations with Frequency for a RFD Device

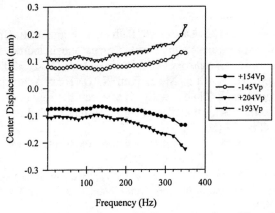

**Fig. 11** Displacement Variations with Frequency for a Thunder Device

It is evident from the results that the parameters to be considered in the final pump design cannot be fulfilled by one of the above actuators as an stand alone diaphragm. Each one of the actuators has advantages and disadvantages for this application and a combination may be needed to achieve the final goal.

## CONCLUSIONS

A comparative study of different type of circular piezoelectric actuators, Bimorphs, Thunders, and RFDs, was performed under specific boundary conditions, clamped around their perimeters.

Capacitance measurements with frequency showed that the RFD overall capacitance is significantly lower than any other actuator making the RFD a very suitable candidate for applications were supplying power is a concern.

Surface mapping of the three types of devices showed that the air volume displaced by the elements varies significantly. The bimorphs, even though have the overall smallest displacement, displaces the most volume. The Thunder devices closely followed the Bimorphs on volume displaced, 18% less than the Bimorphs. The volume displaced by the RFD is much smaller compared to the other two, though the overall displacement, center point movement, is higher.

Finally, frequency performance at different voltages of the three actuators showed that the Thunder devices can easily reach 300 Hz without causing permanent defects on the element. This was not the case with Bimorphs and Radial Field Diaphragms since the elements heat up easily. All of the above conditions need to be taken into account for the design of the final air pump, and none of the devices fulfills all of the requirements for the ideal piezoelectric actuator. A combination of their properties is still needed to obtain the desired final application.

# REFERENCES

[1] J. Mulling, T. Usher, B. Dessent, J. Palmer, P. Franzon, E. Grant, A. Kingon, "Load Characterization of High Displacement Piezoelectric Actuators with Various End Conditions," *Sensors and Actuators A*, **94**, 19-24 (2001).

[2] K. M. Liew, H. K. Lim, M. J. Tan, X. Q. He, "Analysis of Laminated Composite Beams and Plates with Piezoelectric Beams and Plates with Piezoelectric Patches using the Element Free Galerkin Method," *Computational Mechanics*, **29**, 486-497 (2002).

[3] G. Haertling, "Ferroelectric Ceramics: History and Technology," *J. of the Amer. Ceramic Soc.*, Vol. **82**, 4, 797-1615, (1999).

[4] W. Y. Shih, W. H. Shih, I. A. Aksay, "Scaling Analysis for the Axial Dispalcement and Pressure of Flextensional Transducers," *J. Am. Ceram. Soc.*, **80** [5] 1073-78 (1997).

[5] G. H. Haertling, "RAINBOW ceramics—A New Type of Ultra-High Displacement Actuator," *Am. Ceram. Soc. Bull.*, **73**, 93-96 (1994).

[6] T. Idogaki, T. Tominaga, K. Senda, N. Ohya, T. Hattori, "bending and Expanding Motion Actuators," *Sensors and Actuators A*, **54**, 760-764 (1996).

[7] R. W. Schwartz, M. Narayanan, "Development of High Performance Stress-Biased Actuators though the Incorporation of Mechanical Pre-Loads," *Sensors and Actuators A*, **101**, 322-331 (2002).

[8] Z. Ounaies, K. Mossi, R. Smith, J. Bernd, "Low-Field and High-Field Characterization of Thunder Actuators," *Proc. SPIE Smart Struct. Mater.*, **4333**, 399-407 (2001).

[9] K. Mossi, R. Bishop, "Characterization of Different Types of High Performance Thunder Actuators," *Proc. SPIE Smart Struct. Mater.*, **3675**, 738-743 (1999)

[10] D. J. Cappelleri, M. I. Frecker, T. W. Simpson, A. Snyder, "Design of a PZT Bimorph Actuator Using a Metamodel-Based Approach," *Transactions of the ASME*, Vol 124, 354-357, (2002).

[11] Q. Wang, Q. Zhang, B. Xu, R. Liu, E. Cross, "Nonlinear Piezoelectric behavior of Ceramic Bending Mode Actuators Under Strong Electric Fields," *Journal of Applied Physics*, **86** [6], 3352-3360, (1999).

[12] R. Bryant, R. Effinger IV, B. Copeland Jr, "Radial Field Piezoelectric Disphragms," *Proceedings of Actuator 2002*, A1.3, June 10-12 (2002).

[13] R. Bryant, R. R. Effinger IV, I. Aranda Jr., B. Copeland, E. Covington III, "Active Piezoelectric Disphragms," Proc. of SPIE Active Materials, **4699**-40, (2002).

[14] K. Mossi, Z. Ounaies, R. Smith, B. Ball, "Pre-Stressed Curved Actuators Characterization and modeling of Their Piezoelectric Behavior," *Center for Res. Scientific Computation*, SRC-TR00-17, (2003).

# RADIAL FIELD DIAPHRAGM PIEZOELECTRIC PUMPS

Robert G. Bryant
NASA Langley Research Center
MS 226, Hampton, VA 23681

Richard A. Thomas, Jr
Raytheon Technical Services
Hampton, VA 23666

Daniel L. Chattin
NASA Co-Op Student
Christopher Newport University
Newport News, VA 23606

Lisa M. Pietruszka
NASA USRP Student
Rochester Institute of Technology
Rochester, NY 14623

ABSTRACT
   Recently, a new piezoelectric actuator was developed at NASA's Langley Research Center. This actuator, the Radial Field Diaphragm "RFD", has several novel attributes not seen in other high strain piezoelectric actuators including, true conical deformation, actuation profile that is geometrically independent and self-minimized radial and tangential boundary strains. It is the last property that vastly simplifies the design of pumps made using the RFD. Since the RFD's mechanical strains are diminished at the perimeter, non-compliant mounting may be used without affecting the actuator displacement. Thus, passive valve single and double-sided diaphragm pumps (SSDP and DSDP) have been developed with a minimal amount of unique parts. The initial parameters for the 2.2 cm diameter SSDP were between 2-3 mL per minute at 3 Hz with a force of 0.2 N. The overall mechanical efficiency was between 81 – 85% using plastic flapper valves; the power consumption was 50 – 150 milliwatts.

INTRODUCTION
   Over the past decade, research and development of non-resonant piezoelectric micropumps has been sporadic as indicated by the frequency of publications [1-5]. Although there are certain advantages to using non-resonance piezoelectric micropumps such as simplistic design with low power consumption and minimal heat generation using nearly planar architectures and the active element serves as both piston and motor. The disadvantages are the exposure of the electrified

active element, low displacements, low power density and overall efficiency. Recently, a new piezoelectric actuator has been developed by NASA Langley called the Radial Field Diaphragm or RFD (Figure 1). This actuator has several advantages over the conventional unimorph-type element [1-6]. These benefits include; increased displacement - several times that of a geometrically equivalent unimorph and bimorph-type actuators, the RFD is hermetically sealed allowing access to both sides of the element, the electrode patterns minimize the capacitive load, and the RFD is self constraining about its perimeter so that the circumferential mounting of the diaphragm does not limit its performance [7-9]. This paper discusses the initial research, design and characterization of these RFD pumps.

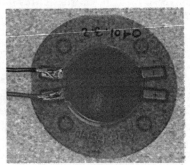

Figure 1. A Radial Field Diaphragm, RFD

EXPERIMENTAL
Parts and Materials
    The unelectroded PZT ceramics were obtained from CTS Wireless Inc. The epoxy adhesive used was E-120HP from Loctite Corp. The polyimide/copper clad used was Pyralux LF 8510 from Dupont Inc. and the release film and press pads were obtained from Pacothane Technologies Inc. The plastic hose fittings were obtained from Small Parts Inc., the Acrylic rod stock was from Norva Plastics Inc., and the burets were obtained from Fisher Scientific Inc.

RFD Fabrication Procedure
    *Assembly of Components*: All materials were cleaned by wiping with ethanol using a lint-free cloth and handled with latex gloves to prevent contamination. Adhesive was applied across both top and bottom copper side of the electrode patterned Pyralux sheets. The wafers were centered on the bottom electrode patterns and the top and bottom electrode patterns were then centered against the wafers. Trapped air pockets were removed by carefully applying pressure to the resulting laminate.

*Curing Process*: A metal plate was placed on a level surface. One press pad was stacked on top of the plate followed by one sheet of release film and the assembled laminate. On this lay-up is placed another layer of release film and one more press pad and a metal plate. The assembly was placed in a vacuum press for 10 minutes with the platens open and the vacuum on. The press was heated to 120°C and ~700 MPa pressure was applied for 1 hour. The press was cooled with the pressure and vacuum released prior to removal of the actuator.

*Pump Housing*: The pump housing was made from machined acrylic rod stock using standard carbide tooling and the valves were made by machining 125 μm thick Mylar sheet (transparency slide).

Characterization

The displacement data was acquired with the use of a Newport 850F LVDT, a Trek Model 609E-6 high voltage amplifier, and a Lab-View data acquisition software program. All RFD's were measured while constrained 2-3 mm from the ceramic perimeter using PMMA circular window clamps constrained about their perimeter at 0.1 Hz sine. The SSDPs were powered with a Trek Model 609E-6 high voltage amplifier controlled from an Agilent 33210A waveform generator. Electrical Power was determined with a Tekronix TDS 210 O-Scope for voltage and current measurements. The SSDP flow rates, head pressure and power output were determined using water filled burets connected to the pump input and output manifold terminals.

RESULTS AND DISCUSSION

There are several factors that determine the RFD's performance, which directly relate to the operation of the Single and Double Sided Diaphragm Pumps, SSDPs and DSDPs, based on the following parameters. These include: the line spacing/pattern that determines the electric field density and vectors; the applied voltage, frequency and resulting strain, which affords displacement; the ceramic composition and geometry, which imparts the base electrical and mechanical behavior; and the adhesive and dielectric package that bestows operational temperature range, processing conditions, environmental resistance and ultimate durability. Of these factors, it is the adhesive and dielectric cover layer that have the greatest influence on the RFD's operational parameters.

Prior to assembly of the SSDP, the displacement of the 2.2 cm dia x 125 μm thick CTS 3195 based RFDs were tested for displacement under quasi-isostatic conditions, and their basic electrical properties evaluated. The line architecture was the intercirculating electrode pattern "ICE" (Figure 2) at a 4/12 line definition, all in mils (0.001") (Figure 3). These RFDs displaced 0.23 ± 0.02 mm at 0.1 Hz sine using 1.5 kV p/p with a +250 V DC bias.

 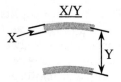

Figure 2.  ICE Electrode Pattern      Figure 3. Line Definition Nomenclature

Several criteria were used to develop the blueprint for the SSDPs and DSDPs, all were related to the goal of a simplistic low cost RFD pump. Hence, this required a pump with minimal unique parts, no glue, no soldered connections and although injection moldable parts would be the most cost effective, machining was chosen to create the working prototypes whose design layout was geared towards obtaining data rather than a final design platform. However, these machined parts were constructed to retain the possibility of future injection molding. The SSDP was constructed out of Acrylic and Mylar flapper valves and was created around the smallest standard wafer size from CTS Corp (125 µm x 2.2 cm) and was operated using only one side of the RFD wafer (single chamber) in order to evaluate the pump valve efficiency and refine the design (Figure 4). The design change for the DSDP is that the lid (1) is replaced by parts 3 – 6. Part 3 can be eliminated if the surfaces are truly matched. The connection to the RFD is made by drilling holes through the pump housing and piercing the electrode pads of the RFD. Nails are then inserted through the housing past the RFD and crimped at the point. The resulting nails serve as both electrical rails to the RFD and hold the pump assembly together without adhesives.

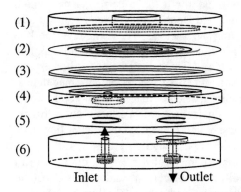

RFD SSDP Diagram Captions Table:
(1) Lid
(2) RFD
(3) Flat O-Ring
(4) Upper Valve Guide/Fluid Chamber
(5) Flapper Valve
(6) Lower Valve Guide/Manifold

Figure 4.  Single Sided Diaphragm pump, SSDP

Since the fluid chamber (4) is a hollowed cylinder (not contoured to the wafer surface) there exists enough dead volume, between the faces of the RFD and the valves, to prevent these pumps from being self-priming (see Figure 5). Thus, the total evacuation of air from the chamber is challenging, and requires operating the RFD at maximum voltage to afford the largest displacements possible. Since, the pumps are running at low frequency any cavitations and compression of these bubbles are assumed have minimal effect. Figure 6 is an actual DSDP without plastic hose connectors.

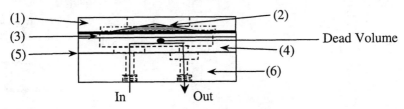

Figure 5. Assembled SSDP, see Figure 4 for RFD SSDP Diagram Captions Table

Figure 6. Acrylic DSDP - Side View.

Water was the medium used to characterize the SSDPs. The experimental setup consisted of two burets (used for input and output flow) with the corresponding hoses connected to the pump manifold. The electrical rails of the pump are connected to the high voltage amplifier controlled by a waveform generator and connected to an O-scope that is used to measure the voltage and current used by the pump. This setup is diagrammed in Figure 7. A stopwatch and conversion factors, from buret volume to column height, were used for flow rate measurements and all the subsequent calculations.

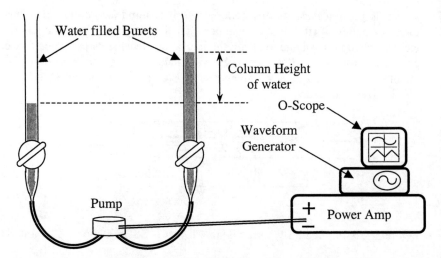

Figure 7. Experimental Setup to Determine Flow Rates, Pumping Efficiency and Power

The first test determined the best operating frequency of the SSDP. The cantilevered flapper valves dictated this frequency. The valve performance is a function of the stiffness, the difference in densities between the fluid medium and the valve material, the viscosity of the fluid, the dead volume of the chamber, and the amount of valve travel, as this effects both response time and the amount of back flow from column head pressure.

Charging the pump with the inlet buret water level slightly higher than the outlet initialized the frequency test. When the height difference of the inlet and outlet burets was zero, (no pressure difference) a two-minute timer was started and the resulting change in column height was measured at the conclusion of the test. Also recorded were the result peak-to-peak current "I", the voltage "V" and the phase angle $\phi$ = 5°. Using equation (1) the power "P" consumed was calculated and shown on Table I where $\cos\phi \approx 1$ at these frequencies (V and I in phase). This value of $\cos\phi$ implies that the RFD is converting almost all the electrical power into mechanical work [10].

Since: $P = V_{rms} \times I_{rms} \times \cos\phi$  and  $V_{rms}$ or $I_{rms} = \frac{\sqrt{2}}{2} \times \frac{V_{p/p} \text{ or } I_{p/p}}{2}$

It follows that:  $P = \frac{\sqrt{2}V_{p/p}}{4} \times \frac{\sqrt{2} I_{p/p}}{4} \times \cos\phi$

Resulting in:  $P = 1/8(V_{p/p} \times I_{p/p})$  (1)

Ceramic Materials and Multilayer Electronic Devices

Table I. Electric Power Consumption for 2.2 cm diameter RFDs

| Freq (Hz) | I (μA) | P (mW)* |
|-----------|--------|---------|
| 2 | 380 ± 80 | 72 ± 15 |
| 3 | 485 ± 120 | 91 ± 23 |
| 4 | 570 ± 120 | 106 ± 23 |
| 5 | 690 ± 150 | 130 ± 28 |
| 6 | 730 ± 120 | 137 ± 23 |

*Voltage was 1.5 kV p/p

The plot, shown in Figure 8, is the result of the 2 minute frequency test for several SSDPs using 2.2 cm diameter RFD. It is apparent, from Figure 8, that from 2 to 10 Hz the values are equivalent. However, when examining Table 1, the higher the frequency, the more power is consumed and the less efficient the pump. Thus, a frequency of 3 Hz was selected to operate the pumps for the flow rate test. Since, the values presented in Figure 7 are nearly identical, an equivalent test was performed over a 15 minute period over a increased frequency range (Figure 9).

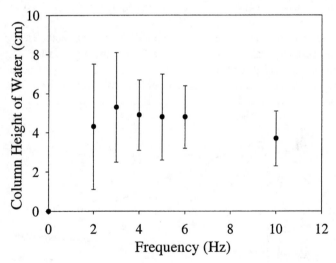

Figure 8. Column Height of water vs Frequency for the 2 Minute Test

From Figure 9, it is apparent that for the frequencies below 10 Hz, the SSDP provides the greatest efficiency and power output. Also shown are the variances in performance of these pumps caused by the RFDs. The reasons for the differences in actuator properties are explained in [9] and are generated during the thermal lamination process.

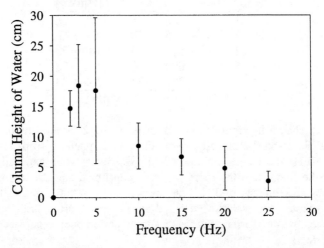

Figure 9. Column Height of water vs Frequency for the 15 Minute Test

The flow rate test was done using two SSDP pumps with RFD actuators of average performance. Once again, the data for the test was started when the input and output column heights of the burets were equal. Time intervals at preselected column heights were recorded and results of this test are shown in Figure 10.

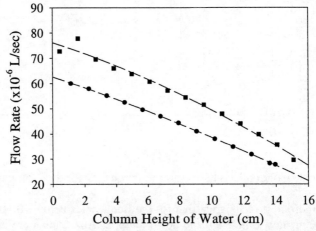

Figure 10. Flow Rate Data at 3 Hz for Two 2.2 cm dia. SSDP fit to 2$^{nd}$ Order Polynomials

The plot in Figure 10 shows a decreasing flow rate as the column height increases. This trend is expected, since the forward flow rate is a function of the column height of water, which is directly related to the backpressure at the pump head. Imposed on the flow rate data is the reverse flow caused by the imperfect valves operating against the water column. In order to calculate the reverse flow as a function of the column height, the outlet buret level was raised above the inlet water level and the change in the water level at different time intervals was record with the pump off. If the valves were perfect, no reverse flow should occur. The results of this test for the two pumps are shown in Figure 11.

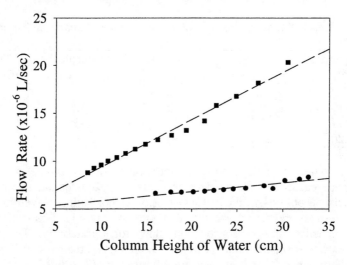

Figure 11. Back Flow Rate Data for Two 2.2 cm dia. SSDP with Linear Fits

The same trend shown in Figure 9 is reversed in Figure 11 with the decrease in flow rates with decreasing column heights. Again, this is expected since increased backpressure (column height) increases the reverse flow through the valves. The ratio of the forward and reverse flow rates affords a simplistic view of the mechanical efficiency of the pump as the dynamics of the sinusoidal signal are not taken into account at the 90° and 270° periods, when both valves may be open and floating as the RFD's acceleration approaches zero. Using the best-fit equations of the experimentally determined forward and reversed flow rates, the electrical power used, the conversion factor of column height to volume of water, and the area of the RFD; the back force, fluid weight, mechanical efficiency and power, and the overall electrical to mechanical efficiency can be approximated. These values for both pumps are averaged and presented on Table II and Table III.

Table II. Calculations of Mechanical Values for the SSDP at Several Different Column Heights

| Col. Height (cm) | Back Force (N) | Fluid Wt. (g) | *Total Flow (μL/sec) | *Back Flow (μL/sec) | % Mech. Efficiency |
|---|---|---|---|---|---|
| 5.0 | 0.086 | 8.8 | 58 ± 9 | 6.2 ± 1 | 90.3 ± 0.1 |
| 5.79 | 0.10 | 10.2 | 56 ± 9 | 6.4 ± 1 | 89.7 ± 0.4 |
| 10.0 | 0.17 | 17.6 | 44 ± 7 | 7.6 ± 2 | 85.3 ± 2.0 |
| 11.57 | 0.20 | 20.4 | 39 ± 7 | 8.0 ± 3 | 83.0 ± 1.4 |

*Calculated from Regression Equations used in Figures 10 and 11.

Table III. Calculations of Power Values and Total Efficiency for 2.2 cm RFD SSDP

| Back Force (N) | Calc. Total Work (mJ) | Electrical Power (mW) | Mechanical Power (μW) | Total E/M Efficiency (%) |
|---|---|---|---|---|
| 0.086 | 4.3 | 91 | 28 | 0.031 |
| 0.10 | 5.8 | 91 | 32 | 0.035 |
| 0.17 | 17.3 | 91 | 43 | 0.047 |
| 0.20 | 23.5 | 91 | 45 | 0.049 |

The values in Tables 2 and 3 do not account for any internal or external flow resistance caused by the external tube diameter and length, internal manifold channels, air pockets, or the inefficiencies of the controlling waveform. However, these results are fairly accurate for the non-optimized pump used as the experimental setup is reasonable and allows for repeatability. The most critical values are those of flow rate, power consumption and the electrical to mechanical 'E/M" efficiency. The flow rates are 2-3 mL/min at 0.1 to 0.2 N, which is in the range of low flow peristaltic pumps. The total efficiency of the pumps can be improved by several methods including, using both sides of the diaphragm, using ball valves, increasing the diameter of any tubing and contouring the diaphragm chamber. By extrapolating the flow rate equations to zero flow rate and converting the resulting column height of water (est. ~22 cm for both pumps) to grams of water (~39 g), the estimated block force based on the SSDP is ~0.4 Newtons and the pressure is 1 kPa.

CONCLUSIONS

A low cost non-optimized pump was been designed using the RFD. This pump affords flow rates from 2-3 mL/min with a mechanical efficiency of 80 – 90%. In order to improve the efficiency of this pumping system, several components will have to be carefully optimized in order to take full advantage of the actuator's capacity.

Future work will involve using the DSDP with ball valves, contoured chambers and block force characterization based on different RFD sizes and thickness, in order to find the best geometries and design criteria for fluid pumps.

REFERENCES
[1] J. A. Waanders, "Piezoelectric Ceramics, Properties and Applications," *Philips Components*, (1991).
[2] M. C. Carrozza, N. Croce, B. Magnani and P. Dario, "A piezoelectric-driven stereolithography-fabricated micropump," *J. Micromech. Microeng.,* **5**, 177, (1995).
[3] D. Accoto, M. C. Carrozza and P. Dario, "Modeling of micropumps using unimorph piezoelectric actuator and ball valves," *J. Micromech. Microeng.,* **10**, 277, (2000).
[4] B. K. Paul and T. Terhaar, "Comparison of two passive microvalve designs for microlamination architectures," *J. Micromech. Microeng.,* **10**, 15, (2000).
[5] S. Böhm, W. Olthuis and P. Bergveld, "A plastic micropump constructed with conventional techniques and materials," *Actuators and Sensors,* **77**, 223, (1999).
[6] K. M. Mossi and R. G. Bryant, "Prestressed Circular Actuators," *Ceramics Trasactions,* **150**, (2003) in press.
[7] Robert G. Bryant, Robert T. Effinger IV, Isaiah Aranda Jr., Ben M. Copeland Jr. and Ed W. Covington III, "Radial Field Diaphragms," *Proceedings of SPIE, Smart Structures and Materials – Active Materials : Behavior and Mechanics,* **4699**, 303, San Diego, CA (2002).
[8] R. G. Bryant, R. T. Effinger IV, and B. M. Copeland Jr., "Radial Field Piezoelectric Diaphragms," *Actuator 2002, 8th International Conf. on New Actuators,* Paper A1.3, 49, Bremen, Germany (2002).
[9] R. G. Bryant, R. T. Effinger IV, I. Aranda Jr., B. M. Copeland Jr., E. W. Covington III, and J. M. Hogge, "Radial Field Piezoelectric Diaphragms," *J. Intelligent Material Systems and Structures,* (2003) Submitted for publication
[10] R. B. Angus, "Electrical Engineering Fundamentals", ch 13 sec 5, Addison-Wesley Pub. Co. Inc., Reading MA (1968).

# HIGH PERFORMANCE PRE-STRESSED PIEZOELECTRIC BENDER ACTUATOR FOR DIGITAL VALVES

Glenn Waterfield
Caterpillar Inc.
TC-E 900
P.O. Box 1875
Peoria, IL 61656-1875
Waterfield_L_Glenn@Cat.com

**Abstract**
The fast response time of piezoelectric actuators makes them very desirable for high-speed digital valve applications. Diesel fuel injection is an example application, where precise delivery of fuel is essential for proper combustion. Pre-stressed piezoelectric bender actuators offer advantages over piezo stack actuators in packaging, simplicity, and stroke. Design, analysis and manufacturing process advancements were combined to develop a bender element and actuator package that meets valve-sealing requirements over a wide temperature range ($-40°$ to $125°$ C).

**Introduction**
Strain from piezoelectric material is typically a few tenths of 1%. This fundamental property has traditionally led to piezoelectric actuators with high force and very small stroke. Small displacement limits some available applications and requires additional displacement amplification in others.

Bimorphs and unimorphs were developed to address the stack's displacement shortcoming, with displacements many times their thickness. Pre-stressed unimorph benders such as RAINBOW and THUNDER®/NASDRIV™ improve force generation and durability.[1-3] Whereas RAINBOW is formed by reducing part of the PZT layer into a metallic layer, THUNDER®/NASDRIV™ benders are formed by bonding metal layers to a thin layer of PZT. Typically, a steel layer around 250 μm thick is bonded to the bottom of a PZT layer of about the same thickness using a hot-melt polyimide adhesive. At the same time, another metal layer, typically aluminum, is bonded to the top of the actuator to act as a stress reliever and electrode. The layers are bonded together at around $300°$

C.[3] Upon cooling, the thermal mismatch in the materials results in a domed configuration that grants numerous benefits. Voltage applied axially results in expansion or contraction in the radial direction, causing the bender to flatten or dome further. Typically a positive voltage causes the bender to flatten while negative voltage causes further doming. These benders have been available commercially for several years.

Several problems existed with the basic disc design.

- The position and stroke temperature dependence of the simply supported device is well known.
- Displacement of the circular benders was inadequate for the target application.
- The translational behavior of the edges of the device made rigid attachment difficult.
- There was no provision to attach a valve or other mass to the bender, and electrical lead attachment was a challenge.

**Technology Description**

It is well known that piezoelectric materials couple electrical energy to mechanical energy and vice versa. This coupling leads to complex interactions within the piezo bender actuator. First, it is well known that the piezoelectric properties of the PZT in the bender are temperature dependent.[4] Second, it is obvious from the THUNDER®/NASDRIV™ fabrication process that the shape of the bender is also temperature dependent. As the shape is temperature dependent, the stress is also temperature dependent. Third, it is known that the piezoelectric properties are stress dependent. This circle of interactions makes the design, control, and application processes challenging.

Piezo stack designers routinely apply an axial preload of up to 40 MPa to promote 90° domain switching and to protect against any tensile stress that is transmitted to the stack.[5] Pre-stressed bender actuators also benefit from certain stress profiles. It has been reported by Li, Furman, and Haertling, along with Schwartz and others that a general tensile stress in the PZT layer can promote 90° domain switching and thereby increase the extrinsic contribution to the piezoelectric effect.[6,7] Exploiting this situation has been the focus of many pre-stressed bender designers in recent years. However, testing by Caterpillar has shown that a circular pre-stressed bender used in a harsh industrial or automotive application can benefit from a net axial *compressive* stress. This compressive stress helps prevent cracking in the PZT that may arise from mechanical impacts and complex dynamic effects that arise from high-speed operation. If the stress profile of the PZT is chosen properly, domain wall motion is still possible while still achieving sufficient durability. Too much compressive stress will result in domain pinning and therefore decreased performance.

*Temperature effects*

By nature of their construction, the doming of thermally pre-stressed bender actuators is temperature dependent. Geometrical temperature dependence complicates applications in which the actuators are used for positioning. For instance, consider a 30 mm diameter bender configured as follows:

| Configuration | | | Dome Height (um) | | | Stroke (um) | | |
|---|---|---|---|---|---|---|---|---|
| OD (mm) | PZT (um) | Metal (um) | -40 C | 25 C | 100 C | -250 V | 550 V | Total |
| 30 | 254 | 200 SST | 587 | 477 | 360 | 70 | 130 | 200 |

Table I

Notice that the dome height change from –40° C to 100° C is 227 μm, or 1.6 μm/°C. This change is more than the available voltage-induced stroke, making the bender unsuitable for use as a positioner or a proportional valve actuator that will be applied over the common automotive temperature range of –40° to 125° C.

There are several ways to address the temperature dependence problem. The first is to make a bender that has more stroke than dome height change, which proves to be difficult in practice. Another method is to rigidly attach the bender actuator to a digital valve that has positive stops (i.e. seats) at each end of its travel. This simple approach limits the dome height growth as temperature changes. Stress in the bender builds as temperature changes, but dome height does not change because it is blocked by one of the seats. This stress can cause an electric field that could oppose the applied field and result in lowered displacement. However, if the actuator remains connected to the power supply as the temperature changes, the charge is free to redistribute. The internal field returns to zero, and the PZT then sees the applied field at full strength. This retains most of the stress-free performance of the bender.

*Changing Stress Profile through Design and Process*

As mentioned above, the stress profile of the bender is critical to performance and durability. The stress profile, along with stroke, force, domain wall motion, and dome height change due to temperature can all be modified through the bender design and bender manufacturing process. Consider the following table that compares benders made with different designs and processes.

Table II

| Disc | OD (mm) | Thickness (um) | | Deflection (um) | | | Stroke (um) | | | Stress @ 25 C (MPa) | Proce |
|------|---------|-------|-----|------|-----|------|-------|------|-------|------|------|
| | | Steel | PZT | 100C | 25C | -40C | -250V | 550V | Total | | |
| 1 | 36.2 | 254 (302 SST) | 254 | 494 | 632 | 755 | 60 | 210 | 270 | 178 | Nor |
| 2 | 36.2 | 254 (1010 ST) | 254 | 222 | 299 | 411 | 85 | 255 | 340 | 90 | Nor |
| 3 | 36.2 | 254 (1010 ST) | 254 | 283 | 354 | 455 | 79 | 221 | 300 | 99 | Hi m |
| 4 | 36.2 | 200 (1010 ST) | 254 | 317 | 386 | 490 | 70 | 260 | 330 | 100 | Hi m |

Disc One was built with a 300 series stainless steel reinforcing layer. This material has a high coefficient of thermal expansion (17 ppm/°C) and results in a bender with high dome height (DH). Total stroke from the bender is 270 μm. When tested, these benders showed highly asymmetric butterfly plots. It was theorized that the high compressive stress of 178 MPa was causing domain pinning, hurting performance. Furthermore, disc one shows a high dome height temperature dependence of 1.86 μm/°C. This high dependence makes operation over a wide temperature range difficult. Additionally, the high tensile stresses in the top metal layer were well into the plastic region, which led to energy losses during actuation.

More stroke was required, so the reinforcing layer in Disc Two was changed to 1010 carbon steel, which has a much lower CTE (11 ppm/°C) but similar modulus. The result was much lower dome height (53% less) and a significant increase in stroke (26% more). Dome height temperature dependence decreased to 1.35 μm/°C. Parallel to the drop in dome height was the decrease in compressive stress. Stroke improved due to increased domain wall motion and less plasticity in the top metal layer. However, the DH decrease and stroke increase resulted in the bender becoming nearly flat at room temperature at 550 V. This situation leads to dangerous tensile stresses in the ceramic layer during high-speed dynamic operation. Endurance testing showed that this configuration was prone to cracking.

The process was changed for Disc Three in order to resolve the durability issues. Using the same adhesive but changing the preparatory process, the melt temperature was raised in order to increase the thermal mismatch. This was successful in raising the DH (18% more) but stroke decreased by 11%. The resulting bender was much less likely to go entirely flat. The increase in compressive stress (10% more) improved durability as testing showed far fewer failures.

The metal reinforcing layer in Disc Four was modified in an attempt to retain the durability gains in Disc Three but regain the stroke of Disc Two. The 1010 carbon steel was retained, but the thickness was reduced from 254 μm to 200 μm to reduce the overall stiffness to increase stroke. Room temperature DH increased by 9% to 386 μm and the compressive stress increased slightly to 100

MPa. Stroke increased by 10% to 330 μm. Together, process and material changes resulted in a bender with high stroke, lower temperature dependence, and low crack occurrence.

*Stacking*

A single bender has limited performance and limited applications. The full benefit of pre-stressed bender actuators is realized when they are used in multiples.

There are two different ways to combine benders: parallel and series. Combinations of benders with stroke x and stiffness k are shown in Figure 1.

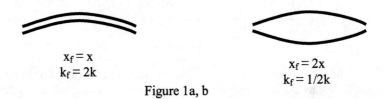

$$x_f = x$$
$$k_f = 2k$$

$$x_f = 2x$$
$$k_f = 1/2k$$

Figure 1a, b

Benders in Figure 1a, also known as the "spoon" configuration, are equivalent to springs in parallel. Benders in Figure 1b, known as the "clam" configuration, are equivalent to springs in series. Due to simplicity in clamping and attachment, the series configuration was chosen for the digital valve application.

The optimized bender in Table II, Disc 4, has the following characteristics:

$$x = 330 \ \mu m$$
$$k = 97 \ N/mm$$

Using Hook's Law, the maximum blocked force generated is therefore

$$F = kx = (330 \ \mu m)(97 N/mm) = 32.0 \ N \tag{1}$$

The stiffness for this bender is quite linear, so the theoretical force vs. stroke plot is as follows:

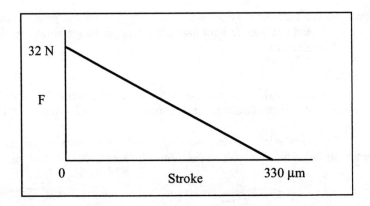

Figure 2

The maximum force is available almost immediately. Force capability is gradually lost as the stroke requirement increases. As expected, when the actuator reaches its maximum stroke it can no longer generate force.

If this bender were to seal against a valve seat 100 μm away, the available seating force would be 22.3 N as is demonstrated below.

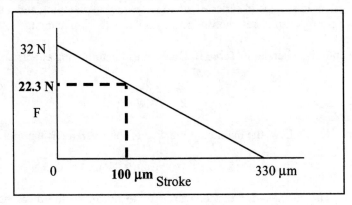

Figure 3

This force is rather low for some rigorous fuel system digital valve applications, so multiple benders are used. In the application discussed in this paper, four benders as described above were used in a parallel configuration. The discs have alternating polarity and each shares an electrical lead with the adjacent disc, similar to a piezo stack. Therefore, four discs have five leads total. The stack should retain the stroke of a single bender, but increase the stiffness by four times.　In practice, the mechanical coupling efficiency of the resultant combination is approximately 85% (discussed in a later section).　Therefore, the new blocked force is:

$$F = 0.85(4)kx = 0.85(4)(97 \text{ N/mm})(330 \text{ } \mu m) = 108.8 \text{ N} \qquad (2)$$

The force/stroke plot is now as follows:

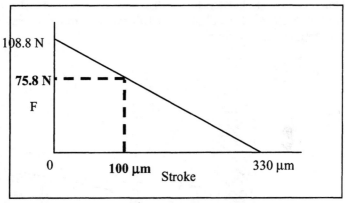

Figure 4

Force on a seat 100 μm away has now nearly quadrupled, allowing the use of the bender actuator on a digital valve.

*Clamping*
It is a challenge to fasten the bender stack to a valve assembly that is exposed to mechanical shock and vibration.　The translation of the edges of the bender as it is actuated makes it impossible to simply weld or bolt it to the valve body.　A spring clamping method was designed to address this condition.

As is obvious from the nature of the bender's movement, a rigidly attached bender will not produce movement.　Also obvious is that most methods of clamping will hinder performance.　At one limit, clamping near the center of the bender disc will completely block part of the movement of the bender.　At the other limit, clamping the bender disc at the outer edge will result in the least impact on performance.　As a benefit, pre-stressed benders have routinely been made with a staggered edge, with the metal reinforcing layer having about a 0.5 mm greater radius than the PZT layer as is shown in the cross section in Figure 5. This ledge makes an ideal place to clamp the bender into place.

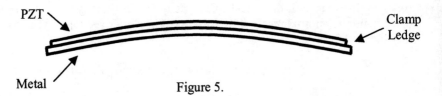

Figure 5.

A nonzero clamping load should be applied around the entire circumference of the bender disc in the form of a ring or cylinder. This load locates the disc and adds stiffness that will improve force generation. However, static clamping loads perform poorly.

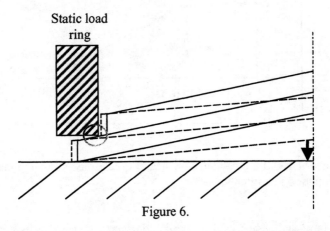

Figure 6.

As is shown by the circle in Figure 6, the load ring separates from the bender disc as the bender flattens during actuation, causing a loss in stiffness (as is demonstrated in Figure 7), and a corresponding loss in force generation.

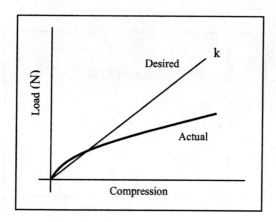

Figure 7

The loss in clamping load also allows the bender disc to lift from the mounting surface. To solve this problem, a spring-loaded clamp ring is used. The result is shown in the following Figures 8 and 9. The circle shows that the clamp ring stays in contact with the bender disc as it actuates. This retains location of the disc and maintains force generation.

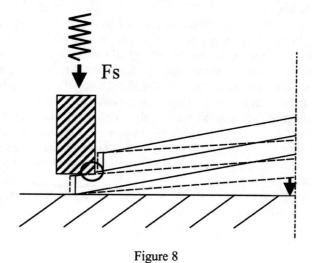

Figure 8

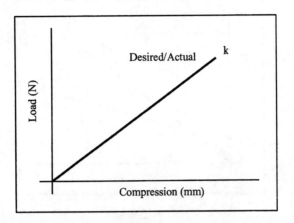

Figure 9

The spring load on the clamping ring should be chosen carefully. Too much load will cause loss of stroke. Too little load causes improper location of the bender disc. The spring load should at least match the force that bender actuator is required to supply in the application.

*Valve Attachment*

There are many applications that require an actuator to move a mass, often in both directions. Solenoids and piezo stacks require a return spring, but pre-stress bender actuators have the benefit of bi-directional actuation. To take advantage of this however, there must be a means of attaching the bender to the mass to be moved. The most durable method is to manufacture the bender with a hole in the center so that it may be bolted to the mass to be moved.

For the application of the digital valve, a 36.2 mm diameter disc (35.2 mm PZT layer) has a 3.5 mm hole drilled through the center. The PZT material removed accounts for only 0.25% of the total volume. Because the piezoelectric effect is volume effect, a loss of only 0.25% of the active material has virtually no effect on bender performance.

The four discs of the bender actuator are stacked together and a bolt is inserted as shown below.

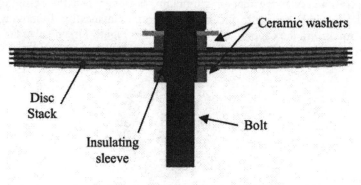

Disc
Stack

Ceramic washers

Insulating
sleeve

Bolt

Figure 10

The bolt is then torqued to specification to the valve. The stack is now clamped in the center and on the outside perimeter, resulting in a highly efficient mechanical coupling between the four discs.

The center hole of the stack contains electrodes of opposite polarity, so certain techniques must be used when using a steel bolt. A ceramic coating or an insulating sleeve may be used on the bolt shaft, while ceramic washers adjacent to the top and bottom discs insulate the bolt from the high voltage electrodes.

The mass to be moved is now rigidly attached to the bender stack, eliminating inertial separation of the actuator from the mass and increasing bandwidth. A return spring is not necessary, reducing the required force from the actuator. An additional benefit is that the mechanical efficiency of the bender stack has been increased.

*Durability*

Electrical lead attachment has long proven a challenge in unimorph benders. Soldering leads to the aluminum top layer has several problems. First, the mass of the solder joint leads to failure of the aluminum and even the PZT during vibration. Second, solder joints cause difficulty when stacking discs. An alternative approach has been to insert leads between layers while the bender is manufactured. This approach solves the stacking problem, but the uneven stress caused by this method leads to failure of the top aluminum layer after several million cycles.

Another approach might be to incorporate the lead into the design of the top aluminum layer, much like the handle of a circular paddle. However, since the aluminum layer is only 25 μm thick, the leads would be extremely fragile.

The leads could be strengthened by a change of material. Copper, for instance, is much stronger than aluminum and is easily soldered. The modulus of copper is roughly twice that of aluminum, however, and the resulting bender structure would be too stiff. Stroke would drop dramatically. Removing 50% of the material from the copper layer as is shown in Figure 11 can solve the stiffness problem.

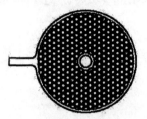

Figure 11

The stiffness and performance of the aluminum design is retained, and the top layer now has a strong integral lead that does not impede stacking. Furthermore, the higher yield strength of copper leads to fewer top layer failures due to plastic deformation.

*Adaptability*

The four discs are stacked together and, along with the spring and clamp ring, placed into a tough metal housing. A connector is welded to the housing, and the integral leads are soldered to the connector pins. The finished package shown in Figure 12 is remarkably similar in size and appearance to a solenoid.

Figure 12

The similarity allows the piezo bender actuator to be retrofitted easily to applications that can take advantage of its speed and other numerous advantages. Other popular piezo solutions would require extensive redesign.

*Control*

The actuator is only half of an actuation system. Just as important to performance and durability are the electronic controller and governing software. The piezoelectric and capacitive properties of the bender actuator are very useful from a control standpoint, while voltage and charge rate control is critical for optimal durability.

A useful property to exploit is the direct piezoelectric effect (strain induces electric field), or "self-sensing" capability, of the actuator. Because the valve is attached directly to the piezo bender actuator, impacts on the valve are also seen by the actuator. These impacts are revealed as reverse voltage spikes and can be monitored by the electronic control module (ECM). Figure 13 shows two voltage traces that were monitored by the ECM. The first trace shows voltage input to an actuator that has no valve seats to hit. The second is the same actuator with a valve seat. The impact and bounce are obvious and easily detectable.

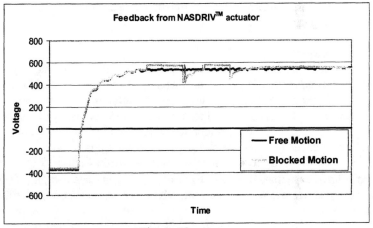

Figure 13

Knowledge of the time of valve impact on a digital pilot valve is extremely valuable, as delays in the control system can be greatly reduced. Software maps that compensate for changes in seat-to-seat time for different situations (temperature, fluid viscosity, etc.) can be eliminated. Most piezo stack designs are not attached directly to the valve and do not offer this benefit.

The capability to determine the magnitude of the valve impact is a second major benefit of seat detection. As can be inferred in Figure 13 above, the magnitude of the returned voltage spike is proportional to the velocity of the valve impact. Two attributes of the bender actuator design become very advantageous at this point: direct attachment of the valve to the actuator and bi-directional capability of the actuator. The velocity of the actuator and valve can then be controlled by changing the charge rate of the actuator. The valve/actuator can be slowed just before seat impact or, if needed, the charge into the actuator can be momentarily reversed. Charge reversal causes a braking effect on the valve/actuator, greatly reducing valve seating velocity and thus seat wear.

*Driving Voltage*

A bi-polar, non-switching voltage strategy was chosen to maximize displacement of the bender actuator. Care must be taken when choosing the voltage limits for this strategy. To minimize fatigue and failures, electric fields over 20 kV/mm are avoided. Switching fields are also avoided in order to minimize fatigue from 180° domain wall motion. Therefore the largest negative voltage used in each situation is always less than the coercive field at that temperature and stress profile. By avoiding the negative coercive field and always passing the positive coercive field, aging, electrical fatigue, and mechanical de-poling are mostly eliminated because the actuator is effectively re-poled during each cycle.[8]

*Power Considerations*

The capacitive nature of piezoelectric bender actuators gives them a significant advantage over electromagnetic actuators. EM actuators (e.g., solenoids) draw current during the entire actuation cycle. They generate a lot of heat and have low efficiency. Piezoelectric actuators need to be charged only at the beginning of the cycle and then discharged at the end of the cycle. Almost no current is needed between the charging and discharging events.

The finished piezo bender actuator shown in Figure 12 (four discs) has a small signal capacitance of only 160 µF. Driving voltage is high (~500 V) but the low capacitance means peak current, which occurs only during charge/discharge, is only 4 A.

The low current requirement also means low heat generation, which is a challenge in co-fired stack designs. The high surface area-to-volume ratio insures that what heat is generated is dissipated quickly. Effective heat dissipation means no special consideration for heat transfer from the actuator, leading to a more simple design.

*Finite Element Analysis*

A finite element model was produced to analyze the complex interactions between temperature, stress, and piezoelectric properties. The modeling techniques are outside the scope of this paper, but dome height, stroke vs. voltage, effective $d_{31}$, and stress can all be predicted at different temperatures. The model is also able to deal with different materials and bender discs of varying diameters.

**Application**

The pre-stressed piezoelectric bender actuator discussed above was designed to actuate the pilot stage of a diesel engine fuel injector. Precise control of the rate of injection of fuel into the combustion chamber is critical to fuel economy and engine emissions. The speed of the piezo bender actuator allows much improved control of the pilot stage, resulting in smaller pilot and post injection quantities as well as smaller dwell times between multiple injection events. The lower power consumption means multiple injections carry a smaller power cost, leading to greater efficiency for the engine.

The pilot valve in this particular fuel injector application is a three-way, two-position poppet valve with 100 µm of travel. There is no return spring. Sealing requirements are 50 N at 28 MPa. The actuator is 39 mm in diameter and capable of 330 µm of free travel. The excess travel is primarily used for two things: applying sealing force on each valve seat, and ensuring that enough stroke is available regardless of temperature. Testing has confirmed that the sealing requirements have been met over the –40 to 125° C temperature range.

In addition to the 36.2 mm discs, benders of several sizes down to 20 mm have been analyzed, built, and tested. Flexibility in the size of the disc ensures applicability to a wide range of fuel injectors, from heavy-duty truck engines to common-rail automotive fuel injectors.

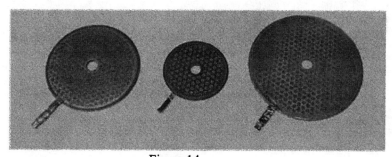

Figure 14

**Conclusion**

Advanced design, analysis, and manufacturing process techniques have resulted in a high performance pre-stressed bender actuator suitable for high-speed digital fuel injection valves.

References:

1. G. H Haertling, "Rainbow Ceramics – A New Type of Ultra-High Displacement Actuator," *Am. Ceram. Soc. Bull.*, **73**, 93 (1994).

2. R. G. Bryant, "THUNDER Actuators," Presented at the Enabling Technologies for Smart Aircraft Systems Workshop, Hampton, VA, May, 1996.

3. S. A. Wise, "Displacement Properties of RAINBOW and THUNDER Piezoelectric Actuators," *Sensors and Actuators, A*, **69**, pp. 33-38, 1998.

4. M. W. Hooker, "Properties of PZT-Based Piezoelectric Ceramics Between – 150 and 250°C," NASA/CR-1998-208708.

5. R. Bindig, G Heilke, "Application of Piezoceramic Multilayer Actuators, Experiences, and Solutions," Actuator 2000, Bremen Germany.

6. G. Li, E. Furman and G. Haertling, "Stress-Enhanced Displacements in PLZT Rainbow Actuators," *J. Am. Ceram. Soc.*, **80**, (6) 1382-88 (1997).

7. R. W. Schwartz et al, "Understanding Mechanics and Stress Effects in Rainbow and Thunder Stress-Biased Actuators," SPIE Smart Structures and Materials 2000 Proceedings, 3992-49.

8. C. Y. Lin, N. W. Hagood, "Compression Depolarization of PZT Piezoelectric Materials under High Electromechanical Driving Levels," SPIE Smart Structures and Materials 2000 Proceedings, 3992-17

# KEYWORD AND AUTHOR INDEX

Microwave processing, 359
Microwave properties, 187
Microwave sintering, 299
Mitic, V.M., 197
Morphotropic phase boundary, 71, 139, 221
Mossi, Karla, 445
Multilayer actuator, 401
Multiplayer capacitor, 359, 367
Multiplayer transformer, 351

Nagata, H., 253
Nam, Song-Min, 33, 205
Nanometer powders, 89
Nb2O5, 197
Neural network, 319
Newnham, R.E., 427
Niwa, K., 401
Noda, Minoru, 125
Nomura, Takeshi, 115

Okuyama, Masanori, 125
Ou, R., 273
Ozonizer, 107

Pan, Ming-Jen, 53
Parallel models, 281
Particle size, 63
Pastes, 309
Patil, Sandeep, 79
Paunovic, V.V., 197
Pb(Zr,Ti)O3, 245
P-E curve, 33
Pejovnik, Stane, 417
Percolation, 63
Perovskite, 3, 139, 171, 289
Phase transformation, 289
Pietruszka, Lisa M., 455
Piezoceramic, 221, 253, 333, 351, 377, 401
Piezoelectric, 445, 467

Piezoelectric actuator, 455
Piezoelectric crystal, 149
Piezoelectric pump, 455
PMNT, 149
PNN-PT-PZ, 401
Pole figures, 265
Porosity, 43
Probability, 63
Processing, 43
Production, 107
Pulsed laser deposition, 125
PZNT, 149
PZT, 245

Radical field diaphragms, 455
Rahaman, Mohamed N., 79
Randall, Clive A., 149, 359
Randall, M., 359
Rapid prototyping, 53
Rayne, Roy J., 53
Resistivity ratio, 281
Resistivity, 265, 273
Resonator, 333
RFD, 455
Rheology, 309
Rocha, Enrique, 107
Rodriguez, Mark A., 289
Rodríguez, Martín, 107

Screen printing, 309
Seeded growth, 139
Semler-Rosenthal, D., 273
Sensor, 377
Series models, 281
Shah, Nipun, 79
Shende, Rajesh V., 43
Shibuya, Akira, 125
Shrout, Thomas R., 149, 359
SiC, 265
Simulation, 63
Singh, Raj N., 139